C000197109

# THE FIRESIDE BOOK OF DEADLY DISEASES

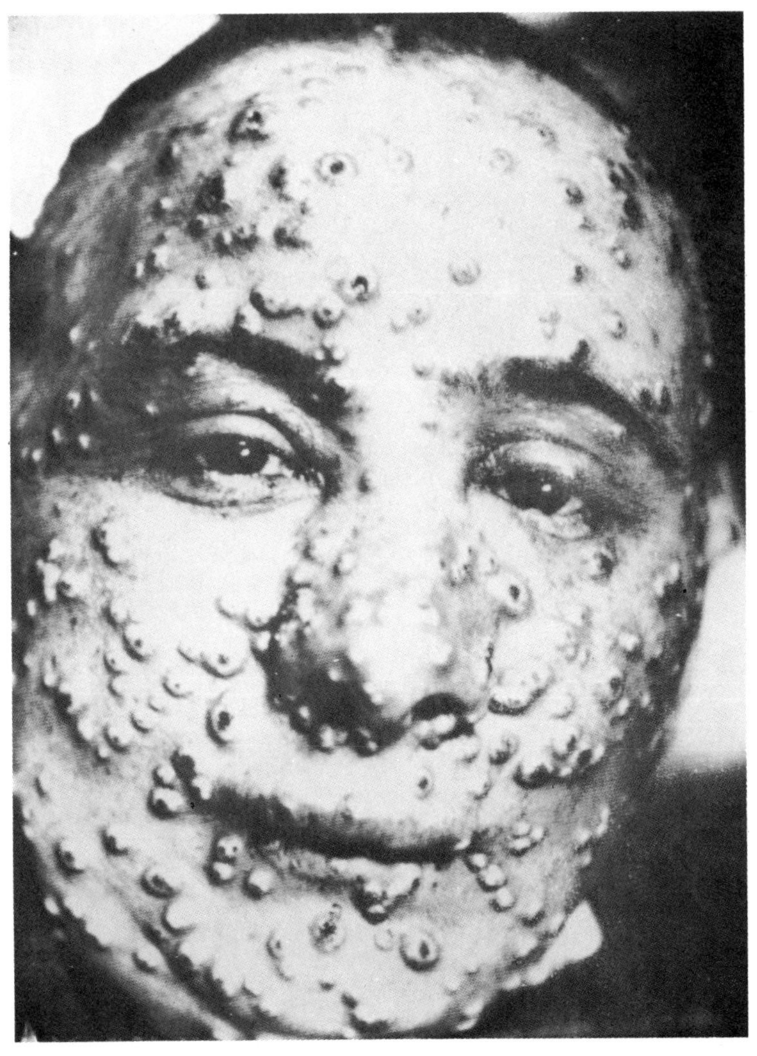

Smallpox pustules, characteristically concentrated on the face

# THE FIRESIDE BOOK OF DEADLY DISEASES

Robert Wilkins

ROBERT HALE · LONDON

*First published in Great Britain 1994*

ISBN 0 7090 4840 8

Robert Hale Limited
Clerkenwell House
Clerkenwell Green
London EC1R 0HT



Photoset in North Wales by
Derek Doyle & Associates, Mold, Clwyd.
Printed in Great Britain by
St Edmundsbury Press Ltd, Bury St Edmunds, Suffolk.
Bound by WBC Bookbinders Ltd, Bridgend, Mid-Glamorgan.

# CONTENTS


*List of Illustrations* ix
*Acknowledgements* xiii
*Apologia* xv

1 DISEASES, ANCIENT AND MODERN 1

2 THREE DEADLY SCOURGES 13

1 The Black Death 13
2 Cholera 32
3 Typhus, disease of dirt 48

3 SMALLPOX, CONQUEROR OF THE NEW WORLD 50

4 DEADLY FIRST COUSINS 69
1 Tuberculosis 69
2 Leprosy 83

5 CREATIVITY AND ILLNESS 95

6 BONES, STONES AND GROANS 115

7 A THERAPEUTIC INTERLUDE 127

8 DISEASES OF THOSE WHO GOVERN 138
1 The Royals 138
2 Leaders 153

9 THE MEDICAL DETECTIVE 166

10 THE THREE MOSQUITEERS – MANSON, ROSS AND REED 175
1 Filariasis 175
2 Malaria 176
3 Yellow fever 192

11 POX AND CLAP: THE GREAT UNMENTIONABLES 197

12 AIDS 230

*Afterword* 241
*References* 245
*Glossary* 260
*Index* 263

*By the same author*

The Fireside Book of Death
The Doctor's Quotation Book

# ILLUSTRATIONS


1 Smallpox pustules ii
2 A cave painting of Cro-Magnon medicine man 1
3 Trepanning of skull in Peruvian mummy 2
4 Guinea worms protruding from a foot 4
5 Beetle found in an embalmed Egyptian mummy 5
6 Bony destruction produced by leprosy 7
7 Congenital syphilis 11
8 Plague doctor, 1720 14
9 Bubo in the groin 27
10 Severe dehydration in a cholera patient 33
11 'Washerwoman's hand' 35
12 Cholera in London 40
13 *L'inhumation précipitée* 42
14 Dr John Snow, the unsung hero of cholera 45
15 Confluent smallpox pustules 51
16 Rameses V, with lesions suggestive of smallpox 52
17 Smallpox pustules on the arm 54
18 Skin reaction to vaccination against smallpox 59
19 Dr Edward Jenner, discoverer of vaccination 62
20 Smallpox pustules on the back of the hand 64
21 A skeleton from Spitalfields 68
22 A skin manifestation of tuberculosis 74
23 Leprosy affecting the face 84
24 'Leonine facies' produced by leprosy 85
25 A leper graveyard 86
26 Mutilation of the hands 89
27 Leprosy and Robert the Bruce 92
28 Beardsley's depiction of *The Lacedaemonian Ambassadors* 96
29 Gillray on gout 115
30 Gout and the big toe 117
31 An unanaesthetized patient 120

32 'Cutting for the stone' 121
33 Breast surgery before anaesthetics 125
34 A self-administered enema apparatus 128
35 A self-administered enema apparatus 129
36 Hot cupping of the buttocks 131
37 A leech on the ear 134
38 Use of a seton to treat a weeping eye 135
39 Cautery with a hot iron 137
40 Feminine attributes of Akhenaton 139
41 Facial destruction in congenital syphilis 145
42 A prosthetic jaw and teeth 156
43 Mass of ascarids in small intestine 164
44 Gross swellings in elephantiasis 175
45 Elephantiasis of the scalp 175
46 Elephantiasis of the scrotum 176
47 Elephantiasis of the legs 176
48 Sir Patrick Manson and Sir Ronald Ross, mosquito pioneers 181
49 Walter Reed, yellow fever investigator 194
50 Saddle nose 197
51 Hutchinson's teeth 198
52 Gangosa 200
53 Gumma 201
54 Syphilis on the penis 203
55 A skin rash caused by syphilis 204
56 Facial destruction in syphilis 205
57 Consulting a venereologist 206
58 The rash of secondary syphilis 207
59 Erotically illustrated condoms 211
60 Nasal destruction in syphilis 215
61 Destruction of the nose in tertiary syphilis 218
62 Blindness caused by syphilis 222
63 Naso-oral destruction in congenital syphilis 224
64 'Crabs' 227
65 A penile gumma in syphilis 228
66 Thrush and AIDS 231
67 Kaposi's sarcoma and AIDS 239
68 Progeria 242

## PICTURE CREDITS

Cassell & Co.: 1, 15, 17, 20. National Museum of Anthropology and Archaeology, Peru: 3. Ballière Tindall: 4, 9, 43. Cambridge University Press: 5. Dr Møller-Christensen: 6, 25. Butterworth Heinemann: 7, 18, 41, 50, 51, 54–56, 58, 60, 61, 63, 65. Oliver & Boyd: 10, 11. Wellcome Institute for the History of Medicine: 12, 14, 19, 29, 48. ACL, Brussels: 13. Cairo Museum Catalogue (E. Smith): 16. T. Mollinson, Natural History Museum, London: 21. Victoria and Albert Museum, London: 28. Department of Anatomy, Edinburgh Medical School: 27. Photographic Department, St Bartholomew's Hospital, London: 37. Praeger: 42. National Library of Medicine, Bethesda, Maryland: 49. British Museum: 57. Christie's South Kensington Ltd, London: 59. Professor M. Adler and the British Medical Journal: 66, 67.

# ACKNOWLEDGEMENTS

First and foremost, I would like to thank my wife, Anne, for her tolerance and understanding. Invaluable help was given by the library staff at the Wellcome Institute for the History of Medicine, the Royal College of Physicians, the Royal College of Surgeons, the Royal Society of Medicine and the British Medical Association. I would also like to thank Belinda Bic; Julian Litten; Theya Mollison (The Natural History Museum); Jeremy Collins of Christie's South Kensington Ltd; Professor Michael Adler and all others who have kindly given me permission to use illustrations.

# APOLOGIA

Micro-organisms produced disease long before the emergence of man: a *Tyrannosaurus rex* suffering the agonies of a dental abscess must have made an awesome spectacle. Despite their rudimentary structure, viruses and bacteria have been waging unintentional but successful war on evolutionarily more sophisticated animals for millions of years. Twentieth-century medical technology has encouraged, in the lay and doctors alike, the spurious notion that epidemic diseases were soon to be regarded as historical curiosities. Such complacency is dangerous. Bubonic plague is not extinct, it merely lies dormant. The sudden reappearance of smallpox – the first disease to be technically 'eradicated' – needs only its release from cold storage in an act of germ warfare.

Antibiotics have not seen off the micro-organism: indeed, the proliferation of drug-resistant strains of microbes has ensured that many diseases, widely regarded as long since conquered, are busily staging a deadly renaissance. It is premature to count out epidemic disease, and much of the widespread anger at the lack of progress made in finding a cure for AIDS is the uncomfortable realization that medical technology is presently unequal to the task.

The influence of disease on human history has been either ignored or significantly underestimated by academics. Disease afflicts both individuals and nations: it was not the Russians who brought about Napoleon's imperial sunset, it was typhus; a major factor in the decline of the Greek and Roman empires was the chronic sapping of energy brought about by malaria; smallpox has been responsible for the extinction of entire royal dynasties and New World civilizations, and is the reason why this book is not written in French: in 1779 an invasion by France was only averted by the enemy fleet falling prey to a microscopic combatant more deadly than even the English tar!

The Third World languishes in disease, and disease arrests human progress. The means already exist to counter such Third World killers as measles, diphtheria, and poliomyelitis – only the money and political will are missing. Most Western drug firms, driven by the quest for profit, are too preoccupied producing superfluous 'me too' drugs to be motivated to help make Africa and India healthy places for human beings to live and thrive.

The effect of disease upon individuals has not always been totally negative. Indeed, many claim a link between illness and creativity, which is examined in detail in this book. Should the world be grateful and indebted to *Mycobacterium tuberculosis* and *Treponema pallidum*, the causative micro-organisms of tuberculosis and syphilis, for enriching European culture with the literary and artistic masterpieces of diseased geniuses such as Keats and D. H. Lawrence, Gauguin and Van Gogh?

This book sets out to place diseases in their historical context and chart their sociological effects through the use of contemporary source material. Not all the diseases are, strictly speaking, 'deadly'; and the two deadliest in our own times, cancer and coronary heart disease, have, by dint of the idiosyncrasy of personal choice, been subordinated to such scourges of old as the Black Death and pox (both great and small).

Disease evokes ambivalence: curiosity goes in tandem with repulsion. I have attempted to satisfy curiosity in the hope that increased understanding will lessen fear.

# 1 DISEASES, ANCIENT AND MODERN

The study of the diseases of antiquity is hampered because researchers are usually limited to those diseases which affect the bones, since skeletal remains constitute the majority of the material that is available for examination. Other sources, such as mummies, or bodies preserved in peat bogs, are not plentiful. Few diseases produce *characteristic* bony changes, and experts have argued about the diagnosis in particular skeletons: some authorities maintain that syphilitic changes occur in European skeletons before the discovery of America; others find the same changes in American Indians (Amerindians) before Columbus arrived in the New World; not infrequently the two sets of experts disagree about the other's findings.

A cave painting of Cro-Magnon medicine man

The bony changes brought about by tuberculosis arouse much less contention, and there is general agreement that this disease was present in Neolithic times and was responsible for the depictions of hunchbacks on Egyptian pottery.

Study of skeletal remains has shown that the operation of trepanation – whereby a large hole was made in the skull – is one of great antiquity, probably dating back to Paleolithic times, some 10,000 years ago. Trepanned skulls have been found in Europe, Africa, Asia and the Americas. Trepanation was probably car-

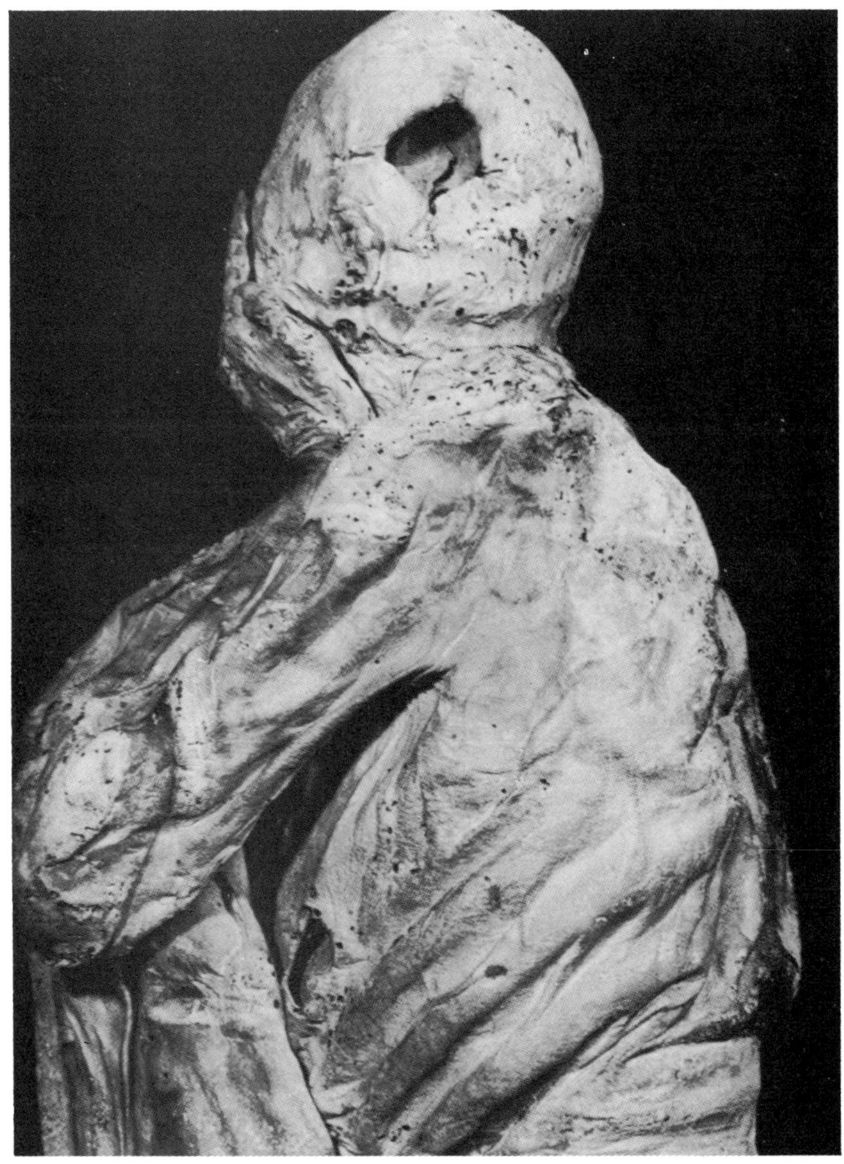

Trepanning of skull in Peruvian mummy (AD1000–1500)

ried out for two major reasons: as a surgical treatment after head injuries (though most skulls show little evidence of physical trauma), or for the alleviation of headache, epilepsy, mental disease and coma, diseases attributed to evil spirits, which escaped through the hole ground in the skull by a stone or flint. If the patient was conscious, partial anaethesia could be obtained by the use of alcohol or opium. The remarkable thing about trepanation is not that it was carried out, but that the patient ever survived – as evidenced by the healing processes discernable at the margins of the hole – and did not succumb to infection of the brain caused by micro-organisms.[1]

## *The variety of diseases*

That early man was not immune to infection by microbes is shown by the caries and abscesses seen in the jawbones of early human skeletons, belying the notion that dental decay is a 'disease of civilization'.

In evolutionary terms, viruses and bacteria represent the most primitive of life forms, which have probably always possessed the potential of causing disease in higher animals. Indeed, viruses cannot survive outside living cells for any length of time, and as soon as they take up residence they can be envisaged as causing greater or lesser disruption within that organism – reflected by severe or mild symptoms of disease.

When primitive man was a hunter his very mobility limited the number and variety of diseases to which he was exposed. But when man began to stay put in one place, to clear the land and to cultivate crops, he inevitably came into closer contact with animals and insects which suffer and transmit diseases: for example, domesticated animals (both those deliberately domesticated such as cattle, and those opportunistically domesticated such as rats) exposed humans to the organisms which cause tuberculosis and endemic typhus. It is certain that when geographically separated communities met up, they shared infections, each falling prey to the other's germs.

Primitive man may have made the link between animals and disease, but most of the causative organisms were far too minute to be seen with the naked eye: the bacterium which causes tuberculosis and the rickettsia which causes endemic typhus, and all other micro-organisms, have only been visualized under microscopes within the last 150 years. But not all agents of disease are invisible. A caveman tucking into a chunk of raw meat or fish would have been well able to see worms crawling about the flesh. He would also have noticed, with varying degrees of disgust, the worms he passed in his own faeces. Parasitic worms come in all shapes and sizes, and are more commonly found in tropical countries. Aristotle distinguished between flat worms (*Taenia*), cylindrical worms (*Ascaris*) and thin worms (*Enterobius*). Celsus described the occasional appearance of a round worm exiting the body through the mouth or nose! It is likely that certain religious food taboos – for example the Hebrew prohibition on the eating of pork – represented an attempt to limit parasitic infestations. (Ironically micro-organisms can sometimes infect man *because* of his religious customs – the spread of cholera is facilitated by communal bathing in the Ganges.)

One of the most widespread diseases caused by worms is schistosomiasis (also called bilharzia), affecting some 150 million persons. The tiny eggs are passed out in human faeces or urine into fresh water where they enter into snails, to be released weeks later as larvae which re-enter the human host through a skin abrasion. Schistosomiasis causes chronic ill-health with damage to the intestines, liver and bladder. The disease is very prevalent in Africa, and the calcified eggs of *Schistosoma haematobium*, one of the parasites which causes schistosomiasis, has been found in the kidneys of Egyptian mummies.[2]

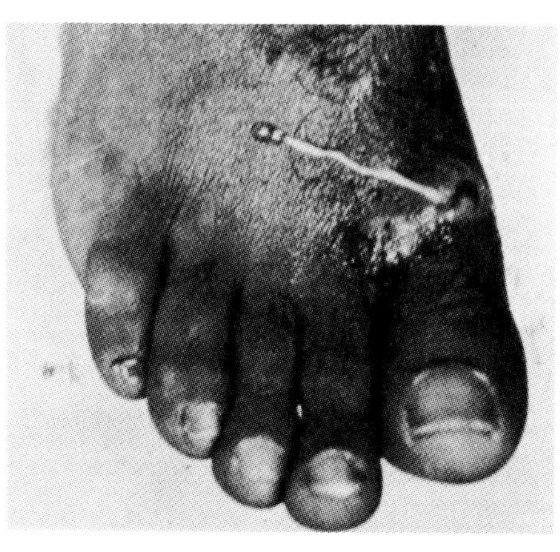

Guinea worm protruding from foot

Nits, lice, beetles and all varieties of creatures have been found in mummies from Egypt and Peru.

## *More about bacteria and viruses*

Man can come into contact with micro-organisms in a variety of ways. Some, such as the *Clostridia*, which cause tetanus and gas gangrene, live in the soil and invade humans by the infection of wounds. Other micro-organisms live in rodents and are transmitted to humans by the bites of insects. The best-known representative of this class is *Pasteurella pestis*, the bacterium responsible for the Black Death, which is transmitted from rat to man by the bite of a flea. Still other micro-organisms primarily affect domesticated animals, the classic example being *Mycobacterium tuberculosis* which man contracts by drinking infected cows' milk.

Micro-organisms can also live in insects: the virus which causes yellow fever also infects the mosquito, *Aëdes aegypti*; and the parasites responsible for malaria need both the female *Anopheles* mosquito and man to complete their life cycles.

Beetle found in embalming of Egyptian mummy

The largest group of micro-organisms need man in order to survive. This group includes the viruses which cause smallpox and mumps, and *Salmonella typhi*, the bacterium which causes typhoid fever. If their human host dies they must quickly find another, or perish. It is probable that these micro-organisms have evolved from 'first cousins' who once infected animals: measles is very like canine distemper, and human smallpox and cowpox are closely related (the latter being used to vaccinate against the former).

Although it may not seem so to a patient dying of an infectious disease, *it is not the intention of the micro-organism to kill its host*. To bring about the death of the host is a sign of amateurism: the ideal is a parasitic relationship whereby the micro-organism gets its needs met with minimal disruption to the host. Those diseases which do kill are probably caused by more recent micro-organisms, evolutionarily speaking. Older micro-organisms have learnt to adapt: *Plasmodium falciparum* is probably the 'youngest' of the malarial parasites since it is the one which inflicts the greatest mortality. The same applies in the animal world: rinderpest was introduced to Africa in 1891 and promptly killed up to 90 per cent of cattle. It could not establish itself simply because the micro-organism ran out of susceptible animals to infect. Over the centuries, scarlet fever, measles and diphtheria have become less virulent in the Western world.

It is also disadvantageous for the micro-organism to induce an immune response in the host since the defenses may destroy the germ and effectively prevent re-infection at a later time. Such micro-organisms include the viruses causing chickenpox and measles, and the bacterium causing whooping cough, which, in order to survive, needs a plentiful supply of non-immune children. If such a reservoir of non-immune humans is unavailable – such as in sparse and widely scattered populations – it is unlikely that these micro-organisms would gain a foothold. This is the most plausible explanation as to why these diseases were unknown in the New World, there being simply too few people to provide a viable environment for the micro-organism. It follows that many diseases which need heavy concentrations of humans are relatively recent, and did not afflict our primitive ancestors. It is not until the first century AD that Scribonius Largus gives a convincing description of shingles – and it is likely that chickenpox dates from about this time, since both diseases are caused by the same micro-organism.

It is not an easy task to determine whether a disease, well-known in our own time, was prevalent in the past. The further back in time, the more blurred things become. And it is unsafe to assume that a particular disease did not exist simply because it is not described. Further uncertainty is introduced by lack of recorded detail, selectivity by the researcher (deliberate or unconscious) and present-day mistranslations of earlier mistranslations! The Bible and the Talmud are books which span many centuries and were written by many authors, and diseases, when they are mentioned, were rarely intended to be clinical descriptions. This fact makes retrospective diagnosis interesting but perilous. Embellishments are likely, especially by those writing many years after the events they describe. The Talmud recounts how Titus, when opened at autopsy, had a sparrow with a copper head and iron nails in his head: medical historians can debate the diagnosis and whether this was a fanciful description of a brain tumour.

The 'bodily discharge' referred to in Leviticus 15:1 ff., is most likely to have been gonorrhoea, but confusion surrounds other descriptions of biblical disease, especially skin eruptions: 'And the men that died were smitten with the emerods' – surely not killer haemorrhoids?

If a medical historian wishes to know whether a particular disease was known in pre-Christian Greece, he would consult the writings of Hippocrates, a physician who lived in the fifth century BC. Hippocrates was a keen observer and has included a number of medical vignettes in his *Epidemics*. He describes Philiskos, who developed a fever, passed black urine, and died on the sixth day; Kriton, whose big toe became red and swollen causing septicaemia and death on the second day; and Pythion, who had pneumonia and coughed up blood. Accurate descriptions are given of consumption, tetanus and malaria, but nothing is recorded about smallpox or

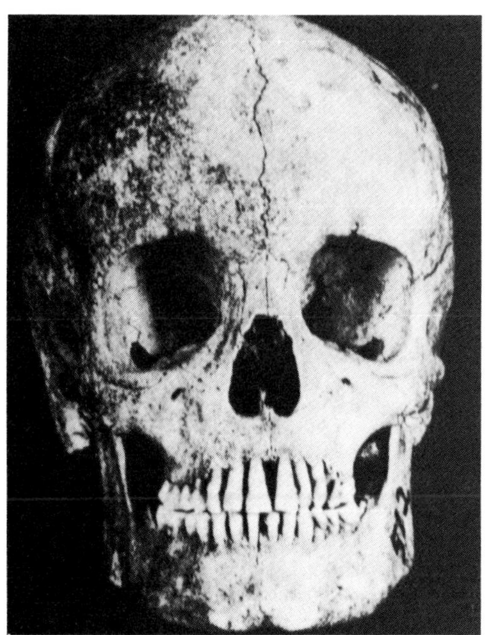

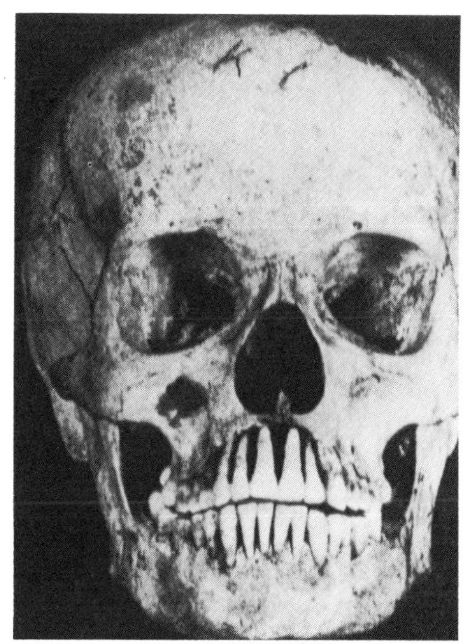

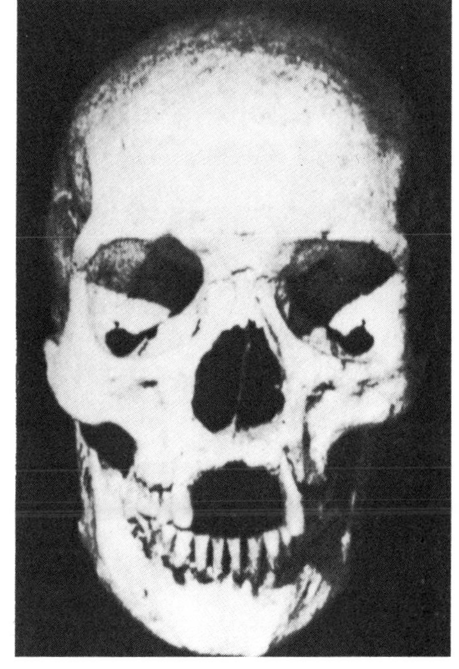

The sequence of bony destruction produced by leprosy affecting the nasal cavity and upper jaw

bubonic plague (Thucydides, a generation later, said that whatever it was afflicting Athens – now thought by many to be smallpox – was 'new'.)

By the same Hippocratic token, ancient Greece was obviously conducive to the mumps virus, but not necessarily to the measles virus. Hippocrates does not mention measles, but his account of mumps is unmistakable: 'Many people had swellings behind one or both ears ... Either early, or after a little time, painful inflammation might occur in one or both testes, sometimes with fever, and the pain severe.' Measles is mentioned in Arab medical writings from the sixth century AD, but it was not until the tenth century AD that Rhazes differentiated it from smallpox, *measles being considered by far the more serious of the two diseases*. (In 1875, in Fiji, measles killed one quarter of the population.)

Syphilis, tuberculosis and leprosy represent a group of diseases whose micro-organisms persist in chronic lesions in the body, and can survive many years in human populations, even those which are widely dispersed. Yet other micro-organisms which infect humans can survive into the host's convalescence: such human 'carriers', who no longer show any symptoms, continue to harbour and transmit the disease to others. Such micro-organisms include those which cause scarlet fever, diphtheria, typhoid, poliomyelitis and infectious hepatitis. Carriers can remain infectious for many months, even permanently in the case of *Salmonella typhi*. (A notorious carrier in America, 'Typhoid Mary', a cook who paid little attention to hygiene, was finally tracked down after she had infected thousands of people.) Since the urgency to find a new host is less critical in carrier states – the micro-organism can bide its time until it makes contact with another, non-immune, human – these diseases can afflict scattered and less populous communities, and are therefore regarded as 'older'. Symptoms highly suggestive of diphtheria are mentioned by Hippocrates, and skeletal deformities characteristic of poliomyelitis are depicted on a stele in Memphis in the XVIIIth Dynasty.

There is abundant evidence to show that diseases have changed considerably over the centuries, probably as a result of the micro-organism's attempt to accommodate to its human host. On purely biological grounds, it is entirely logical to suppose that infectious diseases are constantly changing, that new ones are in the process of developing, and old ones are modified or disappearing. If, indeed, syphilis existed in Europe in pre-Columbian days (and it is a big 'if'), then it bore no resemblance to the virulent disease which broke out among the soldiers at the siege of Naples in 1494. Within decades, the causative spirochaete, *Treponema pallidum*, had lost its virulence, and, instead of causing the death of the host by overwhelming infection (which would have been to its own disadvantage), became a successful parasite: the madness of Baudelaire was testament to the fact that the spirochaete lived on in the author's brain, years after the initial infection.

The history of leprosy in Europe and the Middle East would seem to suggest that it is probably not a biblical disease, that it peaked in incidence in the Middle Ages, and that it began to decline in the fifteenth century. Some experts suggest that most lepers succumbed to the plague; others believe that the leprosy bacterium was ousted by its more successful first cousin, the micro-organism responsible for tuberculosis. Another disease which waxed, waned, and finally disappeared is the 'English sweating sickness'. It made its first appearance in England in 1485, the year when Henry VII defeated Richard III at Bosworth Field, to usurp the throne of England for the Tudors. In 1552, after five epidemics, it disappeared as mysteriously as it came. Unusually, and like poliomyelitis centuries later, the greatest number of deaths occurred in the upper classes. A description of the disease has been left to us by Dr John Caius (1510–73).[3] Because the fever was short-lived, often lasting barely twenty-four hours, Caius suggested re-naming the disease *Ephemera*. He drew particular attention to 'piene in the backe, grief in the stomacke, the passion of the hart, a desire to sleape, and madnes'. Many died within the day. It is believed that the export of the English sweats to the Continent in 1529 caused Luther and Zwingli to abandon their conference, called to discuss ecclesiastical differences, thereby establishing the split between Lutherans and Calvinists.

There are a number of examples of diseases of recent times. There is no reliable account of the existence of poliomyelitis (infantile paralysis) in epidemic form prior to 1840: such a dramatic disease would surely have been commented upon. And it is likely that the virus which causes AIDS is a very recent mutation, previously unknown to man.

As we have seen, over time, a micro-organism can be expected to evolve in order to minimize the damage it produces in its host – after all, tens of millions of micro-organisms live harmoniously on our skins and in our intestines, and *man would not survive without them*! But such a peaceable co-existence between man and microbe breaks down with dramatic results when the micro-organism encounters a virgin population. Colonization by the Old World wreaked havoc in the New. Amerindians who had had no contact with Old World diseases and who, therefore, had acquired no immunity, died in their hundreds of thousands from smallpox, tuberculosis, measles, influenza, plague, diphtheria, typhus, cholera, scarlet fever, chickenpox, and whooping cough. As we shall see later in the book, the victory of Cortés over Montezuma had less to do with military acumen and more to do with the vulnerability of the Indians to smallpox. Further, a disease that struck down Aztec and not Spaniard was regarded as supernatural, and this belief greatly facilitated the Indians' conversion to Christianity. Montezuma's kingdom fell to a foe they could not fight and against which they had no immunity. The conquest of America belongs not to the Spaniards, but to smallpox.[4]

Many questions have been asked about the disparate prevalence of diseases in the Old and the New Worlds. Why was the Columbian trade in deadly diseases such a one-way affair? Why do the Amerindians appear to have been in such robust health before the landing of Columbus? In the Old World there was a long tradition of the domestication of animals. This, as we have seen, brought man and microbe into close contact, and, inevitably, immunity (absolute or relative) developed to common diseases. With the cow, dog and pig came human varieties of cowpox (smallpox), distemper (measles) and influenza. Things were very different in the New World, since there was little attraction to the idea of domesticating the native fauna of North America: bison, moose, elk and antelope. Consequently, these animals kept their diseases to themselves!

Another explanation of New and Old World differences in disease prevalence was the barrier, or 'germ filter', created by the Arctic climates around the Bering Strait, which effectively killed off germs, worms and mosquitoes, and prevented their migration from Russia to Alaska.

In other arenas, disease worked against the European and in favour of the indigenous populations. Malaria saved Africa from early exploitation by the white man. (It has been suggested that the decline of ancient Greece was attributable to chronic debilitation caused by malaria, spread by mosquitoes which inhabited swamps which formed when forests were felled.) The black races, probably by some sort of genetic protection offered by the sickle-cell trait, cope better with malaria. The protozoa, *Trypanosoma gambiense*, produces no discernible ill-effects on the antelope, but when the tsetse fly injects it into man, sleeping sickness is the result. Perhaps this represents an eco-system whereby man, the world's premier killer, would feel disinclined to venture too far on to the African savannah.

A similar geographical and climatic divide exists in China between the warm, moist and disease-ridden south around the Yangtze Valley, and the colder, northern areas around the Yellow River. This difference accounts for the relative underdevelopment of the south: a writer in the first century BC records, 'In the area south of the

Yangtze the land is low and the climate humid; adult males die young.'

If micro-organisms are continuously evolving so as to live more harmoniously with their hosts, can humans look forward to a time when infectious diseases no longer induce illness? Probably not, at least in the near future, since this process takes no account of new diseases, caused either by previously unknown micro-organisms or by long-established micro-organisms which have undergone genetic mutation. It seems that man's battle with the microbe is far from over.

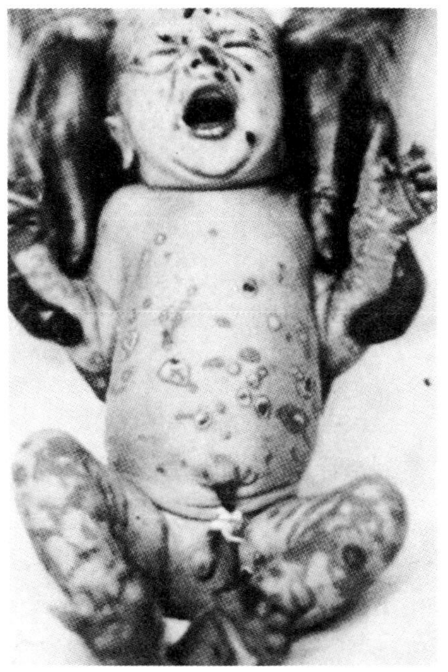

Congenital syphilis

## *Pointing the finger*

There is sometimes a discernible lack of scientific objectivity when it comes to identifying the provenance of deadly diseases. Everyone seems to want to blame any other country but their own. This is well-illustrated by the on-going acrimony which surrounds syphilis and whether Christopher Columbus took the disease with him to America or brought it back with him to Europe. Ironically, the argument is probably academic, since the micro-organism responsible for pinta, which is related to the spirochaete which causes syphilis, probably became established in *Asia* in 15,000 BC. Subsequently, perhaps about 7,000 BC, *Treponema pallidum* evolved to cause the *non*-venereal form of syphilis (i.e. a form of syphilis *not* spread by sexual intercourse), and a mutant form appeared in the late fifteenth century causing a virulent venereal syphilis.

India is thought to have spawned the smallpox virus and the cholera bacterium. Central Asia is attributed with the origin of *Pasteurella pestis*, the micro-organism which causes the Black Death. As commercial trade opened up between East and West, so did human migration, and with the humans went the black rat, its flea and *Pasteurella pestis*. A lethal combination marched westward. As Zinsser observed, 'Man and the rat share ferocity, omnivorousness, utter destructiveness of other forms of life, adaptability and irresponsible fecundity. Neither of them is of the slightest earthly use to any other species of living things.'

Today, arguments rage just as fiercely to lay the responsibility for AIDS at someone else's door. Did this modern scourge originate in Africa, Haiti or America? The answer is important, not because it gives the rest of us someone to blame, but because it may provide vital clues to the eventual conquest of the disease.

# 2 THREE DEADLY SCOURGES

## 1 The Black Death

*The Black Death or the bubonic plague is an infectious disease caused by a bacterium,* Pasteurella pestis, *which is spread from rat to man by a flea. The black house rat,* Rattus rattus, *is the culprit, and not its cousin, the brown field or sewer rat. When a human being is infected it is an accidental occurrence, usually because a hungry flea whose stomach is clogged (a 'blocked' flea), becomes ravenous for a blood meal and resorts to biting anything in its vicinity, humans included. Some of the meal is regurgitated by the flea into the victim's bloodstream, and the plague germs are disseminated throughout the body. The flea also evacuates its bowels, and faeces loaded with bacteria is deposited on to the skin: minor abrasions caused by scratching allow the germs a second portal of entry into the body. When the rats themselves die of the plague (since they are not immune), fleas jump from the carcass on to the first warm-blooded animal that passes by. Human cases of plague were greatest when they came into close proximity with rats and their fleas: pauper hovels were an ideal environment for rats; the stone-built castles of the nobility provided cold comfort.*

*Infection can spread by clothing which harbours blocked fleas. The other, much rarer, way in which the bacterium enters the human body is as a result of being breathed into the lungs when carers get too close to plague victims. Rarer still is infection as a result of the ingestion of contaminated meat (including human cannibalism in those times when famine was so severe that people murdered and ate their relatives).*

*The characteristic sign of infection was the appearance of the* bubo, *a hard enlargement of a gland – usually in the groin, since the flea most often bites its victims' legs. Skin blotches, known variously as 'blains', 'tokens' or 'whelks', appeared at the same time, or shortly after, the bubo. Such was the intensity of pain of the enlarging bubo that many patients threw themselves out of windows to hasten death.*

Plague doctor (Marseilles, 1720). Dressed in leather, his beak filled with purifying spices and carrying a wand to feel pulses at a distance

*Death would ordinarily come on the third or fourth day. The pneumonic plague, spread by droplet infection and breathed into the lungs, was universally fatal. Spitting of blood was the hallmark of this fatal, pneumonic, form of the disease.*

### *From whence came this destroying angel?*

The Black Death has a unique hold on the European imagination.[1] Despite the fact that it is now three hundred years since its last major visitation in Europe, the very name evokes images of panic, pain and precipitous death. The German Dr Hecker, writing in 1846, struck a punitive note: 'That Omnipotence which has called the world with all its living creatures into one animated being, especially reveals himself in the desolation of great pestilences … Nature is not satisfied with the ordinary alternations of life and death, and the destroying angel waves over man and beast his flaming sword.' And never was the angel so destructive as when he brought the Black Death down upon mankind.[2]

Plague comes from the Latin, *plaga*, meaning a blow or a stroke, divinely aimed, and although there are many ancient references to plague, it is not thought that these were all bubonic: the word became a rubric for any infectious disease with a high mortality. The *Black* Death is a relatively recent name given to the epidemic of bubonic plague which devastated Europe with such merciless virulence in 1348 – writers in the fourteenth century called it 'The Great Pestilence', and it was not referred to as 'The Black Death' until the nineteenth century. The origin of the adjective is a mystery, since the disease did not produce blackening of the skin (this was much more characteristic of smallpox). Perhaps it was a fanciful allusion to the plague as a man riding the skies on a black horse.

Recent scholarship has shown that previous estimates of the mortality attributable to the Black Death were unreliable and exaggerated. It is now thought that deaths were nearer thirty per cent than fifty per cent. But stop a moment to fully absorb the magnitude of even such a revised figure, and imagine, in your street, in your work, in your school, if one person in every three were to die within the next week.

Where and when did the Black Death originate? Since biblical references are deemed too unreliable, experts now agree that the first unequivocal description of bubonic plague was the outbreak in the Levant around 300 BC. Eight hundred years later, the Plague of Justinian (AD 542–3), can be confidently regarded as bubonic from the account given by Procopius. For the next 800 years, bubonic plague disappears from Europe, until its re-emergence as the Black Death at the end of the fourteenth century. This second pandemic lasted on and off until the seventeenth century (including the Great Plague of London in 1665), when, again, it went into mysterious decline. Its final appearance on the grand scale was the Indian pandemic in 1896.

Historical research indicates that the source of these pandemics was a reservoir of infected rats in Central Asia. From this focus, merchants travelled to China, India, Russia and the Middle East. And where man went, the black rat and its predatory flea were bound to follow. Heading west, man, rodent and insect took the Silk Road to Syria. This early commercial traffic between the East and the West went largely undocumented. (The only reason we have an account of the travels of Marco Polo was because he was thrown into a Genoese gaol and a literate cell mate thought it worth recording his adventures.) In 1346 *Pasteurella pestis* arrived in the Crimea, brought by a Mongol prince who was laying siege to the town of Caffa.

Rumours had been circulating for some time in Europe about a new infectious disease slowly heading west, but the sheer distances involved ensured that the news evoked only minor interest until the Siege of Caffa. Gabriel de Mussis tells how a group of Genoese merchants had taken refuge in Caffa and how the Mongols surrounded the town and settled themselves down to a lengthy siege – until the appearance of a highly infectious disease began to decimate their numbers. The siege was abandoned, but not before the Mongols had decided to share their misfortune with the Christians: in the first known instance of biological warfare, they catapulted their dead over the walls and into the besieged town. Those who did not immediately succumb took to sea. They sailed into the Mediterranean: dying men, sick rats and blocked fleas.

In 1347 the plague fell upon Constantinople. Nicephoros Gregoras wrote, 'The calamity [affected] men as well as women, rich and poor, old and young ... [It] did not destroy men only, but many animals living with and domesticated by men. I speak of dogs and horses and all species of birds, even the rats that happened to live within the walls of the houses. During that time, Andronikos, the youngest of the king's sons died.' (The King himself, John VI, abdicated in 1355 and retired to a monastery to write a history of the Byzantine Empire.) 'Sputum suffused with blood was brought up and disgusting and stinking breath from within. The throat and tongue, parched from the heat, were black and congested with blood. Great abscesses [buboes] were formed on the legs or the arms, from which, when cut, a large quantity of foul-smelling pus flowed .... Most terrible was the discouragement. Whenever people felt sick there was no hope left for recovery.'[3]

But to return to the ships fleeing Caffa. In 1348 three galleys sought safe haven in Genoa (after all, the merchants were Genoese), but the population had been forewarned of their deadly cargo and saw off the ships by firing burning arrows into their sails. The refugees made for Sicily, and here it was that plague gained its European foothold. By the time the townsfolk of Messina realized something was wrong, it was already too late. The plague ravaged the town, the fleeing population effectively spreading the infection to neighbouring Catania. Friar Michael of Piazza described the suffering of the Sicilians: swellings in the groin would rapidly enlarge from the size of a walnut to that of a hen's egg; people delirious with fever and racked with pain would finally be released from their agonies on the third or fourth day. The onset of a headache was an ominous sign, usually presaging death within seventy-two hours. Some victims, at the onset of their symptoms, and anticipating solitary death, would sew themselves into their shrouds to facilitate removal and burial by relatives. The Patriarch himself died. With some satisfaction the Friar also records the death of Duke Giovanni 'who had carefully avoided every infected house and every infected patient'.

## *The rest of Europe braces itself*

Within three months the plague had made its appearance on mainland Italy, entering at Pisa and raging throughout Tuscany. It was only a matter of time before the waves of infection spread outwards like ripples on a pond to infect the expectant populations of Germany, France, Spain and Britain.

Its ravages in Florence were vividly recorded by Petrarch and Giovanni Boccaccio. Petrarch obviously believed things would never be worse: 'Oh, happy posterity, who will not experience such abysmal woe and will look upon our testimony as a fable.' In *The Decameron*, Boccaccio describes the appearance of buboes in the groin and under the armpits, and the spread of black spots over the rest of the body. He highlights the contagion, whereby healthy people fell sick merely by touching the clothes of plague victims. Animals had no immunity and the houses and streets were littered with the corpses of dogs and cats. Boccaccio tells of two pigs who pushed their snouts into the infected clothing of a plague victim and 'each turning twice or thrice about, they both fell down dead'.

Indiscriminate and undignified death were the hallmarks of the plague: 'all the matter which exuded from their bodies let off an unbearable stench; sweat, excrement, spittle, breath, so fetid as to be overpowering'. There are accounts of some humans, like the two pigs, dropping dead immediately upon contact with a plague victim. The population, often including priests and doctors, fled the towns, but the plague went with them. Neighbouring communities closed their gates on the deadly refugees, but in vain. There was wholesale abandonment of sick relatives. Those rich enough to own country houses wasted little time in packing up and leaving. Bodies piled up, stinking and unburied. There were empty houses full of valuables: one had only to walk in and help oneself – and pray to God that avarice was not punished by death.

Some sought protection through isolation. They barricaded themselves in their homes, and put faith in temperance and shows of piety. Others opted for hedonism, spending their final hours in drunken orgies, there being no shortage of sexual partners. Boccaccio again:

> [Some] banded together, and, disassociating themselves from all others, formed communities in houses where there were no sick, and lived a separate and secluded life, which they regulated with utmost care, avoiding every luxury, but eating and drinking very moderately of the most delicate viands and the finest wines, holding converse with none but one another, lest tidings of sickness or death should reach them, and diverting their minds with music and such other delights as they could devise ... [Others] maintained that to drink freely, to frequent places of public resort, and to take their pleasure with song and revel, sparing to satisfy no appetite, and to laugh and mock at no event, was the sovereign remedy for so great an evil: and that which they affirmed they also put into practice, resorting day and night, now to this tavern, now to that, drinking with an entire disregard of rule or measure ... And it is not only the laity who behave thus, but the nuns in the convent also, neglecting their rules, abandon themselves to carnal lust, and deem that by voluptuousness and excess they will prolong their lives.

Sexual excess became commonplace. In the cathedral of Alby, a fresco depicts sodomy. Homosexuality and incest flourished. Instant marriage was the order of the day – sometimes of a couple who had only known each other a matter of hours. Widowhood was just as rapid, and so too was swift re-marriage – a woman in Nimeguen married three men in six weeks. Toothless old hags, monied by an unexpected inheritance, were courted by handsome young men.

There were those who sought a middle course 'not being so daintily dieted as the first, nor drinking so dissolutely as the second'. These attempted to protect themselves with 'nose-gayes', the sweet scent hopefully warding off poisonous atmospheric miasmas.

Fear of death often outweighed family responsibilities:

And fathers children leave to die
And children from their parents fly

The rich were forsaken by their servants, or persuaded to stay on at vastly increased pay. Victims' cries for water would reverberate around empty houses. Corpses were left unburied or flung into the nearest mass grave by prisoners released from gaol for that very purpose. (Not all victims were bundled into carts and dumped in communal graves. When the plague returned to Venice in 1575–7 it carried off the painter Titian, already in his late eighties. The old man, who had brought so much glory to Venice, was awarded a public funeral, including lying in state, before interment in S. Maria Glorioso dei Frari.) The stench of decomposing bodies filled the air, especially in hot weather. Children in Vienna were described clinging to the breasts of dead mothers or clambering on to the carts so as not to be separated from their parents. The plague was the source of many legends about canine fidelity, when spouses and children would leave the family dog as the victim's only companion. But animals themselves fell victim to the plague and diseased dogs roamed the deserted streets. An instance is cited of a dog's susceptibility to plague being put to good use: physicians suspended a live dog above the mass grave of plague victims – the dog's death after three hours was taken to indicate that the grave was still infectious and that more earth should be heaped on to the existing corpses. Accounts, probably apocryphal, are given of roaming packs of wolves entering houses and devouring untended babies.

Machiavelli's account of the plague in Florence in 1527 paints a similar picture to that of Boccaccio, 179 years before: deserted towns, houses and shops closed and shuttered, crime out of control, the search for scapegoats, and the periods of uncanny silence, interspersed with the maniacal chanting and the singing of grave-diggers. Because the rich were generally the first to leave, the rule of law generally went with them. Gangs of thugs roamed the streets, intent on plunder. Women were raped by lawless grave-diggers then left to die.

For fear of being confined themselves in the pest (plague) house, relatives of victims would keep the deaths secret and hide the corpses under the floorboards.

Similar descriptions are given about later plague visitations. From an account of plague in Naples in 1656: 'The multitudes of birds enticed by the carrion of the corpses, the stench of which is overwhelming.' The air was filled with 'woeful weeping', as people died painful and lonely deaths. Corpses piled up in the streets, gnawed by animals. Noblemen, bereft of their servants, were forced to fend for themselves, to scurry in search of food or to buy oil at extortionate prices so as not to die in the dark. The trappings of wealth became meaningless; only survival mattered.

From a letter written in Danzig about the outbreak in 1709:

> Not far from my lodgings a stout woman who had died was being carried away, and, perhaps, because the bearers were too weak, they stumbled with the coffin, which flew from their shoulders and broke into pieces, so that the naked corpse fell out, revealing such a fearful sight that it so frightened one of the bearers that he immediately sank dead to the ground. No one is sure of his life for a single hour. Although one might think that the proximity of death would act as a deterrent from sin, yet desperate minds seem to be encouraged by the scourge of death to still greater misdeeds.

Gangs entered houses, murdering the sick and stealing their goods. A macabre postscript reads: 'I have often heard that the people are frequently not quite dead and are yet carried away by impatient grave diggers.'

The rapidity of death was chillingly evoked by Boccaccio for future generations to shudder and count their blessings: 'How many valiant and comely young men ... were seen to dine in the morning with their Parents and Friends, and went to sup in another world with their Predecessors?'

Sometimes whole families were wiped out. One tombstone asked passers-by:

> Is it not sad and moving to relate,
> I, Hans Tuchmacher, died with fourteen children on the
> same date
>
> (1533)

Despite all-conquering death, the satirist Francesco Berni (*c.* 1490–1536) was able to find wry humour in times of despair:

> The pestilence time is good ... Firstly, it carries off the rabble, it destroys them, makes holes among them and thins them out – like a housewife among the geese at Allhallowtide! In the churches there are none to press upon you. Besides, none keep any record of buying or borrowing. Yea, buy and make debts, for there will be no creditors to trouble you. And if a creditor should come, tell him that your head aches, that your arm pricks, he straight will go away.

The Black Death entered France at Marseilles only a month or so after its appearance in mainland Italy. Clement VI, the Pope at Avignon, decided on self preservation, and, following the advice of his physician, Guy de Chauliac, retired to his apartments, choosing to be out to all visitors. This set many a papal precedent and a number of pontiffs sought to put hundreds of miles between themselves and their sickly flock: Nicholas V, Pius II, Sixtus IV and Adrian VI. It is not surprising that in the absence of the Head of the Catholic Church, pagan rituals of animal sacrifice experienced something of a renaissance. The King fled Paris for Normandy, but the pestilence followed. In Bordeaux it killed Princess Joan, daughter of Edward III of England, on her way to marry the son of the King of Castille.

The high contagiousness of the plague discouraged physicians doing house calls, and de Chauliac himself admitted that he only visited the sick for fear of disgrace: 'As for me, to avoid infamy, I did not dare absent myself, but still I was in continual fear.' There was no shortage of apologists for absentee physicians: 'No one is so blind and senseless that he should care more for the salvation of others than for his own, particularly in the case of so infectious a disease.' De Chauliac eventually paid the price, succumbing to the plague in 1368.[4]

Cardinals and bishops were usually as scared as physicians and fled as rapidly and as far. Lowly priests, obliged to stay, used to distance themselves from the dying by dipping cotton-wool in consecrated oil, attaching it to the end of a rod, and pushing it through a hole in the door. A similar strategy could be used to offer the host to the dying. Other priests showed a reckless bravery: one, spotting a body move among a heap of plague dead, rushed to give the holy sacrament.

The Church became rich from the gifts of people anxious to propitiate their sins. But, not surprisingly, these practices caused opposition and resentment towards the Church, often from within. 'How contemptible the Church has grown, especially in its most important representatives, who lead a bad life and have sunk even deeper than the others. For the shepherds of the Church feed themselves instead of their flocks, these they shear or rather fleece. Simony has become so prevalent among the clergy ... [they] shamelessly buy and sell ecclesiastical livings.'

Those doctors who chose to stay did not escape criticism.

If the patient was very rich, priests and physicians would vie with one another to be at his bedside. If the victim died, the doctor was responsible; if he survived, it was solely due to the intercession of prayers. On the other hand, if the doctors were too successful and too many of their patients recovered, they were suspected of using black magic. Others blamed physicians for fomenting panic in order that they might receive larger consultation fees. A later visitation of the plague in Marseilles in 1720 shows a doctor dressed in an oiled overall, with a false nose filled with aromatic substances to neutralize the miasma, spectacles to protect the eyes and a wand to feel pulses at a distance.

Laura died of plague in Avignon in 1348 and Petrarch wrote in the margin of his copy of Virgil:

> Laura, illustrious by her virtues, and long celebrated in my songs, first greeted my eyes in the days of my youth, the 6th April, 1327, at Avignon; and in the same city, at the same hour of the same 6th April, but in the year 1348, withdrew from life, whilst I was at Verona, unconscious of my loss ... Her chaste and lovely body was interred on the evening of the same day in the Church of the Minorities: her soul, as I believe, returned to heaven, whence it came.

## *The Black Death enters England*

*Pasteurella pestis* crossed the Channel in 1348 when Edward III sat on the English throne. 'In this year 1348, in Melcombe [now part of Weymouth], in the county of Dorset, a little before the Feast of St John the Baptist, two ships, one of them from Bristol, came alongside. One of the sailors had brought with him from Gascony the seeds of the terrible pestilence and, through him, the men of the town of Melcombe were the first in England to be infected.' The exact date of disembarkation is uncertain, but fell towards the end of June or early July.

Thenceforth the progress of the plague in Britain can be charted by ecclesiastical records, though these have to be interpreted with caution in regard to estimates of mortality. Because of the scarcity of priests – either through cowardice or because they themselves were dead of the plague – vast numbers of victims were denied the sacrament in their last hours. The situation became so serious that in 1349 the Bishop of Bath and Wells wrote, 'If they [plague victims] are on the point of death and cannot secure the services of a priest, then they should make confession to each other, as is permitted in the teaching of the Apostles, whether to a layman or, if no man is present, then even to a woman.' The good Bishop himself, aping the precedent of his pope, stayed safely indoors for six months in Wiveliscombe, a remote village. Those of his clergy who took their duties more seriously often paid with their lives: nearly half of the priests of Bath and Wells died of the plague. The places of the devout clergy were often taken by men of lesser calibre, many of whom were illiterate. This process had profound effects upon medieval hierarchies. Something of the clerical aura vanished forever, and in December 1349, an armed gang vented its anger at the Bishop and attacked him with 'bows, arrows, and iron bars'.

Infection travelled on by sea and overland. Blocked fleas could remain alive in clothing for up to six weeks, snugly hidden in shipments of cotton, grain or furs. Bristol was particularly badly affected, the plague covering the sixty-nine miles from Melcombe in forty-seven days. By the summer of 1349 it had spread to affect virtually every town and village in Devon and Cornwall. Fear prompted exaggeration: '[The plague] consumed nine parts in ten of the men through England, scarce leaving a tenth man alive.' Gloucester tried to introduce a policy of isolation, putting an embargo on all dealings with Bristol, and shutting the city gates against human visitors (but not rodents!). The wealthy were relatively spared, because the rat preferred to nest snugly in the eaves of cottages than in draughty stone castles. This social difference in mortality is well illustrated, albeit in exaggerated form, by the arrival of the plague in Oxford: 'Those that had places and houses in the country retired, and those that were left behind were almost totally swept away.' As the death toll rose, consecrated ground became scarce, and survivors took to burying the dead in plague pits sited outside the city walls.

The relationship between landlord and peasant underwent significant change. Because of the scarcity of labour, the landlord was obliged to pay much higher wages if he wanted the depleted work force to plant and reap. He was even obliged to give over some of his land to the peasants to work themselves. Workers began to travel in order to find landlords willing to pay better wages: labour went on the move for the first time in history. When increased pay and better conditions were not forthcoming, crops rotted in the field.

## *London*

The main onslaught on the capital took place in the early months of 1349. Overcrowding and squalor proved a lethal combination to between twenty and thirty thousand people. The London clergy were particularly hard hit: when John Stratford, Archbishop of Canterbury, died in August 1348 (probably not due to the plague), John Offord was chosen to succeed him: he died of plague in May 1349 before he could be enthroned. His successor, Thomas Bradwardine, died in August 1349. In comparison, royalty got off lightly – except for Princess Joan dying in Bordeaux *en route* for Portugal. Hordes of starving Londoners left the city in search of food and carried plague into the surrounding countryside. Graffiti on the wall of St Mary's Church, Ashwell, Hertfordshire records the anguish of the village: 'Wretched, terrible, destructive year ...' (1350).

In Norfolk, in April 1349, a dispute in law was to be heard between a husband and wife. Despite the fact that courts were held every two months, this case remained unsettled because, by the time of the hearing, all the wife's witnesses were dead, and so too was her husband.

Ireland was not to be spared. Indeed, one of the most haunting accounts of those troubled times has come down to us as an inscription in the margin of *Senchus Mor*, a collection of ancient Irish laws. It reads,

> One thousand three hundred and fifty years from the birth of Christ till this night: and this is the second year since the coming of the plague into Ireland. I have written this in the twentieth year of my age. I am Hugh, son of Conor MacEagen, and whoever reads it let him offer a prayer of mercy for my soul. This is Christmas night, and I place myself under the protection of the King of heaven and earth, beseeching that He will bring me and my friends safe through this plague.

Hugh MacEagen survived, but one third of Britain's population of four million were not so lucky.

## *The search for causes*

In such superstitious times it is not surprising that the blame for the plague was attributed to the wrath of God. It followed, therefore, that the best hope of survival was to propitiate and appease. In Lower Lusatia, they put their faith in a furrow ploughed to encircle the village, driven at midnight by seven naked virgins. We are not told whether this was successful or not.

A more common strategy was to resort to staging miracle plays. The population would promise to mount a large-scale production, on the proviso that God would spare them in order to cast the play and learn the words. Such is supposed to be the origin of the Oberammergau Passion Play: in 1633, Gaspard Schueler left Eschenlohe, where plague was rife, to visit his family in Oberammergau. The plague went with him, and he and eighty-four others died in the following month. A hasty meeting was convened in which the villagers took a solemn vow to produce a play every ten years, in return for God lifting the plague.

Christians tried to find meaning in the indiscriminate slaughter. Cyprian, Bishop of Carthage in 251, wrote:

> Many of us are dying in this mortality, that is many of us are being freed from the world. The mortality is a bane to the Jews and pagans and enemies of Christ; to the servants of God it is a salutary departure. As to the fact that without any discrimination in the human race the just are dying with the unjust, it is not for you to think that the destruction is a common one for both the evil and the good. The just are called to refreshment, the unjust are carried off to torture; protection is more quickly given to the faithful; punishment to the faithless. How suitable, how necessary it is that this plague and pestilence, which seems horrible and deadly, searches out the justice of each and every one and examines the minds of the human race.

Heavenly signs and portents were frequently invoked. The outbreak of 1348 was preceded by the conjunction of Saturn, Jupiter and Mars in Aquarius. People regarded comets with particular unease – especially since the time lag between its appearance and the subsequent disaster often extended over years: in 1618, a large comet spread general terror, and was regarded as the precursor of the calamity which overtook the world fourteen years later. The predictive power of comets waned dramatically when Halley showed that they returned at regular intervals regardless of human sin or divine wrath.

Among a host of other signs of impending doom have been earthquakes, crop failures, children playing at funerals, fireballs, rains of snakes, swarms of locusts or frogs, noisy birds, aborting women, abundance of hazelnuts, apparitions of all types, and an unusual sweetness in the air.

To most, contagion was evident by the experience of their own eyes, and many believed that the disease spread from person to person through noxious air, or miasma. The stench of diseased and rotting bodies inevitably added weight to this theory. It was thought that the breath, even the look, of a victim could kill. Certainly it was thought that anything which had belonged to someone dying of the plague was likely to be contaminated: 'Any that touched the clothes of the sick or aught else that had been touched or used by them, seemed thereby to contract the disease.'

## *The search for scapegoats*

Any minority group was at risk of being blamed for bringing the plague: Arabs were blamed by the Spanish, English by the inhabitants of Narbonne, and lepers by almost everyone. The Jews represented such an identifiable and vulnerable group, made unpopular through their money-lending activities: viewed as the Antichrist, they were deemed capable of all diabolic activities, including the murder of Christian children. Those intent on persecuting and murdering the Jews chose to ignore the fact that Jews died from the effects of the plague just as much as Christians.

Dogma insisted that the Jews were bent on nothing less than the total extermination of Christians. To achieve their end, the Jews, abetted by lepers, were deliberately poisoning water supplies. As early as May 1348, all the Jews in a town in Provence were put to the torch. Other anti-Semitic atrocities were committed at Narbonne. Papal bulls, proclaiming the innocence of the Jews, were ignored. Recalcitrant Jews – those who did not immediately admit their crimes and go on to incriminate others – soon confessed when stretched on the rack. Dispensations were sometimes offered to children, beautiful women, or those willing to be baptised. The people of Strasbourg murdered 2,000 Jews weeks before the arrival of the plague in their city. In Basle in 1348, all Jews were rounded up and confined in a wooden building which was then torched. In Speyer, murdered Jews were bundled into wine-casks and floated on the Rhine. Some Jews pre-empted their fate and immolated themselves. Such persecution was common in Germany, Austria, France, Italy and Spain. In England the Jews were not persecuted – due to the fact that King Edward I had expelled them in 1290! In Poland, Jews were given protection by King Casimir the Great at the behest of his Jewish mistress, Esther.

In 1348 a trial was held of a Jew accused of poisoning the well at Chillon: 'Banditono, a Jew of Villeneuf, was also subjected to slight torture on the rack; afterwards, when taken off the rack, after a long time, he confessed that he had placed a quantity of poison, roughly the size of a walnut, which had been given him by Mussus, a Jew, at Thur, near Vevey, in the well at Carutet, to poison the gentiles.'

Conspiracies need not always involve Jews. In 1530 in Geneva, a young man, Michael Caddod, was seen to throw down a handkerchief in the street. The person who picked it up was aware of its foul smell and became suspicious. Caddod was arrested. Under torture, he implicated Jean Placet, keeper of the pest (plague) house, his wife, and Jehan Dufour, the priest at the pest house. They were all tortured and confessed to drying the purulent discharges from buboes in order to spread the plague, increase admissions to the pest house and rob the victims after their death. The perpetrators had their hands cut off, were then lacerated with red-hot pincers and finally beheaded. Fifteen years later, when the plague returned to Geneva, a similar need to identify conspirators resulted in the conviction and execution of nineteen men and seven women, found guilty of smearing door-handles with material obtained from the amputated foot of a plague victim.

Ambroise Paré, who should have known better, was quite willing to believe in conspiracies:

> [Magistrates] must keep an eye on certain thieves, murderers, poisoners, worse than inhuman, who grease and smear the walls and doors of rich houses with matter from buboes and carbuncles and other excretions of the plague-stricken, so as to infect the houses and thus be able to break into them, pillage and strip them, and even strangle the poor sick in their beds: which was done at Lyons in the year 1565.[5]

Plague, like many other infectious diseases, was sometimes spread deliberately. Barbara Thutin, a servant girl of Konigsberg, gave plague to her master by collecting garments previously belonging to victims. She herself died, but her body was later exhumed and she was publicly hanged.

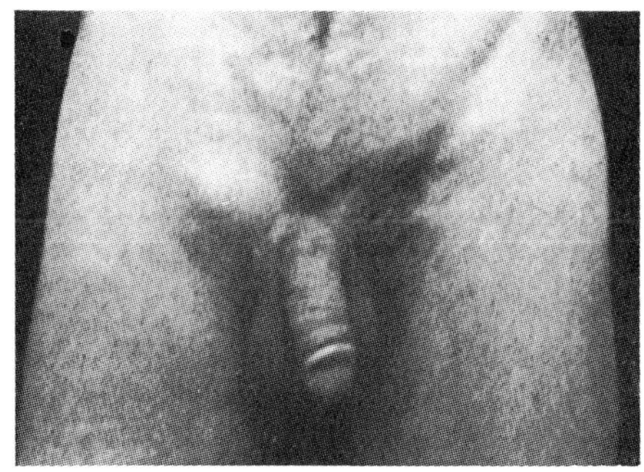

Bubo (as in 'Bubonic' Plague) in the groin

## *Remedies*

> Three little words the plague dispel,
> Quick, far and late, where'er you dwell.
> Start quick, go far and right away
> And with return till late delay.
>
> Rhazes, an Arabian physician

The Black Death was never a Great Leveller like smallpox or malaria: the rich were much more likely to survive than the poor. Consequently the depiction of the Dance of Death – most notably in Basle – showing equality of humankind in the face of death and in the sight of God, did not apply equally to its timing: the rich could follow the advice of Rhazes and greatly lengthen their allotted span on earth.

Popes rationalized Rhazes' advice by persuading themselves that they needed to stay alive in order to give spiritual succour to their flock. As we have seen, many lesser clerics followed papal precedence. Royalty quitted capitals for country palaces, the better to reign over their subjects. Those too poor or too sick to retire to healthier rural areas had the choice of a wide variety of so-called remedies. As we have seen, abstinence and overindulgence were recommended in equal measure. Many remedies depended for their supposed efficacy on the theory that the plague was spread by breathing in foul air. Various substances were burnt in the hope of neutralizing the noxious miasmata: incense, lemon, oak leaves, rosemary, sage, lavender, camphor and sulphur. When these burnings were carried out on a large scale, birds, overcome by the fumes, would drop out of their nests, dead. People carried handkerchiefs impregnated with aromatic oils which they sniffed: eau de Cologne was invented for just this purpose in 1700. Others resorted to smoking tobacco or sniffing snuff. With the benefit of hindsight it can be argued that these aromas discouraged fleas from landing and feeding.

Small birds were kept for the specific purpose of filtering the poisons and keeping the air circulating. Spiders were also considered to purify the air. Warm bread was placed on the mouth of the dying to absorb exhaled poisons. Going to the opposite extreme, because it was erroneously thought that people whose job it was to clean latrines appeared to have an immunity, it was recommended that protection from the plague could be got by standing above a latrine and inhaling the stench!

Others attested to bathing in goats' urine – or drinking one's own urine. Alternatively the urine could be boiled dry and the salts spread on a piece of bread, preferably mixed with menstrual blood. The more disgusting the remedy, the greater its supposed potency.

Still more occult remedies[6] included the wearing of amulets inscribed with words formed into a magic triangle:

A B R A C A D A B R A
B R A C A D A B R
R A C A D A B
A C A D A
C A D
A

If, despite all these prophylactics, one was unlucky (or sinful) enough to contract the plague, isolation was the first line of defense. Quarantine was set at forty days to correspond to the number of days Christ spent in the wilderness. Physicians, if they could be persuaded to visit, might apply a freshly sacrificed pigeon or puppy to the forehead; or prescribe the pus from mature buboes, swallowed in spoonfuls. Using a more scientific approach, physicians sometimes lanced the buboes and cauterized the pus with hot irons.

## *Flagellants and the dancing manias*

The Brotherhood of the Flagellants or Brethren of the Cross originated in Dresden in 1349 and represent a bizarre reaction to the plague, reminiscent of mass hysteria. The movement took root in Germany and comprised large groups of people, some two to three hundred strong, moving in long crocodiles, two by two, men at the front, women bringing up the rear. They moved silently, eyes down turned, faces cowled, dressed in black cloaks with red crosses on the back and front. Barefooted, each carried a three-tailed scourge with which to lash their bodies: through knots in the scourge protruded sharpened iron spikes. In a local church the flagellants would form themselves into a circle, strip to the waist, and throw themselves to the ground as if crucified. They used the scourges to beat their backs and breasts, whipping themselves, quite literally, into a religious frenzy. It was a powerful show, given twice daily. The local people would welcome the flagellants as a much-needed diversion from the miseries of their plague-ridden lives. Initially the flagellants were tolerated by the clergy, even though they often bitterly criticized the Catholic Church. They also directed their wrath at the rich, to the great satisfaction of the poor.

By the time they arrived in London in 1349 they were a spent force, and regarded with indifference. Since they sought to appeal directly to the mercy of God, bypassing the priesthood, it was inevitable that they would eventually come into open conflict with the Church. In the same year, the Pope finally declared them enemies of the Church and popular opinion turned against them. Flagellation was not outlawed – it merely had to be done in the privacy of one's own home! There is little doubt that in their attempts to spread their philosophy they succeeded in spreading the plague.

Another form of mass hysteria were the dancing manias: 'The effects of the Black Death had not yet subsided, and the graves of millions of its victims were scarcely closed, when a strange delusion arose in Germany [in 1374], which took possession of the minds of men, and, in spite of the divinity of our nature, hurried away body and soul into the magic circle of hellish superstition.' Called the dance of St John or St Vitus, the patron saint of epileptics and choreatics, it caused men and women to leap about in frenzy, foam and rage, as if possessed by the Devil. Some danced until they dropped, often half-naked and wearing wreaths in their hair. Totally insensible to others, they would shriek and appear to convulse. On recovery, some would say that they felt that they had been drowning in a river of blood and had to leap high in order not to be submerged. A second epidemic broke out in Strasbourg in 1518.[7]

### *The plague returns to London: Defoe and Pepys*

No convincing cases of plague occurred in Britain before the fourteenth century. This is probably because, before that date, the black rat population was not sufficiently large to initiate or maintain an epidemic. For the plague to re-emerge, a sufficient density of rats was needed, since if there were too few rats then only isolated human cases would result (as in rodents today).

Plague returned to Britain in 1665. Accounts of this visitation have come to us from Daniel Defoe and Samuel Pepys, though Defoe was only six years old at the time. Samuel Pepys lived through the plague in London in 1665/6 but, although intermittently fearful, he was not tempted to leave the capital, nor did it lessen his appetite for pleasure. He first refers to 'great fears of the sickness' in May 1665, and a month later records how 'much against my will, I did in Drury Lane see two or three houses marked with a red cross upon the doors, and "Lord have mercy on us" writ there'. Once, returning home late, Pepys 'met a dead corpse of the plague in a narrow alley'. In July, with plague deaths mounting alarmingly, the court moved to Salisbury, and Pepys moved his wife out to Woolwich.

Despite the dire times Pepys did not lose his ability to enjoy life, and care nothing for the consequences. With his wife safely out of town (in both senses), he went with Mary from the 'Harp and Ball' to take the air in Hampstead, and 'had what pleasure almost I would with her'. On 30 September 1665, at a time when the weekly toll was 6,000, he writes, 'I do end this month with the greatest of content, and may say that these three months, for joy, health, and profit, have been much the greatest that ever I received in all my life, having nothing upon me but the consideration of the sicklinesse of the season during this great plague to mortify me.' He piously adds, 'For all which, the Lord be praised!' His entry for 31 December 1665 reads, 'I have never lived so merrily as I have done this plague time … and great store of dancings we had at my cost at my lodgings. The great evil of this year, and the only one indeed, is the fall of my Lord of Sandwich, whose mistake about the prizes hath undone him.' As for Pepys, he had stayed at his post, faced the pestilence and monopolized all business. As winter approached and the pestilence diminished, people returned to the capital. Noblemen's coaches once again trundled down the grass-grown streets. Mrs Pepys returned, and so did Mr Mills, the preacher, whose first sermon for six months attempted to excuse himself to his flock and explain why he was so quick to leave the city and so reluctant to return. Perhaps he quoted Rhazes.[8]

Defoe's account is far more sombre. In his *Journal of the Plague Year*, he describes the excruciating pain of the ever-swelling buboes – a pain great enough to drive men to suicide. Demented victims even took to burying themselves. His account is a collage of doors daubed with red crosses, the tolling of funeral bells, carts filled to the brim with stinking corpses, and the baneful cries of 'Bring out your dead!'[9]

The children's nursery rhyme

Ring a ring a rosie
A pocket full of posie
Atishoo, atishoo
We all fall down

is supposed to describe the early skin manifestations of the plague, the efforts to neutralize noxious substances with aromatics, the onset of respiratory symptoms and ultimate death.

The sanitizing effect of the Great Fire of London did much to rid London of its rat population and help Britain free itself from plague.

### *The last outbreak of plague in England*

Five miles south of Ipswich, in the parish of Freston in 1910, lived George Chapman, his wife Frances, and four children. On 13 September, Annie, aged nine, was taken suddenly ill at school. Dr Carey was called and found Annie vomiting, and with a temperature of 105 degrees. That night she became delirious, and on the fourth day she died. She was buried one week after her illness started.

The day after the funeral, Mrs Chapman complained of headache and nausea. Again, Dr Carey was called in. He found his patient had developed a fever and a chest infection. Alarmed at the speed of the illness, the doctor asked Mrs Parker from Turkey Farm to nurse her sick neighbour through the night. Dr Carey decided to call in a second opinion, Dr Herbert Brown, from Ipswich, but by the time Brown arrived in Freston, Mrs Chapman was already dead.

Because of poverty, Mr Chapman was obliged to go to work on the morning of his wife's funeral. After the funeral was over and the mourners had left, Mr Chapman took to his bed. So too did Mrs Parker. By now it was clear to the doctors that a rapidly spreading and lethal infection was rampant. Specimens were sent off to Dr Llewellyn Heath in Ipswich for analysis, but before the results were known, both Mr Chapman and Mrs Parker were dead. Funerals were hastily arranged for the following day, and mourners had to have their clothes fumigated and their homes disinfected. The surviving members of the families were isolated in Tattingstone workhouse.

Dr Heath had found *Pasteurella pestis* in the blood samples taken from Mr Brown and Mrs Parker. A government physician, Dr Timbrell Bulstrode, was sent to the area to test the fauna of the district: he found a rat and a hare which tested positive for *Pasteurella pestis*. It is probable that indigenous rats had caught the organism from infected rats which had jumped ship in the Orwell estuary. A concerted effort was made to warn the people of the dangers of too close contact with wild animals (Mr Chapman had recently brought home a rabbit for the family dinner), and a drive was made to exterminate the rat population.[10]

The last fatal cases of naturally occurring plague in Britain were Mrs Bugg and her neighbour Mrs Garrod who died in June 1918 in Erwarton, near Shotley. In August 1962, a research scientist working at Microbiological Research Establishment at Porton Down, Wiltshire, died after accidentally contracting plague.

*Pasteurella pestis* is alive and well ... and living, among other places, in the wild rodents of California. Happily the rodent population is not sufficiently large for the predatory fleas to constitute a threat to human communities, although sporadic, individual human cases are possible.

Plague might well return one day, whether through an upset in the eco-system, or even deliberate biological warfare. Dr Rieux, in Camus's *The Plague*, knew that the crowd's rejoicing was premature, and that the plague bacillus was not dead, but merely biding its time until the day when it would rouse the rats again and 'send them forth to die in a happy city.'

# 2 CHOLERA

*Cholera is an acute intestinal disease caused by a comma-shaped bacterium,* Vibrio cholerae, *ingested in polluted water. Cholera is endemic in many parts of the world, and it can reach epidemic, even pandemic, proportions. Some convalescing cholera patients continue to excrete the organism in their faeces, thus contributing to its further spread.*

*The most prominent symptom of cholera is diarrhoea, leading to fluid loss (sometimes several litres within hours), dehydration, agonizing muscular cramps, electrolyte imbalance, circulatory collapse and death. Death can be avoided by prompt replacement of fluids. A vaccine against the vibrio is available.*

The earliest references to a disease resembling cholera are in Indian Sanskrit writings dating from 400 BC. Inscriptions on a monolith in a temple in Gujrat, written at the time of Alexander the Great, refer to 'the lips blue, the face haggard, the eyes hollow, the stomach sunk in, the limbs contracted and crumpled as if by fire'. Although often compared to the medieval plague, the mortality from cholera was nowhere near as great: fewer than 1 in 100 people died from cholera, compared to 25-30 in 100 from plague. Yet, despite the lower mortality, cholera had the capacity to induce widespread panic at news of its approach. It is clear that only the minority who drank from a contaminated source developed cholera, but if death came, it came rapidly, usually within three or four days, sometimes three or four hours.

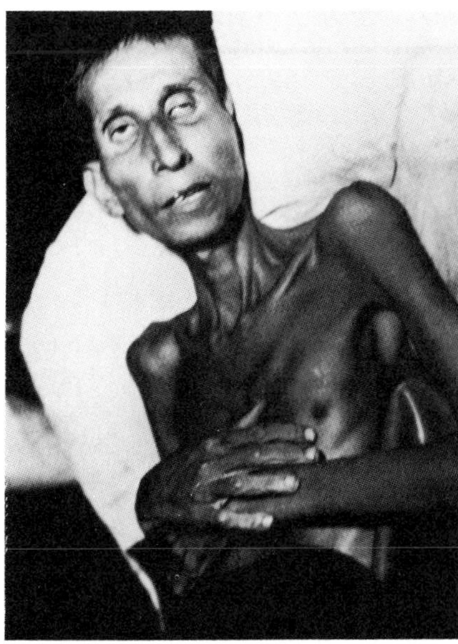

Severe dehydration in a cholera patient

The disease finally broke out of the Indian subcontinent in 1817, spreading along trade routes from its source in Jessore, west to Persia and east to Siam and Burma. A second wave, this time a worldwide epidemic, began in India in 1826, reached Moscow by 1830 and the Baltic by the next year.[11]

Frantic attempts were made by European countries to stop the spread of the disease: strict quarantine measures were applied but appeared ineffective. Because of its disproportionate toll among the poor, rumours were rife that this scourge was the result of deliberate poisoning of the food and water supply. In Hungary the frenzied peasants butchered the well-to-do, and troops murdered their officers. The Germans blamed the British, accusing them of deliberate genocide in India.

Cholera announced its presence some fourteen years before its landfall in England: ample time for vague and academic interest in a disease thousands of miles away, to turn into a mounting unease as the epidemic crept north and west at a slow but inexorable pace, and finally develop into outright panic, denial and recriminations when the first cases were confirmed in Sunderland in 1832.

The relentless progress towards Britain was viewed with trepidation, and fears rose exponentially when, in October 1831, the disease reached Hamburg, only hours away by boat. The British government did its best to be prepared and appointed Charles Grenville as Clerk to the Privy Council. Early on, the Privy Council felt obliged to balance the health of the nation against commercial considerations: quarantine might well prevent spread of the disease, but it would also damage trade. The Privy Council sought the advice of the Royal College of Physicians and got contradictory views regarding the wisdom of quarantine. Hardly an auspicious start! The government decided to set up yet another committee, a Board of Health, which would include six members of the medical profession. The presidency of the board was given to Sir Henry Halford, already President of the Royal College of Physicians.[12] Sir Henry then chose five of his medical cronies ('his intimate friends and toadies'), whom he selected more for their social standing than their medical expertise, still less their knowledge of cholera. *The Lancet*, no friend of the medical establishment, was scathing:

> Emanating from the Privy Council, with Majesty at its head, Sir Henry Halford of course stands prominent; for wherever there is the face of royalty we are sure to find the nose of Sir Henry Halford ... He may be well qualified to instruct us how to endure the noxious atmosphere of a Court, but God protect us from the infliction of his conservative measures ... The appointment of such a person is a scandal to the profession, an insult to those able practitioners who have served in India, and a mockery to the alarmed feelings of the public.

The Board was weighted towards contagionism and consequently quarantine became the primary strategy to counter the advancing pestilence. Although the Privy Council was not impressed with the Board's contagion theory it dared not be seen to ignore its advice and thereby appear to imperil the health of the nation.

When cholera reached Hamburg, barely three days away by sea, the Board's recommendations were watered down. There would be no forcible removal of victims to hospitals – people would go voluntarily or not at all. In this way it was hoped to avoid the riots which broke out on the continent as the workers sensed a middle-class conspiracy. All mention of sanitary cordons was dropped: an omission which was directly responsible for the spread of the disease from Sunderland to Newcastle to Scotland.

There was an early and fundamental disagreement within the medical establishment as to whether cholera was, or was not, contagious, and therefore, whether quarantine of imported goods would, or would not, help to stem its spread. Reluctantly the government agreed to impose quarantine. Grenville observed (erroneously with hindsight), 'All the evidence proves that goods are not capable of bringing in the disorder, but we have appointed a Board of Health, which is contagionist, and we can't get them to subscribe to that opinion. We dare not act without its sanction, and we are obliged to air goods.' Plans were drawn up to isolate infected towns, and to use troops if necessary to enforce quarantine.

The task of preventing or limiting the spread of cholera fell upon the local Boards of Health. Petty bureaucrats came into their own. They, for the most part, lived in parts of towns well away from the

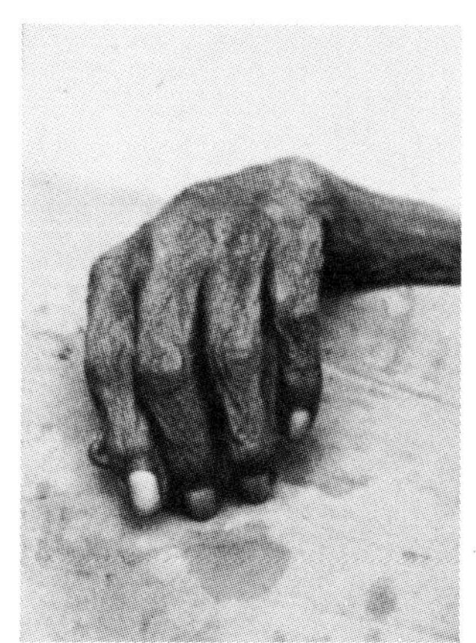

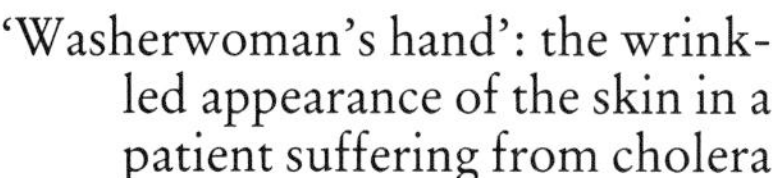

'Washerwoman's hand': the wrinkled appearance of the skin in a patient suffering from cholera

overcrowding and insanitary conditions endured by the poor, where families would have to share a single water tap, or else scoop water by the bucketful from the local river. Water closets were a luxury even for the well-off, and in the majority of homes human excrement drained into a cesspool, or else was dumped in streets or rivers.

The government knew what the symptoms of cholera were from the army medics who had encountered it during postings in India. The disease would usually start with a feeling of general unease or apprehensiveness followed by explosive diarrhoea 'when the whole intestines seem to be emptied at once'. The patient suffered prickly sensations in the limbs and sweated copiously. Any slight movement caused the patient to vomit. The loss of fluid in the diarrhoea would leave the bedroom awash with 'rice-water stools' – actually fragments of the lining of the intestines. Severe dehydration gave the skin a shrunken and shrivelled appearance. Later, excruciating pains occurred in the abdomen, and the skin would turn a deathly blue or black. The pains were likened to a 'sword put in on one side of the waist, just above the hip bone, and drawn through, handle and all'. To obtain some relief the patient sometimes contracted himself into a ball, which proved impossible to be rolled out after death. Dehydration would produce a profound state of collapse, eyes dulled and turned upwards, the victim resigned to his fate.[13]

## *Sunderland, 1831*

In 1831 Sunderland was a thriving port at the mouth of the River Wear. From its quays, ships unloaded cargoes from Russia and Germany. Its population of 19,000 was overwhelmingly working class. In April, the cholera threat was deemed serious enough to impose a fifteen-day quarantine on all goods imported from Russia. Dr Reid Clanny was put in charge: he was assisted by Dr James Butler Kell who had had first-hand knowledge of cholera in India. Unfortunately Kell was not highly thought of among the medical elite of Sunderland, stigmatized by being a surgeon and not a physician, and an *army* surgeon to boot! No one was prepared to heed Kell's advice, even on the death of Robert Henry, a ship's pilot, who had succumbed after suffering severe abdominal cramps and whose fingers and toes had turned blue-black. The most likely cause of Henry's death was that he had broken quarantine regulations, but Kell was never allowed to investigate fully. Thus, the man who knew most about cholera had no choice but to watch those who knew nothing, from the sidelines, growing ever more angry and frustrated.

Initial zeal by the town's doctors soon waned, and attendance at local meetings, called to discuss the impending threat, dropped off precipitously. This was unfortunate since very few were present at the meeting on 30 August to hear one doctor report that he believed he had seen a case of cholera!

In October, Dr Clanny was called in to see Robert Joyce, whose doctor thought might have cholera. Nothing was proved conclusively. A week later, though it did not come to light until three months afterwards, Isabella Hazard, aged twelve, became violently ill in her home in Fish Quay at 4 a.m. Within twelve hours she was dead. Her own mother pointed to the diagnosis: 'What makes the child so *black*?' Neither Clanny nor Kell was consulted about Isabella's death. The first *official* victim of cholera in Britain was William Sproat, who also lived in Fish Quay, only yards from the Hazards. After feeling generally unwell for about a week, Sproat began to vomit and purge. He appeared to improve but later relapsed and died within the week. In quick succession Sproat's granddaughter and son were taken ill.

Despite Kell's experience and first-hand knowledge of cholera, and the opinion of Clanny, the other doctors of Sunderland declared that there was no evidence that Asiatic cholera had entered Britain. Their obstinacy continued despite the death of William Sproat Junior, and of Elizabeth Turnbull, one of the nurses who looked after him at the infirmary. More fatalities followed and a government commissioner was despatched from London. The quarantine was being rigorously applied, but, instead of seeing this as their best chance to limit the spread of cholera, business interests in Sunderland only saw it as a threat to their livelihood. The merchants and ship owners constituted a powerful anti-quarantine lobby, wielding inordinate influence in the town, *even upon the doctors*. A macabre farce was acted out: while people died of cholera, the town worthies were denying that any such disease existed. The Marquis of Londonderry, who had financial interests in the coal trade, considered himself enough of a medical expert to write to the *London Standard* declaring that there was no cholera and that it was all a false alarm.

A group of anti-quarantine business men even managed to take over the Sunderland Board of Health and stop the publication of notices concerning new cases of cholera. Then, incredibly, on 12 November, nearly all the medical men of Sunderland stated publicly that the recent deaths were definitely *not* due to cholera, and that quarantine was quite unnecessary! National reporting of this meeting brought derision down upon the doctors. Many, after a little reflection, claimed that they had been misreported. A face-saving 'compromise' was agreed, which amply illustrated the continuing influence of commercial considerations over those of public health:

> That a disease possessing every symptom of epidemic cholera is now existing in this town ... that there is not the slightest ground for imagining that it has been imported ... that it appears to have arisen from atmospheric distemperature ... and that the interruption of the commerce of the port seems to offer the most probable means of extending the disease, by depriving the industrious poor of their bread and thus placing their families in the depths of misery and distress.

Grenville wrote in his diary that 'the conduct of the people of Sunderland on this occasion is more suitable to the barbarianism of the interior of Africa than to a town in a civilized country.' *The Lancet* could not contain its indignation:

> We will not speak of the conduct of many practitioners in Sunderland in those terms of reprobation which we think it so well deserves. That a posse of starving colliers should threaten to 'burn the doctors' who dare to admit the existence of the disease in that town is scarcely a matter of surprise, but that there should be found a set of well educated men weak enough to pander to the clamorous prejudices of the populace, is almost beyond credibility.

If the medical men could deny the very existence of cholera, it was small wonder that the poor chose to ignore the advice given by the government. Part of the answer to this apparent wanton disregard of commonsense was that the disease had been expected to start suddenly and spread rapidly. Instead, the outbreak was sporadic, sparing the vast majority, its identity a source of argument even among the doctors themselves. Further, sporadic outbreaks of violent diarrhoea had occurred before and had been dubbed 'English cholera', and, despite occasional deaths, had been largely ignored. False alarms in Glasgow, Hull and Margate induced such a nonchalance in investigating physicians that they were unable to identify the real thing when it presented itself in Sunderland. And all the while quarantine was costing money.

Despite denial of its existence, cholera marched on. Rumours were rife about patients forced against their will into hospital, and dissected whilst still alive. Clothes and bed linen, intended to be burnt, were hoarded away, constituting a source of future infection. In December, magistrates decreed that cholera victims must be interred within twelve hours of death, at least six feet deep, and in a separate part of the cemetery. From William Sproat's death on 23 October to the last day of 1831, cholera claimed 215 lives. It was not until 9 January 1832 that Sunderland was officially declared free of the disease it claimed it never had.

## *Cholera's break-out from Sunderland*

When cholera reached Gateshead on Christmas Day 1831 many people again denied its presence, and the folly of Sunderland was destined to be re-enacted – until the time came when the sheer toll of lives put a stop to such dangerous self-deception. A Dr Lawrie wrote, 'The inhabitants of Gateshead fell asleep on the 25 December in perfect security and devoid of panic, but before the sun rose on the 26th fifty-five individuals had been seized, thirty-two of whom were destined not to see it set.' The scenario of denial in the face of the obvious continued in Newcastle, north of the Tyne. Again there were a few scattered cases of diarrhoea, and the medical men hedged their bets, none wishing to be the doctor responsible for initiating quarantine: whilst it *might* be cholera, 'there has been no reason for believing that the cause of death had a Foreign Origin [ie, it could be *English* cholera, a synonym for summer diarrhoea]'.

Edinburgh was infected at the end of January 1832, Glasgow by early February. So anxious were people to dispose of cholera victims that one man in Haddington was 'thrust into his narrow house' whilst still alive. In the village of Dollar, terrified villagers evicted an old woman and burnt down her cottage. She died fifteen hours later, the undertaker leaving her coffin on the turnpike.

The question in most towns now became not 'whether ...' but 'when would the disease arrive?' The increasingly acrimonious disputes between contagionists and miasmatists continued, supported respectively by *The Lancet* and the *Glasgow Medical Journal.* At Dumfries the doctors settled the question democratically by a show of hands, the non-contagionists winning the day.

Doctors debated the treatment of cholera as well as its mode of spread. The two mainstays of treatment were calomel to relieve constipation, and opium to reduce diarrhoea. Paradoxical treatment was even resorted to: since drugs to stop vomiting and diarrhoea were usually unsuccessful, perhaps drugs to exacerbate these symptoms might somehow bring about a cure. Men worn out with purging were given castor-oil as a laxative; women aching with vomiting were plied with mustard and water. Some doctors advocated heat, and one invented an apparatus for blowing hot air under a patient's blankets which was so successful it set the bed on fire. Predictably, perhaps, others advocated ice-cold showers. Bleeding was a common practice: one Penzance doctor bled two patients by long incisions in their scalps. Both died.

## *The victims*

In all, some 32,000 people died of cholera in Great Britain in 1831/2. Very little detail is available about the victims but there was a widespread belief that the majority came from the lower classes. But closer analysis of social status reveals that roughly one in ten came from the middle classes, a proportion which represented the number of the better-off in the population as a whole. One early middle-class victim was Mrs Haslewood, wife of a Sunderland surgeon, who fell ill after attending the post-mortems of Rodenbury and Sproat. Luckily her morbid curiosity did not cost her her life.

The *seeming* predominance of working-class victims gave comfort and a sense of false security to their betters. It also gave the rich the perfect excuse for keeping their distance, although there was no mass exodus comparable to the thousands who fled from the plague. Except in towns like Bilston in Staffordshire, where an explosive epidemic of cholera occurred, there was remarkably little disruption of day-to-day life. In Bilston, social barriers were posthumously broken down by the need for mass burials: 'Some who would not condescend to sit together in the same seat in the house of worship

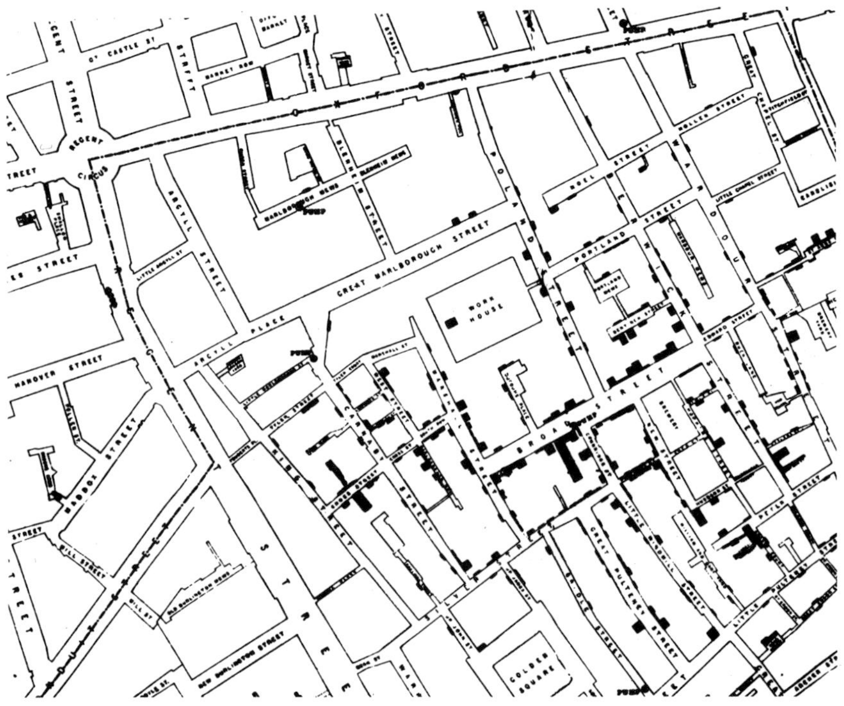


A street map (1854) of the Soho district of London identifying those dwellings in the Broad Street area which housed cholera victims, and the freedom from infection of surrounding areas

are thrown promiscuously into a grave, without coffins or shrouds.'

Cholera was different things to different people. A poster in Lambeth, south London, exclaimed: 'Inhabitants of Lambeth, be not imposed upon by the villainously false reports that the Asiatic cholera has reached London. A set of half-starved doctors, apothecaries' clerks, and jobbers in the parish funds, have endeavoured to frighten the nation into lavish expenditure.' Many saw cholera as the excuse to give 'jobs to the boys', especially minor bureaucrats. According to some, doctors and druggists were making fortunes, having a vested interest in the spread and continuance of the disease. Others saw the cholera scare as a deliberate attempt by the government to divert the attention of parliament and the nation away from the Reform Bill.

Resistance to going into hospital was profound since, by the Anatomy Act of 1832, paupers had replaced criminals as the source of bodies for medical dissection. 'While the neighbours insisted on removal [to hospital], the relations would refuse to allow it, and support their refusal by a denial of the nature of the disease, the poor victim himself suffering during the noisy conflict and aggravation.' Fear of compulsory hospital admission, where it was supposed that cholera victims would be murdered and dissected, was widespread, and sometimes provoked the working class to riot. In Edinburgh, one such crowd, some 2,000 strong, and 'composed of Irish labourers, blackguard boys and ill-tongued women', accosted a surgeon who was visiting a cholera victim. The mob threw stones and yelled 'medical murderer' and 'cholera humbug'. By the time the police arrived the patient had died, but such was the animosity felt for the medical profession that some maintained that her demise was due to the doctor forcing drugs down her throat, 'a drop of which fell on a cloth and burnt right through'. People sought to hide cholera victims from the authorities for fear of unscrupulous doctors, and the medical profession was widely viewed as predatory and out for monetary gain. The status of doctors plummeted further with the publicity given to the activities of Burke and Hare in providing dissecting material for Dr Robert Knox.[14]

In another riot in Paisley (1832) the rabble attacked the cholera hospital: one unfortunate patient was killed when he was struck on the head by a stone. One of the best-remembered riots happened in Manchester. A four-year-old boy who lived with his grandfather was diagnosed as having cholera. The lad was taken to Swan Street Hospital where he died the next day. Their suspicions aroused, the grandfather and his friends exhumed the body: the head had been removed for dissection and replaced with a brick. The hospital was attacked and the patients 'liberated', many to die at home of cholera. It took the 15th Hussars to restore order.

Precipitous burials – often within twelve hours so as to impede spread of the disease – offended working-class sensibilities, denying the deceased 'a good send off'. Wakes were an essential part of an Irish Catholic funeral and usually involved the presence of the deceased in his open coffin. It was usual for funerals to take place on Sundays, in order that people did not have to take time off work. For all these reasons it is easy to understand the widespread resentment voiced against the authorities. Further, such unseemly haste to get the body underground, contributed to fears of premature burial: after all, opium and laudanum, so freely prescribed by the doctors, could produce states of coma virtually indistinguishable from death. Tebb and Vollum, in *Premature Burial and How It May Be Prevented*, vividly illustrate the danger:

> A solicitor living in Gloucester, recently informed the editor that, when first in practice, he had as caretaker of his offices an old woman who, with her husband, had been in charge of the cholera wards,

*L'inhumation précipitée* by Anton Wiertz (1806–65). A grisly depiction of the hazards of hasty disposal of cholera victims

erected just outside the city, at the time of the severe epidemic of 1849, when, in Gloucester alone, there were 119 fatal cases. She told him that as soon as the patients were dead they put them in shells and screwed them down, so as to get them out of the way as quickly as possible, as the same sheds were so crowded. 'Sometimes,' she callously remarked, 'they would come to afterwards and we would hear 'em kicking in their coffins, but we never unscrewed 'em, 'cause we knew they'd got to die! … '[15]

The fate of the cholera victim bundled prematurely into his coffin is vividly evoked by Anton Wiertz's *L'inhumation précipitée*.

Post-mortem muscular spasms, common in cholera, could mimic life even though the patient was truly dead: 'The man was immediately invested with the usual habiliments of death. The first thing the man did, was by the sweep of his right arm, to throw the grave clothes from his breast.'

### *God works in mysterious ways*

The relationship between God and cholera could not be a simple one, since complicated explanations had to be invoked by the clergy to explain the deaths of the righteous and innocent, who, it was to be hoped, would find recompense on the other side. Repentance through prayer was the surest way to avoid death by cholera. If, despite supplication, death came anyway, then the victim either had too much to forgive or was not sufficiently contrite.

Meanwhile it was safest to regard the innocent as suffering for the sins of guilty individuals, a guilty country, or a guilty human race. With a welter of national guilts to choose from, the *Christian Observer* opted for infidelity and profanity.

As to individual accountability, the *Methodist Magazine* in 1832, pored over the victims at Gateshead, and highlighted their moral and social shortcomings:

> On the day following Christmas day two men, one living in the town and the other a few miles in the country, attended a cock fight in the afternoon; and at a public house partook of a supper with the company which had been engaged in this cruel and wicked sport. While at the supper the townsman was seized with cholera, and was a corpse in about 12 hours. The countryman was assailed as soon as he got home, and within two days was also in eternity.
>
> A man in Newcastle, a dreadful swearer and notorious Sabbath breaker, as well as a confirmed drunkard, was seized by cholera; whilst in the agonies of death, he called for ardent spirits and died in a few hours.

Cholera was intimately associated with alcohol in the minds of the pious. There is some scientific corroboration for this putative link, in that the chronic gastritis which often accompanies long-standing drunkenness, serves to reduce the chemical barrier in the stomach which might otherwise have destroyed the cholera organism. Malnutrition would have much the same effect.

When threatened by destruction for their numerous sins, the people of Nineveh declared a fast. In like manner the people of Great Britain declared 21 March 1832 a national day of fasting, repentance and prayer. Churches were packed out as religion sought to compensate for the inadequacies of science. Many thought it pure humbuggery:

> A public day of fasting and humiliation! What does this mean! the rich are not to eat meat, but to limit themselves to such food as 'the earth and the waters under the earth' can accommodate them with (that is, every variety of fish – eggs – vegetables – fruit and wine which wealth can procure and ingenuity render agreeable to the palate), while the

poor, how are they to fast? – to do with less than they do at present, would be absolutely to starve.

*Medicine, the emperor without his clothes*

There was widespread distrust of medical men. And not without cause. Many physicians were ill-educated and ignorant, who would merely purge and bleed their unfortunate patients, accelerating their demise in many cases. One exception, Thomas Latta of Edinburgh, proposed that instead of adding to the body's fluid losses by prescribing purgations, would it not be more sensible to *replace* the fluids lost? By saline solution into a vein, perhaps? Such heresy from a humble rural doctor never stood a chance of acceptance by the medical establishment. Indeed, the contrary argument won the day: if the body was losing great quantities of salt then it obviously had too much of it, and to add more would be illogical. Latta's saline treatment was ahead of its time.

*John Snow, medical detective*

The cholera epidemic of 1832 was regarded as an anti-climax by many: only 31,000 had died, hardly sufficient to warrant all the brouhaha. With such *post hoc* complacency, it is not surprising that few lessons were learnt and that the same mistakes were repeated when cholera returned in 1848 and twice as many perished. In all, four great pandemics swept west in the nineteenth century.

John Snow was born in York in 1813 and apprenticed to a Newcastle surgeon at the age of fourteen. In 1836 he moved to London, and two years later set up as a general practitioner in Frith Street, Soho. He was a shy, hard-working man, a strict teetotaller and vegetarian: doubtless, such beliefs were, in part, responsible for him being widely thought of as 'peculiar'. In his early days in practice, Snow worked long hours for small financial reward. But the discovery of ether and chloroform transformed his career: he took up the study of anaesthetics with enthusiasm and in 1853 was summoned to administer chloroform to Queen Victoria during the birth of Prince Leopold.

Four years earlier Snow had published *On the mode of communication of cholera* in which he argued that the causative agent, whatever it may turn out to be, was carried in polluted water, and not in the air as the miasmatists believed. Snow lacked the flamboyance, ruthlessness and charisma to promote his theory against strong

Dr John Snow, the unsung hero of cholera

opposition, and these personality traits go a long way to explain why his ideas about the method of the spread of cholera took a generation to be accepted.

According to Snow, cholera was a disease of the intestinal tract: all the symptoms, including circulatory collapse and coma, were secondary to the profound fluid loss caused by vomiting and purging. Snow maintained that the cholera poison was swallowed in contaminated water, and that this was the reason that doctors were relatively immune: they simply washed their hands more often. According to Snow, the outbreak in a Merthyr children's home had resulted from a child's habit of putting his dirty fingers in his mouth;

the outbreak in the Yorkshire colliery was because the miners 'always take their victuals with unwashed hands'.

How, then, critics asked, did the disease affect the well-to-do, those that did not live in overcrowded, insanitary slums? Snow had suggested that the cause of a cholera outbreak in Newcastle in 1831 had been a contaminated brook running into a drinking well. Snow decided to draw a large-scale map pin-pointing the cholera deaths which had occurred in the Soho district of London. It was obvious to even a cursory glance that the dead were concentrated in houses whose water requirements were served by the pump in Broad Street. There was a virtual absence of deaths in areas served by the eleven other pumps in the district. Tellingly, Snow specifically cited the seven men who worked at Nos. 8 and 9 Broad Street: although they lived outside the area, they drank the local water. All had died. Two other people, who actually lived on the same premises but who did *not* drink the water, survived.

Nine customers of a coffee shop supplied by the Broad Street pump died, while none of the local brewery workers died because they were supplied with free beer made from water from the brewery's own well. Perhaps the clincher was the case of a lady who had moved away from Broad Street but had acquired such a taste for the local water that she had it delivered every week to her new home in Hampstead. She died of cholera. So too did her niece, a resident of healthy Islington, who had also drunk her aunt's water.

Snow had a unique opportunity to test his theory. In an area of south London there were houses which, though in close proximity, were supplied by two different water companies. The Southwark and Vauxhall Company drew its supply from the polluted waters of the River Thames; the Lambeth Company from a much purer source miles upstream. In the summer of 1854 cholera struck, but not with an even hand. In 286 cases the water came from the Southwark and Vauxhall; in only 15 was water supplied by Lambeth. Given the absolute number of homes supplied by the two companies, the fatalities were 14 times greater in people supplied from the polluted Thames.

Snow had to contend with doubters and with others who claimed that what he was saying was in no way new. Publication of his book setting down his beliefs, left him £200 poorer and with no acknowledgement, financial or professional, for the service he had rendered humanity. He died of a stroke at the age of forty-four. Miasmatists did not give up their fight. In the outbreak of 1866, which killed 6,000 in London alone, one proponent still claimed that cholera was caused by 'a thin transparent bluish haze'.

Cholera broke out on a pandemic scale in 1863 and lasted for nine years. It was about this time that Louis Pasteur was proposing that many diseases were caused by organisms, invisible to the naked eye. The search was on to identify the organism responsible for cholera, and national pride was at stake. When cholera broke out in Egypt in 1883, both France and Germany sent out their best scientists to crack the problem once and for all. Robert Koch, who had the year before isolated the organism responsible for tuberculosis, was despatched from Berlin; Roux and Thuillier travelled from Paris. Both set up separate research centres and worked independently. The French were the first to claim victory – alas, prematurely. Soon Thuillier lay dying of cholera, and Koch paid him a visit. He asked Koch, 'Have we found it?' Overcoming his antipathy to France and all things French, Koch generously replied, 'Yes, you have found it!' Believing that they had been successful, the French team decamped to publish their findings.

Koch was more circumspect and, when the outbreak was diminishing in Egypt, he decided to travel on to India, the home of cholera. Working day and night at the Medical College in Calcutta, Koch finally isolated a comma-shaped bacterium from specimens taken from dead and dying cholera victims. He proved finally and conclusively that the organism was not breathed in, but swallowed, and that it could also be carried on clothing, thus vindicating those who had advocated quarantine. Germany had beaten the best of Britain and France, and it feted its hero in a way that Snow never was. In an irony, which was partially duplicated years later by Ronald Ross (see pp.176–92 on malaria), Dr Charles Macnamara bitterly complained that the Indian Medical Service had not given him leave to carry on his researches into cholera, and had allowed the accolades to be heaped upon a foreigner.

The last major outbreak of cholera in Europe occurred in Hamburg in 1892, causing 8,000 deaths. Koch was summoned and was soon able to identify the source of the polluted water. But his enemies refused to be convinced either about the causative organism or its spread in the water supply. Foremost of Koch's critics was Max von Pettenkofer, Professor of Hygiene at the University of Munich. He asked Koch to provide him with a culture of the cholera bacillus, sufficient to poison a whole regiment. Koch complied and von Pettenkofer swallowed the lot. 'Even if I be mistaken, and the experiment I am making emperils my life, I shall look death quietly in the face, for what I am doing is no frivolous or cowardly act of suicide, but I shall die in the service of science as a soldier perishes on the field of honour.' Von Pettenkofer lived, but happily his reckless gesture did not take away from the truth. Nine years later, with his theories widely discredited, von Pettenkofer committed suicide.

Koch's wife divorced him in 1893 when he was fifty. Two months later he married an eighteen-year-old art student, an act for which his native town showed its disapproval by removing the commemorative plaque on the front of his former home.

### *Twentieth-century update*

Despite all our knowledge of cholera, the disease continues to be a major cause of death in the Third World. The vibrio flourishes whenever and wherever there are insanitary conditions. Communal bathing, especially on a mass scale at religious festivals, has been held responsible for recent outbreaks in India.

## 3 TYPHUS, DISEASE OF DIRT

*Epidemic typhus (not to be confused with typhoid) is caused by the organism,* Rickettsia prowazeki, *which is spread from person to person by the body louse. The louse defecates on the victim's skin and the infected faeces gain entry into the body by being scratched into the abrasion made by the insect's bite.*

*The rickettsial organism, which is between a bacterium and a virus in size, produces intense and prolonged fever, and a characteristic rash of pink spots which initially fade on pressure. Before modern treatment became available, typhus was fatal in up to sixty per cent of cases, patients usually dying of heart and brain complications.*

*Trench fever, another louse-borne disease caused by* Rickettsia quintana, *was widespread among the troops in World War I. It produces fever, but does not cause death. Endemic (murine) typhus, a much less serious disease than epidemic typhus, is caused by* Rickettsia mooseri *and is transmitted from rats to man by the flea,* Xenopsylla cheopis. *The most serious present-day rickettsial disease is Rocky Mountain spotted fever, caused by* Rickettsia rickettsii, *and is spread from wild rodents to man by ticks.*

*Effective treatment of all rickettsial diseases is provided by antibiotics.*

The humble body louse, and the typhus that it spreads, has had an enormous, though immeasurable, influence on human history. It has been a combatant in all human conflicts where insanitary conditions have prevailed (especially siege and trench warfare), often responsible for determining which side was the victor and which the vanquished. Whenever standards of hygiene are compromised, the louse flourishes, warm, snug and well-fed within the layers of clothing of its human host.

Although the Romans considered cleanliness to be next to godliness, in later societies personal hygiene was not rated particularly highly: if you began to stink, you simply put up with the smell or ladled on more perfume and powder. Some insight into twelfth-century mores can be gleaned from an account written about Thomas à Becket:

> The Archbishop was murdered in Canterbury Cathedral on the evening of 29 December. The body lay in the cathedral all night, and was prepared for burial on the following day. The Archbishop was dressed in an extraordinary collection of clothes. He had on a large brown mantle; under it, a white surplice; below that, a lamb's wool coat; then another woollen coat; and a third woollen coat below this; under this, there was the black, cowled robe of the Benedictine Order; under this, a shirt; and next to the body a curious haircloth covered with linen. As the body grew cold, the vermin that were living in this multiple covering started to crawl out: 'The vermin boiled over like water in a simmering cauldron, and the onlookers burst into alternate weeping and laughter'.

It is likely that the louse has always sought out humans for food, warmth and protection. When the human dies, the louse must scurry off to find another as soon as possible, or die itself. Since the human body louse is unable to use any other species as host, scholars used to debate if Adam and Eve were lousy. In Sweden in the Middle Ages a mayor was elected by a louse: candidates sat around a table, beards on the table, and a louse was placed in the middle!

Reboux, writing about the education of a medieval French princess, observed, 'It is improper to take lice or fleas or other vermin by the neck to kill them in company, except in the most intimate circles.'

Aztecs and Incas were lousy before Columbus afflicted them, so typhus is one disease which cannot be laid at the door of the Old World. In Aztec society poor peasants who had nothing else to offer would collect bags of lice to give to their ruler.[16]

## *Postscript*

Typhus killed both Ricketts and von Prowazek, the two doctors, one American, one Austrian, who had done so much to elucidate the nature of the organism.

# 3 SMALLPOX, CONQUEROR OF THE NEW WORLD

*Smallpox is an infectious disease caused by a virus,* Variola major. *The virus is breathed into the lungs from the exhalations of victims, or from off corpses, clothes, blankets etc., which can remain infectious for months. Patients remain infectious from just before the appearance of the rash until the scabs fall off, three weeks later. In the first week there are no signs of illness, but by the ninth day the patient develops headache, fever and chills, sometimes with vivid and terrifying dreams. There is a temporary improvement as the fever subsides, but the patient's condition worsens with the appearance of the rash. Characteristically, the rash consists of pustules, particularly on the face, arms and legs. Many die in the first few days of the rash as a result of irreparable damage to vital internal organs. Others die before the rash appears. The body stinks and the skin often sloughs off. One quarter die. Those that survive have lifelong immunity but are frequently left hideously scarred or blinded.*

*Another variety of smallpox, caused by the virus* Variola minor, *produces a milder disease with a mortality of only 1 in a 100. Recovery from either major or minor forms of the disease, confers immunity to both. The viruses belong to the same family of organisms which cause cowpox, camelpox and monkeypox, but the smallpox virus does not cause disease in these animals.*

Since its eradication from the world, it is difficult to convey the sheer horror that was smallpox, one of mankind's most ancient scourges, and one of its most dreaded. If smallpox failed to kill, it frequently left its victims so cruelly and permanently disfigured that they would wish themselves dead: 'Grooms would recoil in horror at the sight of their brides; mothers would abandon babies, their faces rendered unrecognizable by a grotesque confluence of black-centred pustules.' Many, unable to endure the destruction of their beauty, plunged into depression and sought release in suicide. Talleyrand (1754–1838), the

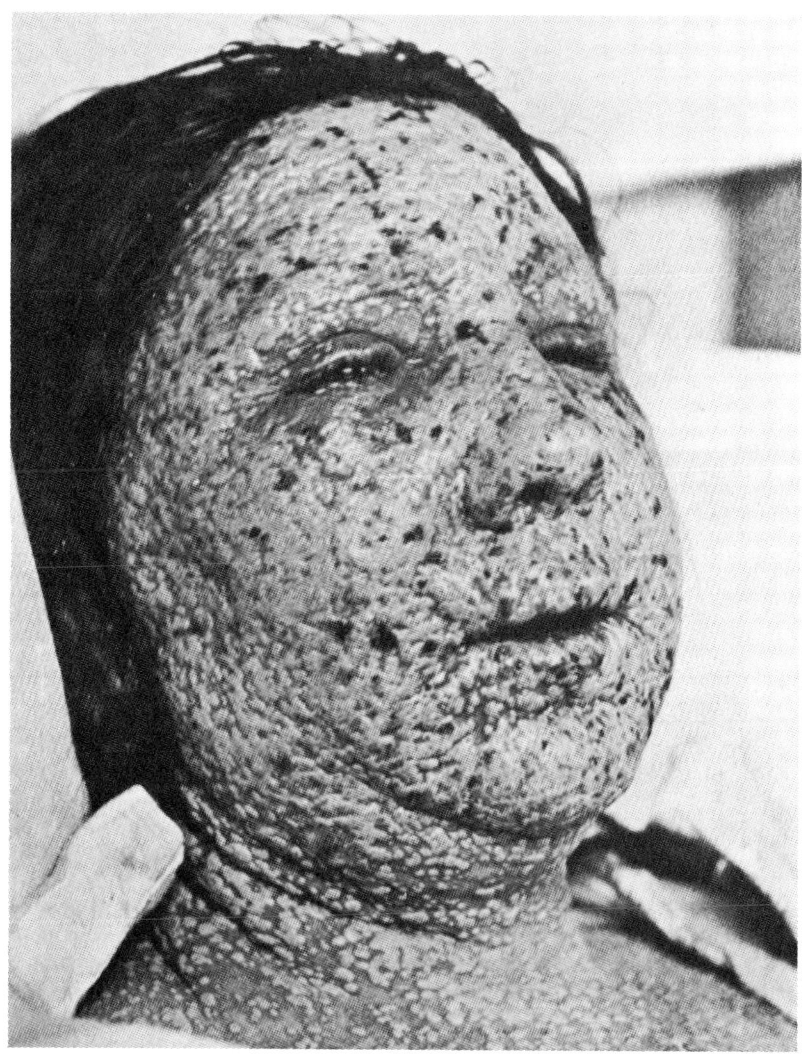

Confluent smallpox pustules obscuring the features of the face

French statesman and a great lady-killer, had his features rendered hideous by smallpox.

There is convincing evidence that smallpox was known to the ancient Egyptians: three pock-marked mummies, dating from 1570–1085 BC, including Rameses V, are presumed to have suffered from the disease. Contemporaneously, clinical descriptions suggestive of smallpox appear in the medical and religious texts of India:

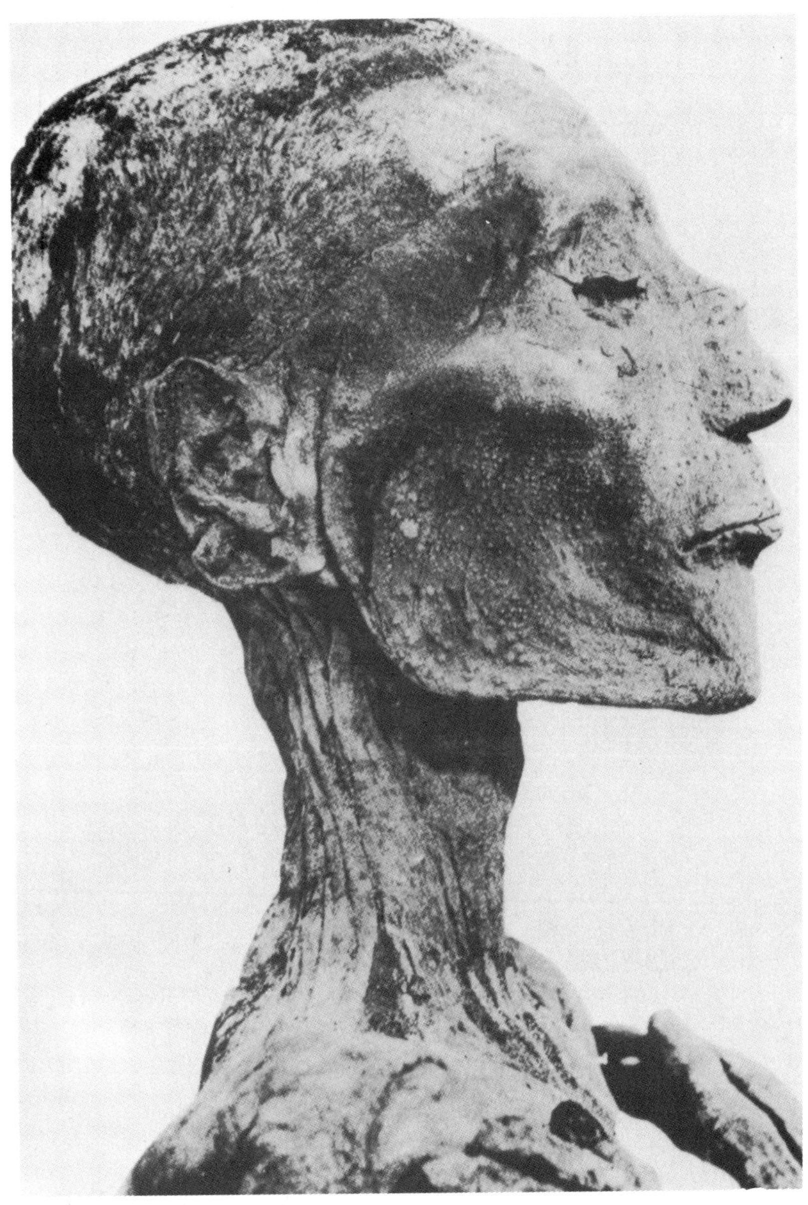

Ramases V with lesions suggestive of smallpox

the *Susruta Samhita* describes red, yellow and white pustules which later turned black and became excruciatingly painful. Inoculation, even cowpox vaccination, has been practised in India since ancient times.

Smallpox was brought to China by the invading Huns around 250 BC: not unnaturally, the Chinese called it 'Hunpox'.

## *The Plague of Athens*

Academics disagree about whether Hippocrates (500 BC) knew the disease, though it is generally agreed that the Plague of Athens, a virulent disease which struck that city in 430 BC, was smallpox. A first-hand account of this plague was penned by Thucydides, writing at the time of the Peloponnesian War. Each year, at the approach of the Lacedaemonian army, the citizens of Athens, on the orders of Pericles, would flock within the city walls, to withstand a siege. Such was the overcrowding and insanitary conditions that pestilence was certain: it broke out in the second year of the war. Mortality was high and the people turned in their grief upon Pericles. But he was already a broken man, having lost his two legitimate sons, Xanthippus and Paralus, his sister and many others of his family. As he laid a wreath on the body of Paralus, the great statesman was overwhelmed with anguish and sobbed bitterly. The pestilence finally claimed Pericles himself.

Thucydides wrote:

> The disease is said to have begun south of Egypt in Ethiopia: thence it descended into Egypt and Libya, and after spreading over the greater part of the Persian empire, suddenly fell upon Athens ... I was myself attacked, and witnessed the sufferings of others.
>
> Many who were in perfect health, all in a moment, and without any apparent reason, were seized with violent heats in the head and with redness and inflammation of the eyes ... the breath became unnatural and fetid. There followed sneezing and hoarseness; in a short time the disorder, accompanied by a violent cough, reached the chest; then fastening lower down, it would move the stomach and bring on all the vomits of bile. [The body] was of a livid colour inclining to red, and breaking out in pustules and ulcers. The internal fever was intense: the sufferers could not bear to have on them even the finest linen garment. They insisted on being naked and to throw themselves into cold water. And many of those who had no one to look after them actually plunged into the cisterns, for they were tormented by unceasing thirst ... They died on the seventh or ninth day, or if they survived, then the disease descended into the bowels and there produced violent ulceration and severe diarrhoea ... If a person got over the worst [the disease] would often seize the extremities, attacking the privy parts and

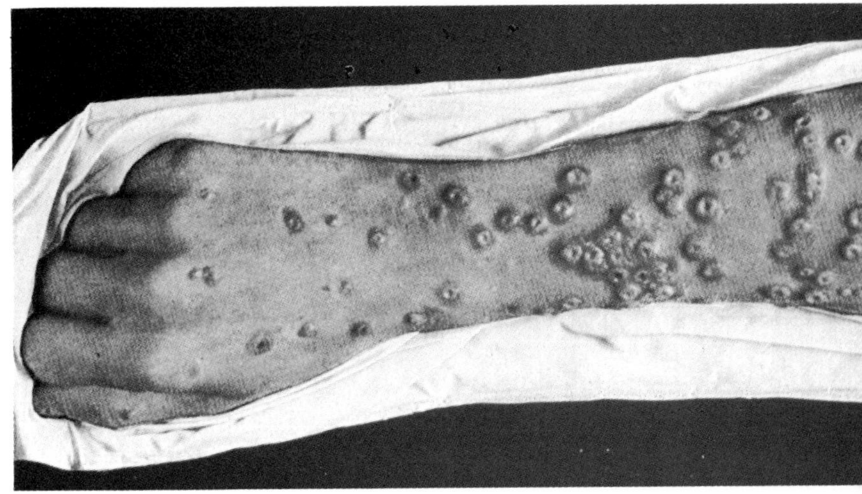

Smallpox pustules on the arm

the fingers and the toes; and some escaped with loss of these, some with the loss of their eyes. Some again had no sooner recovered than they were seized with a forgetfulness of all things and knew neither themselves nor their friends.

The birds and animals which feed on human flesh, although so many bodies were lying unburied, either never came near them, or died if they touched them. This was proved by a remarkable disappearance of the birds of prey, who were not to be seen either about the bodies or anywhere else: while in the case of the dogs the fact was even more obvious, because they live with man.

Most appalling was the despondency which seized upon anyone who felt himself sickening: for he instantly abandoned his mind to despair and, instead of holding out, absolutely threw away his chance of life. Appalling too was the rapidity with which men caught the infection: dying like sheep if they attended upon one another. When they were afraid to visit one another, the sufferers died in their solitude, so that many houses were empty ... or if they ventured they perished, especially those who aspired to heroism. For they went to see their friends without thought for themselves and were ashamed to leave them.

The newly arrived suffered most, perishing in wild disorder. The dead lay as they had died, one upon another, while others, hardly alive, wallowed in the streets and crawled about every fountain craving for water.

Men who had hitherto concealed their indulgence in pleasure now grew bolder. For seeing the sudden change – how the rich died in a moment, and those who had nothing immediately inherited their

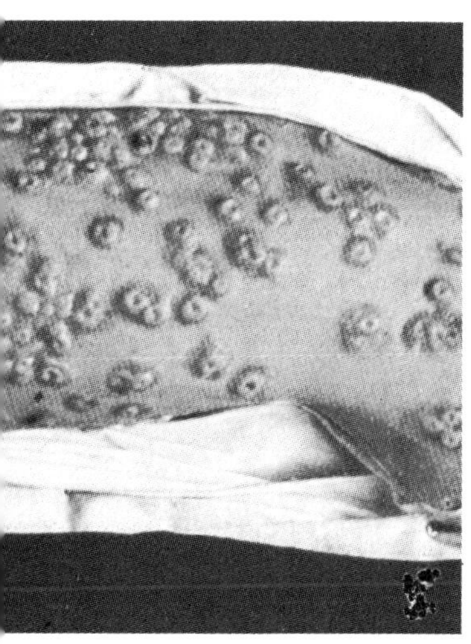

property – they reflected that life and riches were alike transitory, and they resolved to enjoy themselves while they could, and to think only of pleasure. Who would be willing to sacrifice himself to the law of honour when he knew not whether he would ever live to be held in honour? ... No one would live long enough to be called to account. Already a far heavier sentence had been passed and was hanging over a man's head: before that fell why should he not take a little pleasure?[1]

The plague raged for three years, and the toll on the Athenian army has been judged by historians as a major contribution to the Spartan victory.

## *Smallpox after the birth of Christ*

An epidemic, widely believed to be smallpox, struck Rome in the reign of Emperor Marcus Aurelius Antonius (known as the 'Plague of Antonius') and was described by the Emperor's physician, Galen (130–200). Galen is uncharacteristically brief in his description, and this might be because the good doctor fled the city at high speed to avoid falling victim himself. The disease raged for fully fifteen years, claiming the life of the Emperor himself, and is regarded by some as contributory to the decline in the influence of Rome.

Gregory of Tours described the effect of the smallpox outbreak of 580, when monasteries opened their doors to women whose beauty had been destroyed by smallpox. Among those who sought refuge from the world was Countess Eborin, who 'was so covered with the vesicles, that neither her hands, nor feet, nor any part of the body, remained exempt, for even her eyes were wholly closed up by them.' Another victim, Count d'Angoulême, died, 'his corpse appeared black and burnt, as if it had been laid on a coal fire'.

## *Princes and peasants*

Queen Elizabeth I, writing from Hampton Court to Mary, Queen of Scots, on 15 October 1562, broke off her letter when she became feverish and started to shiver. Dr Burcot, her German-born physician, was summoned: he bluntly declared, 'My liege, thou shalt have the pox.' It was clearly not what Elizabeth wanted to hear and she retorted, 'Have away the knave out of my sight.'

Soon after, the Queen became incoherent and slipped into a coma. The sense of panic in the court was palpable: the Virgin Queen might die, and her very virginity, and lack of an heir, placed the succession in doubt and the country in peril. A little later she recovered consciousness sufficiently to proclaim that Lord Robert Dudley should be appointed Protector of the Realm, and to vouchsafe that no impropriety had ever occurred between them. It was later that same night a rash began to spread over the Queen's body, leaving the diagnosis no longer in doubt.

Messengers were sent to bring Burcot back to the royal bedside. His physician's pride had been deeply wounded. He replied, 'By God's pestilence, if she be sick, then let her die. Call me a *knave* for my good will!' Burcot's show of independence was short-lived, and he was soon persuaded to change his mind: he was told that he would be put to death immediately if he did not comply with the Queen's wishes. When Burcot confirmed his earlier diagnosis the Queen began to complain about how loathsome she found the pox. Burcot, devoid of bedside charm, wrapped her in a 'great length of scarlet cloth' and laid her on a mattress in front of the fire.

To everyone's surprise and relief the Queen began to show signs of recovery. Within a month she was at Somerset Palace and writing again to Mary, Queen of Scots, about how she had escaped without scaring or baldness (though other accounts refer to tell-tale pockmarks on the Queen's face). She rewarded Burcot with money, land, and a pair of gold spurs which belonged to her grandfather, Henry VII. One of the women of the court who attended the Queen, Lady Mary Sidney, was not so fortunate: she was so disfigured by smallpox that she never appeared in public again without wearing a mask.[2]

Royal physicians like Burcot walked a dangerous tightrope, and some were not as lucky as he. When the Merovingian Queen Austrigilde caught smallpox she blamed her doctors. During her illness she asked King Guntram that if she did not survive, 'Give me your solemn word … that you will cut their throats the moment that my eyes have closed in death. If I have really come to the end of my life, they must not be permitted to glory in my dying. When my friends grieve for me, let their friends grieve for them.' Both physicians were executed.

A disease which threatens the lives of queens is no respecter of social standing, cutting a swathe through all societal levels and felling princes and peasants alike. It is truly remarkable how many royal victims have been claimed by smallpox and the consequent changes brought about in the course of national and world history.

Across the Channel, the Duke of Alençon, who had once sought the hand of Elizabeth, caught smallpox.

> When he emerged from his chamber after a dangerous bout of smallpox, there was little left of the promising young prince. His appearance was totally changed: his face was deeply pitted, his eyes bloodshot, his voice thin and reedy, and his nose almost doubled in size. His spirit too had undergone a profound change. He found that he no longer had a part to play in that world in which handsome faces and virile bodies were given first prize.

Elizabeth cited Alençon's pockmarks as a reason for not marrying him.[3]

In the seventeenth century, as plague, leprosy and syphilis reduced in incidence and virulence, smallpox continued unabated, causing havoc in the royal families of Europe. Prince Balthazar Carlos, heir to the Spanish throne, died in 1646; Prince William II of Orange in 1650; Ferdinand IV, the Emperor-elect of the Holy Roman Empire, in 1654. Leopold I, who succeeded Ferdinand, had two children die of smallpox: 'My youngest daughter, born only last year, was sick barely three days, and this morning was seized with such terrible cramps that her innocent soul winged its way to heaven.'

## *The end of the Stuarts*

In England, the Stuart line was extinguished by smallpox. In May 1660, when Charles II was restored to the throne of England, he brought with him his brother, Henry, Duke of Gloucester. Henry died of smallpox four months later. The King welcomed back to England his sister Mary, widow by smallpox of William II of Orange. She was dead of smallpox within three months. When Charles II died, he was succeeded by his Catholic brother, James, as King James II. After three years, James had to flee the country and was succeeded by his Protestant daughter, Mary, and her husband William III of Orange. In 1694, the 32-year-old Queen contracted smallpox.

Macaulay, in his *History of England*, gives us this account of the dignified way in which Mary prepared for death.

> [The King] had good reason to be uneasy ... Sir Thomas Millington, who was physician-in-ordinary to the King, thought that she had the measles; but Radcliffe, who, with coarse manners and little book

> learning, had raised himself to the first practice in London chiefly by his rare skill in diagnostics, uttered the more alarming words, smallpox ... [then regarded as] the most terrible of all the ministers of death. The havoc of the plague had been far more rapid; but the plague had visited our shores only once or twice within living memory; and the smallpox was always present, filling the churchyard with corpses, tormenting with constant fear all whom it had not yet stricken, leaving on those whose lives it spared the hideous traces of its power, turning the babe into a changeling at which the mother shuddered, and making the eyes and cheeks of the betrothed maiden objects of horror to the lover ... [The Queen] received the intimation of her danger with true greatness of soul. She gave orders that every lady of her bedchamber, every maid of honour, nay, every menial servant who had not had the smallpox should instantly leave Kensington House. She locked herself up during a short time in her closet, burned some papers, arranged others, and calmly awaited her fate.

Mary died childless. When her husband William III died he was succeeded by Mary's sister, Anne. Only one of Anne's eighteen children, William, Duke of Gloucester, survived into childhood. He died, aged eleven, of smallpox. The Stuarts had run out of heirs – smallpox had seen to that – and it was time for the Hanoverians to be brought from Germany to assume the monarchy of England.

## *Other VIP victims*

In the eighteenth century, smallpox, that most regicidal of killers, carried off, among others, an Emperor of Austria, a Dauphin of France, and a Tsar of Russia.

When Emperor Joseph I caught the smallpox in Vienna on 7 April 1711 he was only thirty-three years old. Ten days later he was in his coffin. It is possible that the Emperor contracted smallpox from a visit he had made to a local hospital. In Joseph's death, Austria lost not only its Emperor but also lost the Habsburgs the Spanish succession.

Three days before Joseph I died, death by smallpox snuffed out the life of Louis, 50-year-old heir to the French throne: 'inside [the chamber] lay the disfigured corpse of the man who, only a few hours before, had been heir to the crown of France, the object of flattery and homage, and the centre of hopes, ambitions and intrigues'. (One notable French royal to recover from smallpox was the nine-year-old Louis XIV, back in 1647.)

Tsar Peter II, was crowned in the Kremlin in January 1728, at the age of fourteen. By the end of the month he was dead of smallpox on what was to have been his wedding day. In a macabre deathbed drama, the Dolgorukys, the power behind the throne, attempted to ensure the succession. 'During the final moments, Prince Dolgoruky in desperation thrust his daughter into the expiring Tsar's bed. Coitus having taken place, the Prince was to announce Catherine the rightful successor to the throne.'

## *Turning the tables*

For centuries the surest safeguard against smallpox was to isolate victims and pray that oneself did not become infected. Other predictable remedies included purgatives, bleeding, or chewing noxious substances, such as powdered horse excrement. One specific and unusual treatment was the belief in the healing power of objects or substances which were red. Such erythrotherapy was mentioned in ancient Japanese texts. The Hindu goddess of smallpox is depicted

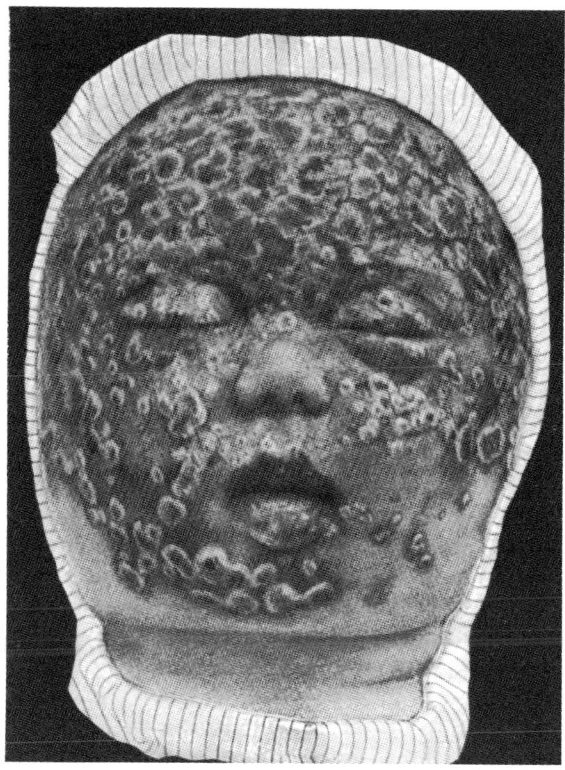

Skin reaction in a baby caused by vaccination against smallpox

draped in a red sari. Red blankets, powders and drinks were given to victims. In 1314, Prince John was made to 'suck the juice of a red pomegranate and to gargle with red mulberry wine'.

In 1629 London introduced 'Bills of Mortality' which recorded the cause of death. Between 1650 and 1699, smallpox accounted for an average of twenty deaths a week in the capital. Around about 1700 reports began to reach Europe about a Chinese way of preventing smallpox: by taking bits of infected material, drying and powdering it, and blowing the dust into the nostrils. The response in Europe was less than enthusiastic. Then, in 1717, Lady Mary Wortley Montagu, wife of the British ambassador, wrote to her friend, Sarah Chiswell, shortly after her arrival in Constantinople: 'The small-pox, so fatal, and so general amongst us, is here entirely harmless, by the invention of *ingrafting*, which is the term they give it.' The letter described how 'matter' from smallpox lesions was used to tip the end of a needle which was then scratched into a vein. A mild feverish illness followed, after which recovery took place without residual scarring. Lady Montagu knew of no fatalities and intended 'to try it on my dear little son'. One does not know the reaction of Sarah Chiswell to her friend's advice, though one can guess that she was not moved to follow suit: Sarah Chiswell died of smallpox nine years later.[4]

At last physicians were beginning to take notice of inoculation, a process whereby material from smallpox lesions, introduced into the body of a recipient, induced only a mild fever and conferred immunity from the real thing. Royals became particularly interested in inoculation and were in the vanguard of those seeking to protect themselves and their heirs. Charles Maitland, the physician who inoculated Lady Montague's son, was granted royal permission to conduct clinical trials on six condemned prisoners at Newgate Prison in 1721. Following these, presumably successful, trials, Caroline of Anspach, the wife of the Prince of Wales (later King George II), had her two daughters inoculated.

Although royalty might have been convinced of the efficacy of inoculation, the poorer classes remained suspicious, partly due to the belief that one should not deliberately seek to contract a disease which the Almighty had not chosen you to suffer. This reluctance remained unswayed by official statistics published in 1723 which showed the chances of dying from smallpox were nearly twenty times less if inoculated.

In France, opposition to inoculation was strong and widespread, partly, no doubt, because the English were seen to be enthusiastic. Voltaire despaired the ignorance of his countrymen and was vociferous in his advocation of inoculation, 'for the sake of staying alive and keeping our women beautiful'. Inoculation was finally introduced into France in 1755.

Spain and Russia both lost young monarchs more than two years after Caroline's daughters had been inoculated. Luis Ferdinand succeeded at the age of sixteen years to the Spanish throne in January 1724 on the abdication of his father, Philip V. He ruled for a mere seven months before succumbing to smallpox, whereupon the throne returned to his father.

But even in England enthusiasm for inoculation was not total. Critics of the procedure would point out that inoculation sometimes killed and that immunity was not lifelong. The heavy mortality of smallpox in London in 1752 did much to re-stimulate interest in inoculation. Improved techniques served to reduce complications, but inoculation could not be regarded as completely safe: in 1783 Octavius, four-year-old son of George III, died a few days after inoculation – happily, the last member of the British royal family to suffer from the disease.

Even though the French royal family resisted inoculation, the Austrian and Russian royal families, headed by Maria Theresa and Catherine the Great, embraced the new ideas with gusto. Catherine sought the services of Dr Thomas Dimsdale of London, who travelled to Russia to inoculate her and her son, Grand Duke Paul: 'To your skill and integrity will probably be submitted nothing less than the precious lives of two of the greatest personages in the world.' The responsibility served to unnerve the doctor: 'Many corroding cares disturb me, and embitter all this greatness which I am not able to enjoy.' Happily all went well and Dimsdale, like Burcot before him, was amply rewarded.[5] The child, from whose arm the virus was taken to inoculate the Empress, was ennobled. Catherine was congratulated by Voltaire who wrote admiringly, 'You have been inoculated with less fuss than a nun taking an enema.' The Empress showed herself as a realist: in the event of tragedy, she had provided relays of horses to be ready to enable Dimsdale to flee the country. Russian aristocracy eagerly followed the example of the Empress and were generous in their gratitude. One noble presented Dimsdale with a bag of gold so heavy that he limped while carrying it out of the room.

Opinions in France about inoculation changed radically when smallpox claimed the life of Louis XV in 1774, at the age of sixty-four, after a reign of fifty-nine years. The diagnosis came as a profound shock since everyone believed that the King had been made immune by an attack of smallpox contracted thirty years earlier. It was not a dignified death: 'The body of the King was falling to pieces in a state of living putrescence, and the smell was horribly fetid.' No autopsy was carried out. One observer commented, 'If the body is opened, neither you nor I nor anyone present will be alive a week later.' The body was placed in a double lead coffin, covered with lime, vinegar, spices and wine, and hastily taken to St Denis. It was widely rumoured that the King had contracted smallpox from a teenage girl coerced into his bed a few weeks before. His heir, Louis XVI, was promptly inoculated.

There is an irony in the death through smallpox of Louix XV. The patron saint of smallpox is St Nicaise, who was beheaded by the Huns in 451 outside his cathedral at Rheims, after surviving an attack of smallpox the year before. St Nicaise looked down from the great rose window on the coronation of Louis XV – not that it did the King any good!

Dr Edward Jenner, English general practitioner and discoverer of vaccination

Perhaps it was as well for England that France did not take to inoculation with greater alacrity. It may be the reason that the French, and their Spanish allies, failed in their plan to invade England in July 1779. The combined armadas – vastly superior to anything that England could muster – gathered in the Channel, and yet did not attack. And the reason? Smallpox had broken out among the crews and was causing carnage. More than 8,000 sailors died. How might the history of Europe have been changed if variola had not ruled the waves? Perhaps this book would have been written in French.

### *Edward Jenner, country doctor*

It had been known for a long time that a human who contracted cowpox became safeguarded against the more virulent disease of smallpox. Using this knowledge, Edward Jenner (1749–1823), on 14 May 1796, inoculated a boy, James Phipps, with cowpox material taken from the hand of Sara Nelmes, a milkmaid. Phipps developed a mild reaction a week later. On 1 July, Jenner inoculated Phipps again – *this time with pus taken from a case of smallpox!* No reaction occurred: Phipps had become immune to smallpox by having suffered from cowpox. Jenner wrote to the Royal Society to share with them the momentous news. The response he received was uncompromising: if he valued his reputation he had better stop promulgating such nonsense. Undeterred, Jenner inoculated five more children with cowpox and then challenged them with smallpox: all failed to contract smallpox.

Jenner was probably not the first. In 1765, a Dr Fewster read a paper to the London Medical Society entitled, *Cowpox and Its Ability to Prevent Smallpox*; and in 1774 a Dorset cattle breeder named Benjamin Jesty inoculated his two sons with cowpox. Jenner was never knighted nor was he made a member of the Royal Society of Medicine – but Napoleon appreciated him: on several occasions Napoleon liberated captured Englishmen after receiving a petition from Jenner, saying, 'Ah! Jenner! I cannot refuse Jenner anything!'[6]

## *The nineteenth century*

Inoculation using material from cowpox became known as vaccination, and represented a major leap forward: it was simple, cheap, safe, and those who were vaccinated did not have to be isolated since it was impossible for them to spread smallpox. But there were objectors, especially those who had earned their living from inoculation. One woman complained that after vaccination her daughter had 'coughed like a cow and had grown hairy all over her body'.

Although many still debated the duration of immunity, England made vaccination mandatory in 1853; France followed forty-nine years later. But pandemics still occurred with unacceptably high mortality, mainly due to public complacency and the fall-off in immunity over time. Unfortunately compulsion went against the grain of British democratic concepts and people were able to refuse vaccination by conscientious objections. Nevertheless, revaccination was instituted: indeed, in 1867 inoculated cows were led from door to door to deliver fresh material.

The worst pandemic, 1870–75, was a direct consequence of the long-standing disruption caused by the Franco-Prussian War. Almost half a million people died, shocking Europe out of its complacency about smallpox as a bygone disease.

Great Britain became free of smallpox in 1935. In 1973, a research worker was taken ill in London and found to have contracted smallpox. Two people, visiting a patient in an adjacent bed, contracted the disease and died. In 1978, in Birmingham, the virus 'escaped' from a research laboratory, into the ventilation system, and infected a medical photographer who worked on the floor above. The victim, Mrs Janet Parker, aged forty, died one month later. Whilst the research staff were in quarantine, the laboratory's director, Professor Henry Bedson, committed suicide. Smallpox had claimed its last human victim.

### *Smallpox in the Old World …*

Smallpox was introduced into China from Central Asia by the Huns around 250 BC. When it passed on to Japan some thought that it was a punishment for embracing Buddhism. Buddhist nuns were hunted down, stripped and flogged – to no avail. When the pendulum swung the other way, the population sought to propitiate the Buddha and built a huge statue in the hope that the scourge would be brought to an end. Standing fifty-three feet high it was the world's largest bronze, but had no impact on halting the spread of smallpox.

It was the Chinese who first practised inoculation by collecting scabs from mild cases of smallpox and blowing the crusts into the nostril. Despite inoculation, smallpox continued to claim its royal victims. Emperor Fu-lin died of the disease in 1661. In order to protect the dynasty, the next Emperor, Hsüan-yeh, was chosen, the third of eight sons, simply because he had already recovered from an attack of smallpox. As Emperor K'ang Hsi, he occupied the dragon throne for sixty-one years, and made sure his family and troops were inoculated.

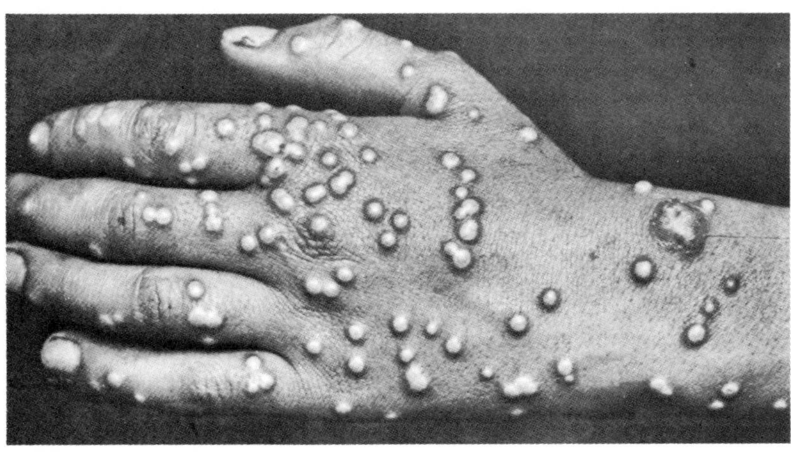

Smallpox pustules on the back of the hand

India has long known the ravages of smallpox. Like the Chinese, the Indians have practised a form of inoculation for centuries. Edward Jenner, who was anxious to 'export' vaccination, hit upon the idea of arranging for volunteers to be vaccinated in succession on the long sea journey to India, so that viable material was available on disembarkation.

### *... and the New*

Smallpox was unknown in the Americas before 1492, and was another gift bestowed on a vulnerable population by Christopher Columbus. The first epidemic of smallpox in the New World occurred on Hispaniola in 1507, when it exterminated entire tribes of native Indians.

In November 1519, Hernando Cortés met the Aztec Emperor Montezuma at Tenochtitlan. A following fleet sent from Cuba landed near present-day Vera Cruz in April 1520, and smallpox disembarked on mainland America. The local Amerindians 'died in heaps, like bedbugs'. In June 1520 Cortés did battle with Montezuma and lost a third of his men. The Aztecs should have pursued the Spaniards and consolidated their victory: instead, Montezuma's men were enfeebled and dying with smallpox, thereby allowing Cortés' soldiers to rest and regroup. Within a year, Cortés was back, to win a permanent victory. Much has been made of the advantage given to Cortés by artillery and the awesome power of armoured horses charging into the Aztec lines. But the Spaniards' greatest ally was an invisible virus: Montezuma's kingdom fell to a foe they could not fight and against which they had no immunity. The Indians reasoned that a disease which struck down Aztec and not Spaniard must be supernatural. Smallpox, not the Spaniards, conquered America.

Smallpox reached the Incas of Peru in a devastating epidemic in 1524, killing an estimated 200,000 people in a four-year period. The Inca leader, Huayna Capac, succumbed. He had himself 'sealed with stone into his house where he was left to die unattended. After a wait of eight days his minions went in, took out his half-decomposed body, embalmed him, dressed him in his finest armour, and carried his body on their shoulders to Cuzco where he was buried'.

Between 1617–19 smallpox wiped out nine-tenths of the Indian population along the Massachusetts coast. Such biological carnage greatly facilitated ethnic cleansing for the incoming pilgrims from Europe. Increase Mather (d. 1723), a Puritan clergyman and President of Harvard College, had no doubt that God had entered the fray on the side of the White Man in his battle with the infidel. Smallpox moved on to ravage the Huron Indians of Lake Ontario, and then the Iroquois. Dying Indians were baptised by Jesuits, though it is likely that the kissing of crucifixes merely served to hasten the spread of the disease. One trader, angered by loss of his equipment, and bent on revenge, invited the local Indians to smoke a pipe of peace. He presented the Indians with a keg of rum, wrapped in a flag that had been smeared by smallpox pustules.

The white settlers were not totally immune, only relatively so, and periodic epidemics occurred in cities like New York and Boston, often with long disease-free intervals. A mass exodus of the population of Boston took place when smallpox struck in 1751. In some parts of the city, one in five died. Philadelphia became infamous as a repository of smallpox. Benjamin Franklin wrote in 1731: 'We have had smallpox here lately ... Mr George Claypole (a descendant of Oliver Cromwell) died first, suddenly; within a short time died his best negro; then two children buried at the same time; then two more: so that I saw two double buryings come out of the house in one week. None were left in the family, but the mother and one child.'

Increase Mather's son, Cotton, also a Puritan preacher, began to investigate the possibilities of inoculation when, in May 1721, smallpox visited Boston. He asked the co-operation of the local physicians, but only one, Zabdiel Boylston, volunteered his help. On 26 June 1721, Boylston inoculated his six-year-old son, Thomas, and two Negro slaves with the pus from a smallpox patient. All three developed mild infections and became immune. Despite this success, the voice of opposition was indignant and deafening. Boylston had to hide from the mob; Mather's home was bombed.

In the same month, Cotton Mather's son Samuel came home from Harvard following the death of his roommate through smallpox. Samuel had not yet shown any symptoms. Father agonized in his diary: 'Full of distress about Sammy. He begs to have his life saved by receiving the Small-pox, in the way of Inoculation ... and if he should after all die by receiving it in the common Way, how can I answer it?' The decision was taken to inoculate, and Samuel was the only one of Cotton's sixteen children to survive him.

Benjamin Franklin, who lost his four-year-old son, Francis, to smallpox, became an ardent advocate of inoculation. Children were invited to 'inoculation parties'. The need to isolate those who were inoculated limited its application as a measure of mass eradication. George Washington insisted that his troops were inoculated, and this factor has been cited as a major factor in the colonists eventually gaining their independence from Great Britain.

Benjamin Waterhouse became first Professor of Medicine at

Harvard Medical School in 1782. In 1800 he vaccinated his five-year-old son Daniel, the first in the United States. His crime, in the eyes of many, was to profit from an attempted monopolization of vaccination. He offered to supply vaccine in return for one-fourth of the profits from its use, and attempted to mask his financial greed under the mantle of claiming the need to maintain the high standards and quality of vaccine.

After vaccination had become fully established in America, two unlearnt Old World lessons led to its decline: complacency and the lack of appreciation of the need for revaccination. A pandemic in 1836–40 served to wipe out many of the native Indian tribes: Mandan, Assiniboin, Crow, Dakota, Pawnee, Apache and Comanche. Of its effects on the Sioux: 'they died a ghastly death, with their bodies swollen, and covered with pustules, their eyes blinded, hideously howling their death song in utter despair'. Not surprisingly, the Indians regarded vaccination as a white man's trick.

On 19 November 1863, Abraham Lincoln delivered his Gettysburg Address. At the White House that night he felt unwell with headache and fever. Two days later a rash appeared and a diagnosis of smallpox was eventually made. He was probably infected by his youngest son, Tad, aged ten. Lincoln's smallpox was mild, but he passed it on to William Johnson, his black valet, who died and was buried at Arlington National Cemetery at Lincoln's expense. The illness of a President at war is a serious affair: fortunately, Lincoln's did not last long and had a happy outcome.

### *The world eradicates its first disease*

Jenner foresaw the eventual eradication of smallpox, but it was a long time coming. The advent of freeze-dried vaccine, which maintained its potency in hot climates without refrigeration, was a major step forward, enabling treatment in tropical areas of the world.

The reason that smallpox was chosen by the World Health Organization (WHO) as the first disease to be targeted for eradication was the fact that the virus which causes human smallpox cannot survive in any other animal. Therefore, if everyone in the world is vaccinated and immune, there is nowhere for the virus to survive, and consequently the disease would be completely eradicated. In 1966 the WHO called for global eradication within ten years. The deadline was met with just one year to spare. On 16 October 1975 a Bangladeshi girl became the last known case of endemic smallpox in the world.

And yet ... Can we be absolutely sure that the virus will never

again return to blight human kind? No, we cannot be sure. The virus is known to exist and multiply in tissue cultures in research laboratories, both East and West, ready for use in biological warfare. American servicemen are still vaccinated in case an enemy resorts to using smallpox as a weapon, in ways reminiscent of the genocide of the Amerindians.

And can we be sure that the virus does not linger somewhere, snug and dormant, waiting to be revitalized? In 1986 in Spitalfield Church, London, it was decided to clear the crypt of its centuries-old coffins. All went well until some of the sealed coffins were opened and workers gazed upon the bodies, some with skin still adhering to bone. Could it be possible that the smallpox virus had survived? Happily, no.

A skeleton from Spitalfield Church, London. During the clearing of the crypt, it was feared that the smallpox virus may have lain dormant for centuries, and might re-infect a vulnerable population. Happily such fears were unfounded!

# 4 DEADLY FIRST COUSINS

## 1 Tuberculosis

*Tuberculosis (consumption, scrofula, phthisis) is a chronic disease which is caused by a bacterium,* Mycobacterium tuberculosis. *There are three types of tubercle bacilli which infect man: human, bovine and avian. Spread of the human form of the disease occurs when a person breathes in bacilli exhaled by someone suffering with tuberculosis. Caucasians have a better natural resistance to tuberculosis than Africans, Amerindians and Eskimos. Bovine tuberculosis is contracted by drinking infected milk, but its incidence has decreased dramatically since pasteurization. The decrease in the incidence of the human form of the disease, conspicuous in the West until recent times, has been brought about by improved nutrition and higher standards of hygiene and sanitation.*

*The disease is so called because of the nodules or 'tubercles' which appear throughout the organs of the body and which are recognizable at autopsy. Many people have no symptoms and the disease is only discovered on routine chest X-ray examination. Although tuberculosis affects every tissue and all organs of the body, it is primarily a disease of the lungs, characterized by a persistent cough and spitting up of blood. Wasting and debilitation follow. Consumption is a good descriptive term for the ravages brought about by this disease. On occasion, tuberculosis may run a fulminating course to rapid death – 'galloping consumption' – but more often it is characterized by waxing and waning in the severity of symptoms. Tuberculosis may produce serious disease by destruction of bones, larynx (voice box), kidneys, adrenal glands and brain.*

*The disease is diagnosed using a skin test, by growing the bacterium from a sample of a patient's sputum or urine, or by characteristic changes on chest X-rays. Drug treatment (e.g. Streptomycin) kills the bacterium, but resistant strains are becoming more common. A live vaccine (BCG) is available as prophylaxis.*

### *Keats and Lawrence: two tubercular Englishmen*

A little over a century separates the deaths from tuberculosis of John Keats and David Herbert Lawrence. Quintessential Englishmen, they died abroad, each searching in vain for a climate which would help to heal lungs destroyed by consumption.

John Keats died of tuberculosis in 1821 at the age of twenty-six. Some, including his friend Shelley, would contend that his sensitive nature turned tubercular when his poem *Endymion* received such a poor reception from the critics. More realistically, Keats contracted tuberculosis from his mother whom he nursed during her terminal illness in 1810, when he was only fourteen. Eight years later Keats did the same for his younger brother, Tom, when he contracted the disease. In February 1820, Keats caught a high fever and took to his bed. One morning he coughed and recognized the taste of blood in his mouth: having studied medicine at Guy's Hospital in London, Keats needed no one to tell him its ominous significance. 'The blood is my death warrant, I must die.' According to the practice of the time, Keats's doctors bled him frequently, thereby exacerbating his anaemia and listlessness.

In September 1820 Keats set out for the gentler clime of Italy, hoping to recover his strength and revive poetic inspiration. The long sea journey to Naples completely exhausted him. His sense of impotence and frustration boiled over: 'Oh! what a misery it is to have an intellect in splints!' The final leg to Rome by chaise drained his last reserves of energy. He put himself under the care of Dr James Clark, the physician to the English community, who bled him more and fed him on a prison régime of a single anchovy and a morsel of bread. Keats complained that 'a mouse would starve on it'. When his landlady suspected that the Englishman was suffering from tuberculosis, Keats was unceremoniously evicted. On 23 February 1821, John Keats died peacefully in his sleep. He was wrapped in his winding-sheet with Fanny Brawne's letters next to his heart. His self-composed epitaph testifies to the inpermanence of being:

> Here lies one whose name was writ in water[1]

D.H. Lawrence never conceded that he suffered from tuberculosis. He attributed his chronic cough and chest problems to 'bronchitis', despite his being told the true diagnosis by numerous doctors. In the end tuberculosis killed him, and it is probable that he would have lived longer and written more if he had acknowledged the seriousness of his condition and accepted proper treatment.

David Herbert Lawrence was born in 1885, his father an illiterate coal-miner, his mother a school-teacher. Early in childhood he suffered with his chest and, years later, described himself as 'a delicate brat with a stuffy nose'. At school he was forever troubled by a hacking cough, which became his hallmark. At eighteen, Lawrence was a student at Nottingham University and went on to become a school-teacher in south London. In 1911, the year after his mother's death, he contracted pneumonia after waiting for a train in a downpour. This illness made him decide to give up teaching and devote himself to writing.

For the rest of his life Lawrence found it difficult to stay in one place for any length of time. He and his wife, Frieda von Richthofen (a cousin of the German air ace, Baron von Richthofen), travelled constantly. During the First World War they returned to England where, unsurprisingly, he was found to be unfit for military service. In 1919, he set off again on his travels and subsequently was only ever to return to England on brief visits. He was always on the move, always restlessly searching. When in Mexico City in 1925 he was examined by a Dr Uhlfelder who told Frieda, 'Mr Lawrence has tuberculosis' and gave him but a year or two to live. Two months later, Lawrence was feeling better and referred in a letter to his 'malaria, typhoid condition and flu'. The Lawrences were on the move again.

In 1926, Lawrence began to spit up blood. The next year he had a severe bronchial haemorrhage but stubbornly persisted in calling his illness 'bronchitis'. By 1927 he was gravely ill. Dr Hans Carossa, an expert in tuberculosis, commented, 'No medical treatment can really save him.' A friend described Lawrence thus: 'No doubt he was gravely ill. Tuberculosis, the miner's disease, had emaciated his tall bony body and stooped his shoulders. It looked as if his suit was much too large for him. But the pale triangular face with the large front and the little reddish goatee was illuminated by a spiritual vitality which triumphantly denied all physical decay.' *Spes phthisica*, a misplaced optimism characteristic of tubercular patients, was hard at work. When other friends visited Lawrence in Florence in 1928 they resolved 'not to postpone to the future our time with him, but seize each passing day'. Lawrence wrote, 'My health is enough to depress the Archangel Michael himself. My bronchials are really awful. It's not the lungs.'

By 1930 Lawrence was so ill that he was advised to enter a sanatorium in southern France for treatment. In February he finally agreed. 'It's not a good place – shan't stay long – I'm better in a house – I'm miserable.' He insisted on moving into a rented villa in the village. Frieda tells that the day after the move he cried out in agony and asked for morphine, 'so Aldous [Huxley] went off to find a doctor to give him some. After a while he said: "I am better now" ... and then again: "I am better now".' He died at Vence on 2 March 1930, aged forty-five: 'The moment came when the thread of life tore in his heaving chest, his face changed, his cheeks and jaw sank, and death had taken hold of him.'

## *One of man's oldest*

The disease which afflicted Keats and Lawrence, and countless other lesser mortals, is one of man's oldest. Naturally, no pulmonary evidence of tuberculosis remains from ancient times, but the disease is evident from suggestive bony destruction. Tuberculosis has been identified in the skeletal remains of Neolithic people buried near Heidelberg. Bony evidence of the disease has been found in Egyptian mummies dating back to 1000 BC, and obvious depictions of tuberculous skeletal deformities adorn ancient pottery. In Deuteronomy is one of the few biblical references to tuberculosis: 'The Lord shall smite thee with a consumption, and with a fever and with an inflammation.' Many more descriptions are to be found in Hindu, Greek and Roman writings, though it is important to be aware that not all the ancient references to 'consumption' can be assumed to be cases of tuberculosis, since this was often the name given to any chronic wasting disease. The Greek word 'phthisis' was meant to signify a shrivelling up, a melting away of the body, a 'consumption'.[2]

Although tuberculosis is a disease of great antiquity, its greatest harvest was gathered in with the poverty and deprivation of the Industrial Revolution. It is probable that tuberculosis also affected the better-off, but such was its stigma that the relatives of richer victims could persuade doctors to enter a more acceptable diagnosis on the death certificate.

One form of tuberculosis, scrofula, was the name given to large swellings of the lymph glands in the neck. There is a long tradition among French and English kings of curing scrofula – thereby known as the 'King's Evil' – by the touch of a royal hand. Scholars – not always without a little nationalist bias – have long argued in which country this tradition originated, but it is now generally accepted that the first to touch was King Clovis, who reigned in fifth-century France. The practice continued in England until relatively recent times. The largest number touched for scrofula was in 1684 when many were trampled to death in the rush to get close to King Charles II.

One of the most celebrated persons to receive the royal touch was Dr Samuel Johnson, an event described in *An account of the life of Dr Samuel Johnson from his birth to his eleventh year, written by himself*. The first entry records, 'I was born almost dead', neatly setting the scene for the life of medical crises to follow. For fear that he might not survive his birth, the baby was christened that same night. But survive he did, and was subsequently farmed out to a wet nurse, Joan Marklew, from whom, he claimed, he contracted scrofula. Whether Johnson was infected by Marklew or some years later, when he was two-and-a-half years old he was touched by Queen Anne who had been encouraged to revive the flagging tradition to demonstrate to her subjects the divine right of kings, a firmly held Stuart tenet. Johnson's mother had to get a certificate from the doctor to certify that Samuel had not been touched before, and the boy had to be examined by the court surgeon to verify the diagnosis, before he was finally given his entrance ticket and allowed to join the other 200 hopeful of a miracle. Johnson was also given a 'touch-piece' as a memento of the occasion which he wore around his neck for the rest of his life. Anne had patently lost her touch and Johnson subsequently had to submit to surgical drainage of his neck glands. James Boswell, Johnson's biographer, observed that the scars 'greatly disfigured a countenance naturally harsh and rugged'. Johnson's life was not foreshortened by tuberculosis: he died, aged seventy-five, the scrofula scars showing up prominently on his death mask.[3]

### *How did tuberculosis spread?*[4]

Many people over many centuries had believed tuberculosis to be contagious, communicated either through the air or by handling objects belonging to the sick person. It was Fracastorius (the same man who gave syphilis its name) who did most to popularize contagion as the method of spread of tuberculosis. Others, noting how tuberculosis appeared to run in families, argued that this might indicate a hereditary disposition. Other ideas were rather more unorthodox: the physiologist Van Swieten contended that the kiss of a wife dying of phthisis had taken the hair off a spot on her husband's head; Panarolli, an Italian physician, said that he saw a man fall down dead from stepping on tuberculous spittle (the poor chap probably slipped and broke his neck).

Contagion was so widely accepted that legislation was passed in Italy to forbid autopsies on tubercular corpses. The possessions of the dead were often burnt and their houses replastered to guard against

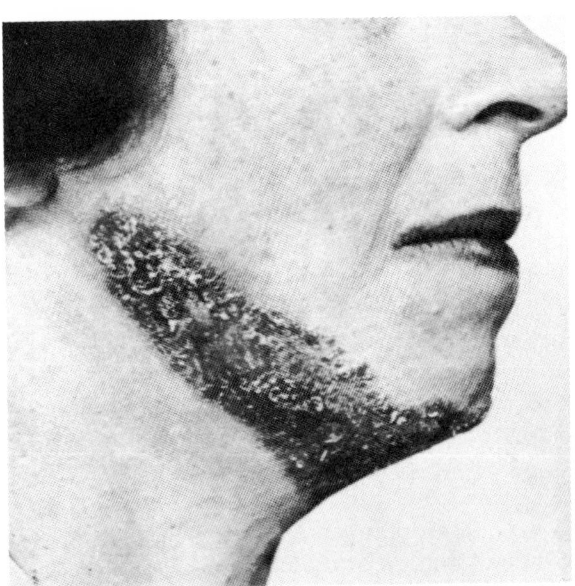

A skin manifestation of tuberculosis

contamination. Over time, and usually due to commercial rather than medical considerations, the regulations were relaxed. Nevertheless in 1818, Paganini, the virtuoso violinist, was turfed out of his lodgings in Naples when the owner discovered the maestro to be suffering from tuberculosis. The French writer, René de Chateaubriand, tried to sell his carriage in order to raise money to care for his friend, Madame de Beaumont, who was in the final stages of consumption. He was unsuccessful since people had seen Madame de Beaumont riding in the carriage and therefore considered it to be contaminated – Chateaubriand was ordered to burn it.

Frederic Chopin met the same reaction when he went to stay on the island of Majorca. He wrote,

> I have been as sick as a dog the last two weeks; I caught cold in spite of 18 degrees C of heat, roses, oranges, palms, figs and three most famous doctors of the island. One sniffed at what I spat up, the second tapped where I spat it from, the third poked about and listened how I spat it. One said I had died, the second that I am dying, the third that I shall die … All this has affected the Preludes and God knows when you will get them.

When the local population found out that Chopin was consumptive they would have nothing further to do with either him or George Sand. The landlords wanted to evict them immediately and insisted that they pay for replastering the house. They were refused carriages. Sand wrote, 'We had to go three leagues through deserted roads in "birlocho", that is, in wheelbarrows. When we arrived in Palma, Chopin had a terrifying haemorrhage; the following day we boarded the only steamship that comes to the island and which is used to transfer pigs to Barcelona.'

Transmission by suckling was long suspected. Sir Walter Scott was born in 1771, one of twelve siblings, six of whom perished in infancy. Scott probably survived tuberculosis only as a result of dubious medical ethics: 'I was an uncommonly healthy child, but had nearly died in consequence of my first nurse being ill of a consumption, a circumstance which she chose to conceal, though to do so was murder to both herself and me. She went privately to consult Dr Black, the celebrated professor of Chemistry, who put my father on his guard. The woman was dismissed and I was consigned to a healthy peasant.' Posterity is indebted to Black's breaking of medical confidentiality, for the Waverley novels and other masterpieces.

Protagonists of the hereditary spread of tuberculosis could point to many famous families, including royalty, in which tuberculosis affected successive generations. The Bourbons in France were particularly affected. It is likely that the anal fistula of Louis XIV was tubercular in origin. When conservative treatment failed, an operation was advised. The King was not enthusiastic and the story is told how the surgeon Felix practised his technique on lesser buttocks before being let loose on the royal rump. Sychophantic courtiers, anxious to share the King's discomfort in convalescence, applied surgical dressings to their rears and imitated His Majesty's limp.[5]

The best-known example of tuberculosis running in a family is that of the Brontës. The Reverend Patrick Brontë hailed from Ireland and married Maria Branwell of Cornwall in 1812. They had six children in the next seven years. The family lived, frugally and without creature comforts, in the parsonage at Haworth in Yorkshire. Throughout his long life, in hot weather or cold, Patrick Brontë always wore a cravat which covered his neck, reaching right up to his ear lobes. Many believed that by this device, the Reverend Brontë hoped to conceal the swellings or scars of scrofula. Life was hard and the climate harsh. Maria, Elizabeth, Charlotte and Emily were sent to Lowood School to be educated. Some idea of the bleakness of Lowood can be gained from reading *Jane Eyre*: 'as the dense mist penetrated to the shivering frames, I heard frequently the sound of a hollow cough.' A few months after the arrival of the Brontë girls at Lowood, an epidemic broke out in the school. Its exact nature will never be known but Maria and Elizabeth fell ill and had to be sent home. They died soon after.

After some years away the remaining Brontë children came back to live together at Haworth. They began to pursue their literary careers. *Jane Eyre* established Charlotte's literary reputation. Branwell squandered his talent and opportunities by overindulgence in alcohol and a dependence on opium which he took to suppress his constant coughing. His addictions and ill-health finally overtook him in September 1848. At his funeral Emily caught a cold and her condition steadily worsened, her breathing becoming increasingly laboured. She refused to rest or see a doctor. She died, three months after her brother, aged thirty. Two weeks later the doctor pronounced his verdict on Anne: advanced consumption. Charlotte decided that she would take her only surviving sister to the seaside at Scarborough. They were there barely four days when Anne died, aged twenty-nine. Charlotte returned to Haworth and her literary career. She married in 1854 and became pregnant. A few months later she, too, was lying in the churchyard, aged thirty-eight. Patrick Brontë survived his wife and all six children and went on to live until the age of eighty-five.[6]

## *Diagnosis*

Generally speaking, tuberculosis was not a difficult condition to diagnose. Severe emaciation associated with night sweats, chronic cough, spitting up blood and diarrhoea, were usually sufficient to point to the correct diagnosis. Charlotte Brontë wrote of her sisters: 'One by one they fell asleep in my arms and I closed their glazed eyes.' In her prose she highlights the slow decline brought about by tuberculosis: 'The sick girl wasted like any snow-wreath in thaw; she faded like any flower in drought.' One did not need to be a doctor like Keats to be able to diagnose tuberculosis: Katherine Mansfield (1888–1923), the New Zealand writer, knew immediately:

> I woke up early this morning and when I opened the shutters the full round sun was just risen. I began to repeat that verse of Shakespeare's: 'Lo, here the gentle lark weary of rest', and bounded back to bed. The bound made me cough – I spat – it tasted strange – it was bright red blood – I don't want to find this is real consumption, perhaps it's going to gallop – who knows? – and I shan't have my work written. *That's what matters*. How unbearable it would be to die – leave 'scraps', 'bits' ... nothing real finished.

(Shades of Keats's 'When I have fears that I may cease to be/Before my pen has glean'd my teeming brain.')

Other wasting diseases, such as cancer, usually had much more accelerated courses compared to the slow, steady decline brought about by tuberculosis. Autopsies of tubercular patients revealed cavities in the lungs, and often small nodules or tubercles, resembling millet seeds, scattered throughout the organs of the body. Sometimes the tubercles would be hard to the touch; others would have a soft centre of cheese-like material. Slowly, over centuries, it became increasingly possible to link clinical symptoms with later post-mortem findings.

Today, if one visits a doctor with a chest complaint, it would be unusual if a physical examination was not carried out. The two methods of examination of the chest – tapping (percussion) and listening with a stethoscope (auscultation) – are so familiar that it is difficult to think that they are both of relatively recent origin. Percussion was 'discovered' by Leopold von Auenbrugger, an Austrian physician, and described in his *Inventum novum* in 1761. The principle is quite simple: by tapping the chest with the fingers one is able to elicit notes of different pitch, reflecting the inner structures. A high-pitched sound signifies tissues filled with air, while a duller note signifies more solid structures. No doubt Auenbrugger, the son of an innkeeper, remembered how his father used to tap barrels to find out how much beer remained in them. Over time, and with practice, physicians became able to locate tubercular cavities by eliciting their characteristic percussion sounds, and to distinguish between empty cavities and those filled with fluid.

It was the brilliant Frenchman, René Théophile Hyacinthe Laënnec, who, in 1804, first brought together the various clinical and pathological findings into a coherent theory. He contended that the tubercle was the characteristic lesion of consumption and that the diverse manifestations of the disease represented the effects that tubercles had upon the organs which they invaded. A tubercle may grow, soften, rupture and form cavities.

It had been well known that some of the inner sounds of the body could be distinctly heard if one puts one's ear directly to the skin. This was not a popular practice of doctors, doubtless because of the unhygienic state of many of the bodies. Laënnec's aversion to applying his ear 'to the perfumed but unbathed bosoms of his patients' moved him to invent the prototype of the modern stethoscope. One day, so the story goes, while sitting in the garden of the Louvre, he watched fascinated as children played with a long plank of wood: a child would hold one end and scratch it with a pin; a second child, with his ear to the other end, would distinctly hear the sounds transmitted through the wood. Laënnec hurried back to the Hôpital Necker, found a large piece of card, and formed it into a cylinder. He put one end on the chest of a patient and put the other end to his ear. He was delighted to be able to hear the chest sounds with such clarity.[7] As with percussion previously, physicians were soon able to differentiate between the various pops, squeaks and bubbles, and to learn what each signified in the tubercular processes, and link them to autopsy findings. But auscultation was not welcomed by all. Forbes, the doctor who translated Laënnec's work on auscultation into English, was far from convinced himself! 'It must be confessed that there is something even ludicrous in the picture of a grave physician proudly listening through a long tube applied to the patient's thorax, as if the disease were a living being that could communicate its condition to the sense without.'

Laënnec was able to refine many of his auscultatory techniques by placing his stethoscope on his own chest: thus was he able to chart the course of the tuberculosis from which he himself suffered, and which finally killed him in 1826. Deteriorating rapidly, he had decided to quit Paris for the healthier air of his native Brittany. But his illness was too far advanced. On the last day of his life he calmly removed the rings from his fingers and placed them on a table, stating that he wished to spare others this melancholy task.

## *Animalculae and germs*

Benjamin Marten first postulated the existence of germs as long ago as 1722:

> The Original and Essential cause, then, which some content themselves to call a vicious Disposition of the Juices, others a Salt Acrimony, others a strange Ferment, others a Malignant Humour, may possibly be some certain Species of *Animalculae* or wonderfully minute living creatures that, by their peculiar Shape or disagreeable Parts, are inimicable to our Nature; but, however, capable of subsisting in our Juices and Vessels.

Such a theory would explain some of the mysteries surrounding the spread of tuberculosis. Marten again:

> It may, therefore, be very likely that by habitual lying in the same Bed with a consumptive Patient, constantly eating or drinking with him or by very frequently conversing so nearly as to draw in part of the Breath he emits from the Lungs, a Consumption may be caught by a second person.

Marten's book was promptly forgotten, and when rediscovered in 1911, only four copies could be found.

The germ theory was considerably advanced by a French army

surgeon, Jean-Antoine Villemin, who, in the 1860s, injected some of the caseous material from a patient who had died of tuberculosis under the skin of rabbits. When the rabbits were killed some months later their organs were found to be infiltrated with tubercles. When the rabbits were inoculated with tuberculous material taken from cows the disease was more rapid and more severe. In later experiments Villemin used tuberculous sputum and material from scrofulous glands in his inoculations, and produced the same results, proving that the causative agent was a germ. Again, as so often in the history of tuberculosis, traditionalists opposed to contagion theories, carried the day. The British government set up an experiment to replicate Villemin's research. Sure enough, out of fifty-three guinea-pigs inoculated with tubercular material, fifty developed lesions of tuberculosis. By way of comparison, two guinea-pigs had wads of cotton inserted in the shoulders in an attempt to set up a local inflammation: one of these animals developed what appeared to be tuberculosis. On the basis of this one guinea-pig – who may have had pre-existing tuberculosis – the English researchers found Villemin's claims unproven.

Despite setbacks the germ theory continued to gain ground and converts until, in 1882, the tubercle bacillus was visualized under the microscope by the German, Robert Koch. It had not been an easy task since the bacillus needed to be stained with unusual dyes in order to show up on the microscope slide, and because it took fully ten days to grow in culture media. A theory evolved to explain the origin and manifestations of an infection with the tubercle bacilli. Infection of an individual is usually by inhaling infected sputum or drinking infected cows' milk. Many people who contract tuberculosis show no symptoms; in others the disease lies dormant only to be reactivated at a later time. Once established, the tubercle bacillus can spread by way of the blood to affect all the other organs of the body. That some people have more natural resistance than others was shown by a remarkable mistake which happened in Lubeck in 1926. 249 babies, due to be vaccinated were given instead enormous numbers of living, virulent tubercle bacilli: 76 died of acute tuberculosis but 173 developed only minor lesions. Susceptibility and mortality seem to be lower in the range five to fifteen, the so-called 'golden age' of resistance to tuberculosis.

Bacterial considerations must not blind us to the importance of constitutional or hereditary factors in regard to susceptibility, course and outcome in tuberculosis. Exposed to the same dose of bacteria, the healthy and well-fed will succumb less easily than the sick and malnourished.

### *The nineteenth century: tuberculosis and the arts*

In 1815 Thomas Young estimated that tuberculosis was responsible for the death of a quarter of Europe's population, especially men and women in the prime of their lives. It has been calculated that half the population of England suffered from scrofula. Unquestionably, tuberculosis was the single greatest cause of death in the Western world: truly, 'The Great White Plague'.

With so many poets, novelists and artists falling prey to tuberculosis it is hardly surprising that the disease figured prominently in the arts. There had always been something *meaningful* and *significant* about an artist dying of tuberculosis – preferably poor, young and alone. (It is known that Keats treated himself with mercury – presumably for syphilis. This prompts one to ask: 'If the poet had died of the pox rather than consumption, would this fact have altered posterity's view of the man and his work?')

Around the turn of the nineteenth century there arose the 'graveyard school' of romantic poetry, which dwelt more on the expectation of sorrow and death than on love and happiness. Decay and disease were imbued with beauty and a weeping romanticism prevailed. Children and young people in Victorian novels fell prey to tuberculosis, either to increase the pathos, or to take them swiftly out of the plot: Little Blossom in *David Copperfield*, and Frances Earnshaw in *Wuthering Heights*. Colds had a nasty habit of settling on the chest, especially in those of a sensitive nature:

> As light winds wandering through groves of bloom
> Detach the delicate blossom from the tree.
> Close thy sweet eyes, calmly and without pain.

Pain was the reserve of villains.

The archetypal French consumptive was Marguerite Gautier in Dumas's novel *La Dame aux Camélias*, modelled on the courtesan Alphonsine Plessis, who later changed her name to Marie Duplessis. Despite terminal consumption, Duplessis was determined to live life to the full. Her body finally surrendered to death in 1847 when she was only twenty-three years old. She was widely and genuinely mourned, lovers bringing camellias to her grave in Montmatre. Verdi based his opera *La Traviata* on her life story.

Opera has always wallowed in tuberculosis and some of the best known arias have been given to consumptives in their death throes – even if the dramatic impact has been compromised by a wasting disease which leaves its victim weighing 300 pounds! The original Mimi, the emaciated heroine of *La Bohème*, was a flower girl in Paris in the 1840s. Despite her consumption she joined a group of impecunious artists, who met in a club called Bohemia. She moved in with Henri Murger, one of the leaders of the group, who, after her death in 1848, immortalized her in his novel, *Scènes de la Vie de Bohème*, which became a play and the basis for Puccini's opera.

Social realism became fashionable in the literature of the later nineteenth century, the brothers Edmond and Jules Goncourt going to great lengths to record their impressions of Parisian life in the raw in their *Journal*. They witnessed people dying of tuberculosis in the Hôpital de la Charité and incorporated the material into their novel *Philomème*. Soon their own servant was to enter the hospital to die. Despite describing in detail the ravages of the body, the Goncourts still regarded tuberculosis as a refined disease in which the mind triumphs over the body. Dickens, in *Nicholas Nickelby* puts it thus:

> a Dread disease in which the struggle between soul and body is so gradual, quiet, and solemn, and the result so sure, that day by day, and grain by grain, the mortal part wastes and withers away, so that the spirit grows light and sanguine with its lightening load, and feeling immortality at hand, deems it but a new term of mortal life; a disease in which death and life are so strangely blended that death takes the glow and hue of life, and life the gaunt and grisly form of death …

After 1800 it became the height of fashion to impersonate a corpse: women were meant to appear wan and delicate and to drape themselves in thin clothing, regardless of the season. Rouge was abandoned and whitening powders applied to the face. Better still to be carried off with consumption. Edgar Allan Poe's first wife, Virginia, was made the more attractive for him by her 'morbidly angelic' features. On one occasion, whilst singing and playing the harp in the half light, she suddenly coughed blood over her white breast. Poe considered his wife's illness a strange charm which 'rendered more ethereal her chalky pallor and her haunted, liquid eyes'. Delicate women, given to faints, were highly prized, and their young deaths regarded the highest form of poetry.

This idealized woman was captured on canvas by the Pre-Raphaelite painters. Much use was made of Elizabeth Siddal, wife of Gabriel Rossetti, whose phthisic looks inspired a generation of imitators. It was especially the gaunt frame, prominent eyes and sensuous mouth which came to encapsulate tubercular women. The chronic cough was considered a bonus! But consumption dragged Siddal down, and she finally resorted to laudanum, dying of an overdose at the age of thirty in 1864.[8]

Men were not immune to the tubercular look. Byron told a friend he would like to die of consumption. When asked why, he replied,

'Because the ladies would all say, "Look at that poor Byron, how interesting he looks in dying!"' Even the robust and sensuous Alexandre Dumas made occasional attempts to look frail and consumptive: 'It was good form to spit blood after each emotion that was at all sensational, and to die before reaching the age of thirty.'

### *The quest for a cure*

Some sufferers were less enamoured with their disease, and dearly wished to be well again. Galen (*c.* 130–201) was one of the first physicians to recommend a change of climate and sent his patients to breathe in the volcanic air of Vesuvius. Keats and Shelly (who was also tubercular) heeded similar advice and decided to head south to restore themselves to health.[9] The most favoured destinations were Italy and southern France. In Nice the *émigrés* from colder climes would promenade, bejewelled but deadly pale – so pale that one observer wondered if the local cemetery had allowed its inmates to escape for the night. It was to Nice that the violinist, Nicolo Paganini, went to spend his last winter in 1839. Like Keats ravaged by the twin scourges of tuberculosis and syphilis, he performed before audiences looking like 'a dead man risen from his grave, a vampire with a violin.' People feared that when he took a bow his whole frame would crumble into a heap of bones. Somehow he found the strength to perform a brilliant musical improvization on his deathbed.

Katherine Mansfield tried to find a cure by finding herself. She had heard of George Gurdjieff and his Institute for the Harmonious Development of Man, which was transplanted from Moscow to Fontainebleau, outside Paris, in the years following the Russian Revolution. Gurdjieff's philosophy embraced the simple life in an attempt to discover one's 'inner being'.

When Mansfield arrived at Fontainebleau on 16 October 1922 it was obvious to all that she was dying. Gurdjieff agreed to her staying even though he knew he risked his reputation if this famous writer should die. (Gurdjieff was known for decades later as 'the man who killed Katherine Mansfield'.) Mansfield entered into the ethos of the community, despite having to rise at 7.30, wash in ice-cold water, do strenuous exercises and take her rest in a hay loft where she could inhale the breath of cows with all its health-giving properties. She wrote that the place would suit D.H. Lawrence, if it was not for his pride.

Christmas and New Year came and went, and from Mansfield's letters it is clear that she realized that death was closing fast. Her husband, Jack, visited on 9 January 1923 and they spent the evening joining in the activities. In going up to her room, Katherine for once forgot her illness and bounded up the stairs. At the top she turned back to Jack and a torrent of blood came from her mouth, like a duck with its head chopped off. She said, 'I believe I'm going to die.' People came rushing and she was helped to her bed. Fully conscious, the blood continued to gush while she frantically pressed a towel to her mouth. Two doctors came and ushered Jack from the room. But it was too late: Katherine Mansfield was dead.[10]

### *Twentieth-century update*

By the 1970s the battle against tuberculosis was as good as won. Successful vaccination of children, improved public health and a triad of drugs had effectively put pay to one of man's oldest adversaries. Or so it seemed. Now, in the 1990s, it appears that optimism and complacency were premature: the disease is on the increase, and *mycobacterium tuberculosis* strains are appearing which are resistant to currently available drugs. The situation is worst in the Third World: of the three million deaths each year, ninety-five per cent are in developing countries, especially in Asia. Tuberculosis has been described as a 'time bomb constructed by social and economic inequality and ignited by the HIV epidemic'.

Serious research into tuberculosis stopped long ago, with the result that 'the diagnostics are stone age and the immunology is bronze age': because of the bacterium's notoriously slow growth, most hospitals still take four weeks to confirm the diagnosis, during which time drug-resistant varieties have killed the patient. Money spent on tuberculosis programmes are a throw-back to the years just after World War Two: today very few doctors are competent to diagnose and treat tuberculosis competently. Drug resistance is facilitated by sloppy approaches to treatment which do not emphasize the paramount importance of continuing to take combined therapies for an extended time. The motivation of multi-national drug companies to replace ineffective drugs is low, since there are no large profits to be made in Third World diseases.[11]

## 2 LEPROSY

*Leprosy (Hansen's disease) is caused by the bacterium,* Mycobacterium leprae, *first discovered by Armauer Hansen in 1874. The disease affects about ten million people worldwide, more commonly in tropical countries. Although its precise mode of transmission is unclear,*

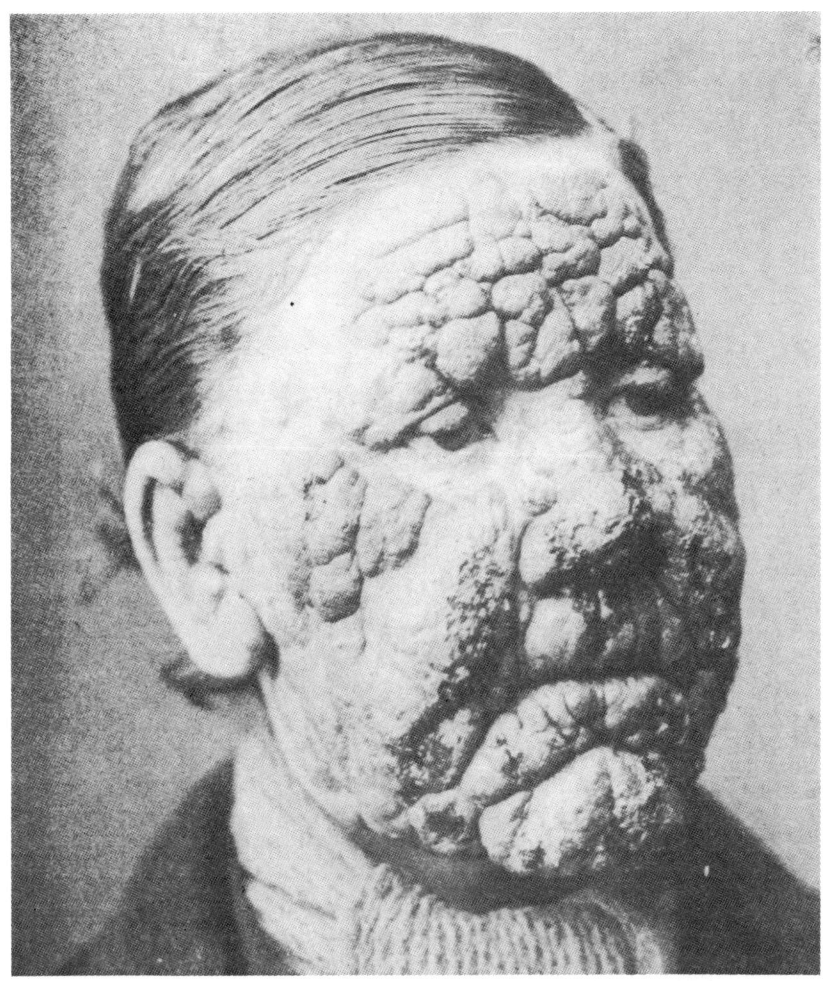

Leprosy affecting the face

*prolonged exposure to someone suffering from the disease is usually required. The bacterium is probably breathed in or gains entry to the body through cuts or abrasions. The incubation period can be many years, even decades. Leprosy usually affects those who are already ill-nourished, poor and unhealthy. The disease is protean, but most often affects the skin and nerves. Cutaneous manifestations include thickening of the skin of the face ('leonine facies'). Nerve involvement includes loss of sensation to temperature, touch and pain, producing loss of fingers. Destruction of the nasal bones lead to saddle nose. Nerve damage causes blindness and crippling. Long-term drug therapy is the treatment of choice.*

## *How old is leprosy?*

> Let him, whose body is covered with pustules like the bubbles of foul air that rise from the marsh and burst as they come to the surface, hide and live in isolation on a dunghill, with pariah dogs and other filthy beasts. Let us drive him from our village with stones and cover him, who is himself a living excrement, with ordure. May the immortal rivers reject his corpse.
>
> Hindu poet, 2,400 BC

Much mystery and confusion surrounds leprosy. It was once widely

The 'leonine facies' produced by leprosy

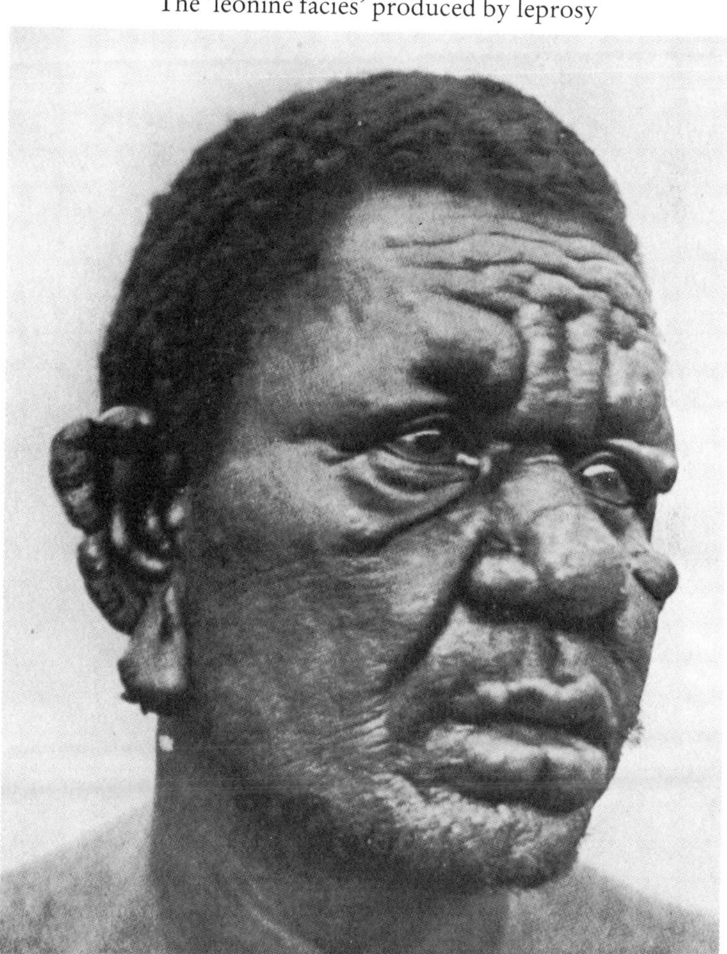

accepted that Lazarus, the biblical beggar who was covered in sores, suffered from leprosy. Medieval leper hospitals were known as lazar-houses, and the Knights of St Lazarus dedicated themselves, in theory at least, to improving the lot of lepers. Further confusion occurred when Lazarus the beggar became identified with Lazarus of Bethany, whom Jesus raised from the dead. Now, Lazarus of Bethany had a sister Mary, who has been associated with the welfare of lepers, to the extent that the Knights of St Lazarus (the Lazarus who was not actually a leper), became the Knights of St Lazarus and St Mary (the sister of the resurrected Lazarus). It seems almost predictable that this Mary would soon be confused with St Mary Magdalene, and the latter was made the patron saint of lepers in England. On the continent, St George, England's patron saint, was adopted as the patron saint of lepers.

Lazarus, George and the two Marys apart, is Biblical leprosy the same disease as the one we know by that name today? The surest way of answering this vexed question is to examine ancient skeletons and look for the characteristic changes which denote leprosy. Foremost among the bony hallmarks of leprosy are the destruction which occurs around the area of the nasal cavity, the loosening and loss of the upper front teeth, and the destruction of the roof of the mouth (the palate). This triad of skull changes is referred to as *facies leprosa*. Additional corroboration of leprosy can sometimes be obtained from bony changes in the legs, fingers and feet.

A leper graveyard

Møller-Christensen, the Danish expert on leprosy, has examined thousands of skeletons. Originally a general practitioner, his interest in leprosy began in 1944 when he unearthed the skeleton of a young woman who had died in the thirteenth century. He wondered if the unusual deformities of the skull could be an indication that the woman had died of leprosy. Since no one could enlighten him, he decided to become his own expert. The logical approach was to examine the bones of people who were definitely known to have died of leprosy. All he had to do was to find a leper graveyard and start digging. Easier said than done, since it took him fully four years to locate a medieval leper hospital and cemetery at a farm in Naestved, near Copenhagen. By 1968, two years after the townsfolk of Naestved had bought and made a gift to him of the farm, Møller-Christensen had examined more than 650 skeletons, and had become the foremost authority on leprosy in the world.

Armed with the knowledge of the bony changes to be found in leprosy, Møller-Christensen turned his attention to Egyptian mummies. He was only able to find strong evidence of leprosy in two skeletons: a man whose skeleton is in the Royal College of Surgeons in London; and a woman whose skeleton is in Cambridge. This dearth of early lepromatous skeletons led Møller-Christensen to the conclusion that leprosy was not a common disease in Europe and the Middle East before the time of Christ. Furthermore, he concluded that the disease probably spread westward from Asia rather than northward from Africa.

If leprosy was not common in Old Testament times, how does one explain the references to the disease which occur in the bible? The most likely explanation is a mistranslation of the Hebrew word *tsara'at.* Biblical leprosy is probably modern psoriasis, a chronic and scaly skin condition. True leprosy would appear to have been a rarity in early Christian times. Certainly Hippocrates, who lived in the 5th century BC, was not describing leprosy as we know it today when he wrote of a scaly skin disease which itched furiously and healed quickly.

## *The rise and fall of leprosy*

Leprosy, as we know the disease today, flourished in the Middle Ages but then disappeared from Europe in the fifteenth century, probably edged out by tuberculosis, its bacterial first cousin. Only in countries around the Baltic Sea did leprosy persist to any great degree into the nineteenth century. The increased numbers of leper hospitals established in the early Middle Ages did not mean that leprosy was on the increase at that time. Rather, the rich had hit upon the idea of founding leper hospitals in order that the patients within might pray for the soul of their benefactor. It was considered a shrewd investment: for the minimal cost of keeping, say, twenty local lepers, in food and accommodation, one's soul was guaranteed speedy transit to paradise. Although admission fees, gifts, tolls and taxes helped in the upkeep of leper hospitals, the major source of a hospital's income came from endowments. The vast majority of lepers were too poor to pay admission fees: intriguingly, some people *who were not lepers*, paid the admission fee and lived at the hospital, simply to be looked after in their old age. Food too rotten to sell was sent to 'ye hous of ye lepir men'. Henry II, after the murder of Becket, left legacies to several leper hospitals. Many hospitals appointed a proctor to go out into the community and beg alms, sometimes in exchange for indulgences.

Leprosy is a mutilatingly grotesque disease which, in its most florid form, is unmistakable. It has one of the longest incubation periods, sometimes taking fifteen or twenty years after infection before signs of the disease appear. It is a very difficult disease to catch, fewer than one in ten of those who are exposed to the bacterium contract the disease, and only half of those show the typical lepromatous changes. It is probably caught by inhalation, and was likely to have been much more contagious in the Middle Ages. It was once thought that leprosy could be caught by having sexual intercourse with a woman who was menstruating. The association of leprosy with increased sexual appetite was taken to infer a venereal cause, though it is easy to imagine that a newly diagnosed leper, faced with the prospect of a lifetime of enforced isolation, would become preoccupied with the opposite sex.

In its early stages leprosy is difficult, if not impossible, to diagnose. Until quite recent times, the diagnosis often depended upon a 'wait and see' approach. In the Middle Ages it was not unusual for neighbours to accuse others of being a leper. Joanna Nightingale of Brentwood in Essex (just north of London) was accused of being 'infected by the foul contact of leprosy' in 1468. She refused to submit 'to be diligently viewed and examined by certain discreet and loyal men of the county'. Ultimately she was examined by royal physicians and deemed not to be a leper, and issued with a certificate stating that she was free of the disease and did not have to go into isolation. Joanna Nightingale's case was unusual for its involvement of doctors: more commonly, priests and local worthies constituted the examination panel, since the services of doctors came expensive. In 1772, Margaret Abernethy of Shetland, was summoned by the parish council 'next Wednesday in order to be examined and inspected' and to be 'set apart if she be found unclean'. In 1648, in

Föglö on the Aland Islands (between Sweden and Finland), a woman called Kaisa was ordered to 'present herself by the church wall on the next Sunday so that the people can decide whether she is leprous or whether she should remain under observation'. No doubt a public leprosy examination added some prurient spice to an otherwise dull sabbath. In Kaisa's case the diagnosis remained in doubt and she was confined to her house to await the next annual inspection.

If the decision went against the examinee, and the diagnosis of leprosy was confirmed, the consequence was swift and absolute: social isolation. It was expected that a leper would cut himself off from society, for if he did not go voluntarily he would be cast out by force:

> Although, Oluf Hendhersson, I have repeatedly advised you that Nills Rosenkrantz of Hallkilais in Pemar parish should present himself for admission to hospital he had done no such thing and can easily infect his brothers and sisters with whom he daily lives. In order to force him to comply with the order made against him the aldermen and six of the strongest men who are themselves lepers should be sent by boat to take him from his farm by force.
>
> (Finland, 1670)

Lepers, whatever their station in life, must 'betake themselves to places in the country, solitary and notably distant from the city and suburbs'. Defiance could result in burning of the cheek or cutting out the tongue. Rigorous rules of behaviour were imposed. The leper was

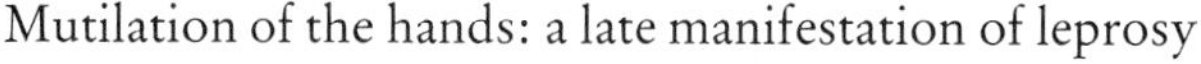
Mutilation of the hands: a late manifestation of leprosy

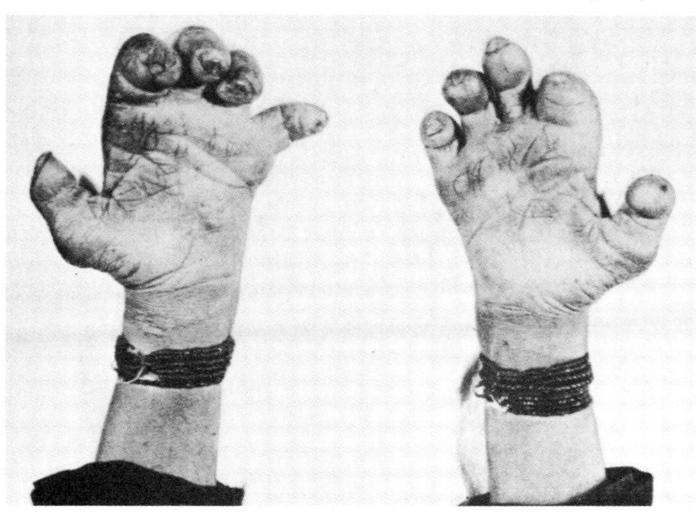

forbidden to mix with others; if he wished to buy something he would touch the article with a stick and have it put in his bowl (one wonders how the vendor sanitized the leper's money); he had to announce his presence by ringing a bell or rattling his clapper; if he stopped to talk to anyone he was obliged to stand to the leeward; he must avoid narrow alleys where he might brush against the healthy; his only companions were to be his wife and fellow lepers.

The process of ostracism was even dignified by a church ceremony, a 'goodbye' mass. He was pronounced dead to the world and cast out from the village in which he had been born and grown up. Black was the predominant colour, of the church and of the leper. The unfortunate leper was expected to stand in a freshly dug grave, holding a candle, while the priest shovelled earth over him, and the congregation sang. The priest then read a list of 'don'ts' which forbade the leper to touch others (except his wife) and forbade him from ever again going into a church. Lepers were forced to wear a uniform of a white or grey woollen robe and gloves. In some countries a large letter 'L' was sewn onto the robe.

Not that all lepers were poor. One rich leper, Zodicus of Constantinople, built the first leper hospital in the fourth century. Noble lepers within colonies usually set themselves apart, as did leprous priests or nuns.

Leprosy had far-reaching implications for married couples. In Welsh laws of the tenth to twelfth centuries, leprosy, 'foul breath' and failure to have sexual relations, were cited as legitimate reasons for a wife to leave her husband and reclaim her dowry. Leprosy was not considered a bar to marriage, provided the leper could find a mate. A spouse might accompany the leper and be admitted to hospital, provided that they promised not to live as husband and wife. In other cases the admitted leper and the spouse who remained in the community *both* had to take vows of perpetual chastity. Most hospitals demanded that the leper, on admission, make a will, leaving two-thirds of his goods and chattels to benefit the hospital and its inmates.

Society looked upon lepers as evil, lustful, sly and paranoid, but few wondered whether these traits might be the result of being cast out and shunned by society. Lepers, like the Jews, were routinely blamed for calamities. In England, King Edward I buried them alive. Shakespeare has Margaret of Anjou ask, 'Why dost thou turn away and hide thy face? I am no loathsome leper, look on me!' The Church regarded leprosy as divine punishment for lustful living: those that flaunted their sexuality would pay for their immorality by forfeiting their good looks, and people who once seduced, now only repulsed. And yet the Church also believed that lepers were guaranteed salvation. This seeming paradox had a biblical precedence, since Lazarus, who suffered as a leper on earth (albeit psoriasis!), went to heaven, while the rich man went to hell. Eternal recompense for a lifetime of being cast out by society.

Leprosy does not kill quickly, but a sense of death is rarely far from a leper's consciousness. From the time that his skin becomes lumpy and his voice becomes hoarse, the spectre of the Grim Reaper haunts his every day. Sentence of death has been passed but the execution day has not been determined.

## *A royal leper*

History books swell with famous people who caught the plague, smallpox and tuberculosis. But where are the illustrious lepers? Perhaps because leprosy is generally a disease of the poor, rich and powerful victims were a rarity. But there is one possible candidate for the title of leprous monarch: King Robert the Bruce of Scotland. Let us carefully examine the evidence.

The Act of Union between Scotland and England is a well-remembered date. Much less well known is the Treaty of Northampton, signed in 1328, by which England gave up all claims to Scotland. Scottish independence was solely due to the efforts of Robert the Bruce, who was able to unite his fellow Scots and wage an unrelenting war against the English Plantagenets. And yet within a year of the Treaty of Northampton, Robert the Bruce was dead – and in mysterious circumstances which have caused comment ever since. After his death, and according to his wishes, Robert the Bruce's heart was cut from his body, encased in a silver casket, and transported around the neck of his loyal lieutenant Sir James Douglas, to the Church of the Holy Sepulchre in Jerusalem. Unfortunately Sir James never arrived: he became embroiled in a local skirmish *en route* in Spain and was slain. The dead knight was returned to Scotland together with the silver casket. Robert the Bruce's heart was finally buried in Melrose Abbey, but what became of the king's body remained shrouded in mystery. Until 17 February 1818.

On that date, work was well advanced on the rebuilding of the choir of Dunfermline Abbey. As the workmen removed the top layer of soil from an area around what was the high altar of the *old* abbey, their spades struck a horizontal stone slab. With mounting excitement the men cleared away the soil: a tomb was revealed. Embedded in the stone were three pairs of iron rings, long since rusted in their sockets. On lifting the slab an inner vault came into view, occupied by a body encased in lead. Peering through cracks in

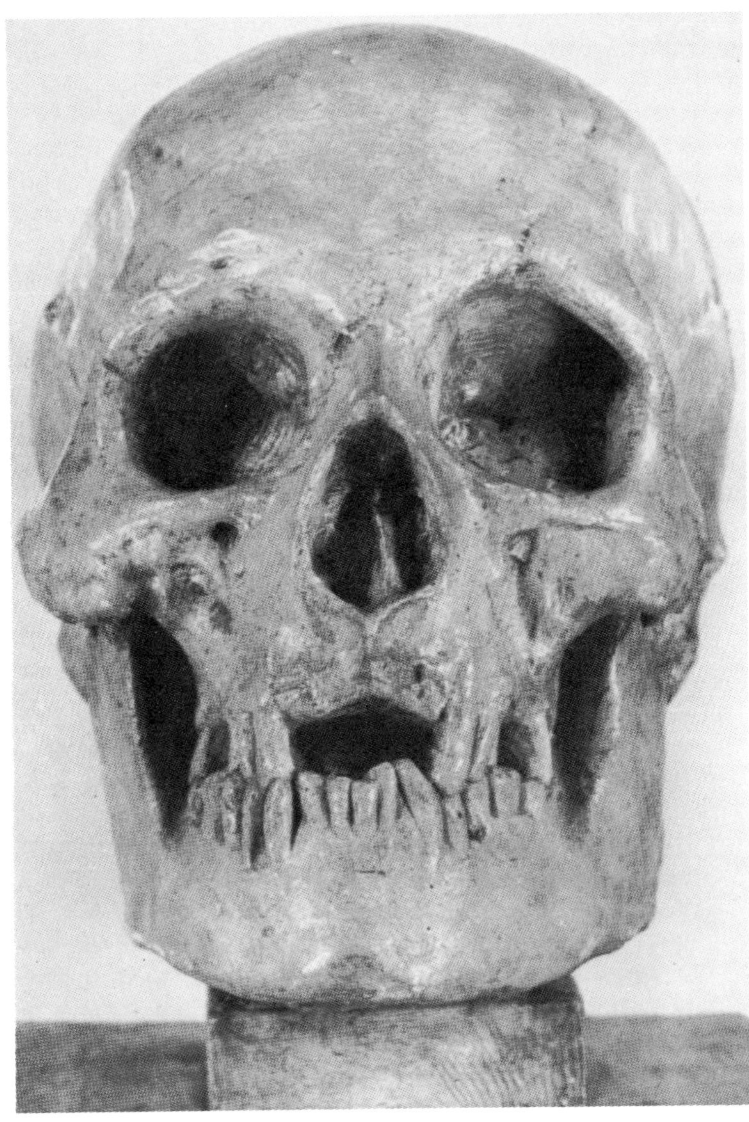

A plaster cast of the skull of Robert the Bruce showing typical bony destruction around the nasal cavity and upper jaw caused by leprosy

the lead, workmen were able to identify the bones of its occupant. Some thought they spied a crown. There was much speculation as to whose corpse had been discovered, but such speculation had to wait while the tomb was resealed, on the orders of the government, to allow time for contemplation about how best to proceed.

The question on everyone's lips was: Could this be the 'lost' tomb of Robert the Bruce? Certainly it was in the right place – immediately in front of the altar in the very monastery in which he had desired to be buried and in which at least nine other Scottish kings were interred. His queen, who predeceased him, had been laid to rest at Dunfermline. When excavation work resumed on 5 November 1819, most believed that they were about to gaze on the remains of Robert the Bruce himself.

Doctors and scientists moved in to pick over the bones – literally. The skeleton was of a man and measured five feet eleven inches. The breast bone was split along its length, no doubt to facilitate removal of the heart meant for the Holy Land. Five days later the identity of the skeleton seemed to be placed beyond all doubt, when a copper plate was found with the inscription *Robertus Scotorum Rex.* Unfortunately this proved to be a hoax. Ultimately, the bones were reinterred in the exact spot where they had been discovered, and there Robert the Bruce lies peacefully to this day.

One of the party of experts who examined the king's remains was an artist called Scoular who had the forethought to make a cast of the skull before it was reburied. This cast has been the focus of medical speculation ever since. The most striking feature about the skull was the missing upper incisors and the erosion of the front of the jaw, just below the nasal cavity. Could these anatomical findings provide a clue as to the cause of the king's death in 1329, at the age of fifty-five?

The English had long maintained that Robert the Bruce was a leper, and yet contemporary descriptions left the matter in doubt. There was never a hint that the king was a social outcast or that visiting dignitaries were afraid to be in his presence. His chronic illness, whatever its nature, was borne philosophically by the king. The matter was finally resolved in 1968. In that year the Danish general practitioner cum world's expert on leprosy, Møller-Christensen, examined Scoular's cast in Edinburgh Medical School. Unhesitatingly he diagnosed *facies leprosa* and Robert the Bruce as a leper.

### *A disease which remains a social stigma*

Leprosy has never been a disease of societies or civilizations. It is quintessentially a disease of individuals, constituting a personal scourge with very public manifestations. The sense of abhorrence remains in our language and attitudes centuries after the disease has ceased to be prevalent: the taunt of 'social' or 'moral' leper conveys the medieval sense of stigma and ostracism.[12]

There is one final irony. Among the most effective of the modern drugs used to treat this mutilating disease was one that produced its own mutilating side-effects: thalidomide.

# 5 CREATIVITY AND ILLNESS

It has long been postulated that tuberculosis and creative genius were somehow linked, that the processes which wasted the body fuelled the mind. The ancient Greeks recognized *spes phthisica*, a type of nervous energy displayed by consumptives, a feverish urge to achieve before being overtaken by death, combined with a misplaced optimism for eventual recovery. 'It is often astonishing to behold the sinking man make plans for the future, engage in new enterprises, plan long voyages ... arranging for his marriage a few days before his death.' The state of mind has been likened to the influence of narcotics or alcohol. With the discovery of the tubercle bacillus, Erich Stern conjectured a toxin circulating in the blood which specifically energized the creative brain. It has even been mooted that the decline in tuberculosis in our present time explains the decline of standards in literature and the arts! But one must beware of confusing coincidence with causation when considering the putative role tuberculosis may play in the genesis of creativity and genius. After all, tuberculosis does not usually kill quickly: rather, it weakens the body but not the mind, and enforces rest and solitude. In what should be the prime of life, tuberculosis puts one in touch with one's mortality, and concentrates the mind on how one would wish to be remembered by posterity.[1]

When I have fears that I may cease to be
Before my pen has glean'd my teeming brain

Keats was not the only consumptive who valued every extra day of life and endowed it with significance.

Many, while not believing that tuberculosis causes genius, nevertheless contend that it may fan into flame an otherwise dormant spark. Others might concede the increased output of those dying of consumption but take issue as to its quality. D.H. Lawrence's tubercular impotence served merely to increase the eroticism of his writing. Aubrey Beardsley's eroticism also fed off tuberculosis, his impotence sublimated in increasingly obscene drawings. It was said

AUBREY BEARDSLEY

of Beardsley that he 'knew he was a doomed man even on the threshold of manhood, and he strove with feverish intensity to get a lifetime into each twelvemonth.'

Opponents of the notion of the tubercular genius would cite Robert Louis Stevenson. Granted, he wrote some of his best known works when he was physically disabled with tuberculosis, but his genius did not leave him in his periods of relative good health. Too many whose object is to prove a link between tuberculosis and genius omit to take due cognizance of non-tubercular geniuses, and the virtual universality of exposure to infection in the eighteenth and nineteenth centuries which should have produced a surfeit of creativity.

And could it be that tubercular tranquillity was merely a manifestation of that peace of mind that many feel who are about to die? Chekhov, a doctor, playwright and consumptive, wove disease into his fiction. In *The Black Monk* he describes the pre-terminal euphoria thus: 'He saw on the floor, close to his face, a large pool of blood, and from weakness he could not utter another word, but an inexpressible, a boundless happiness filled his whole being.'[2]

## *Opium muddies the creative waters*

> I need not tell you that opium cures nothing, though by setting the powers of life at ease, I sometimes flatter myself that it may give them time to rectify themselves.
>
> Dr Samuel Johnson

In the nineteenth century opium was the drug of first choice in the treatment of tuberculosis, used primarily to suppress coughing. And since many consumptives took large doses of opium – geniuses included – the close association of the drug with the disease makes it well-nigh impossible to tease out their separate effects on creative processes.[3]

Samuel Taylor Coleridge (1772–1834), poet and philosopher, author of *The Ancient Mariner*, first took opium at the age of nineteen for relief of the pain of rheumatic fever. He took it in the form of Kendal Black Drop: 'In an evil hour I procured it: it worked miracles – the swellings disappeared, the pains vanished.' According to De Quincey the effect on Coleridge of his opium addiction was to

*Opposite:* The *Lacedaemonian Ambassadors* by Aubrey Beardsley, amply illustrating how the artist's tubercular impotence was channelled into pornography

stimulate him as a philosopher but to kill him as a poet. Running contrary to this assertion was the fact that Coleridge claimed to have composed *Kubla Khan* with no effort, after waking from an opium-induced dream. Coleridge believed that his addiction was harmful but found himself impotent to rid himself of his habit. He is exasperated by the injunctions of others: 'You bid me rouse myself: go bid a man, paralytic in both arms, to rub them briskly together and that will cure him.' In the depths of his depressions, Coleridge drank laudanum by the half-pint. Ultimately he did manage to exercise some measure of control with the help of James Gillman, a Highgate surgeon, with whom Coleridge lived for the last eighteen years of his life. He died in 1834, aged sixty-one.

A generation of addicts in the 1820s attributed their dependence on opium to Thomas De Quincey (1785–1859) and the day they first read *Confessions of an English Opium-Eater*. De Quincey, a precocious scholar, took opium for the first time when a student at Oxford. In *Confessions* (which first appeared anonymously in the *London Magazine* in 1821) he describes taking opium at the suggestion of a friend to counter the agony of toothache or perhaps trigeminal neuralgia:

> By accident, I met a college acquaintance, who recommended opium. Opium! dread agent of unimaginable pleasure and pain! I had heard of it as I had heard of manna or of ambrosia. It was a Sunday afternoon, wet and cheerless; and a duller spectacle this earth of ours has yet to show than a rainy Sunday in London. On my road homewards – I saw a druggist's shop, where I asked for the tincture of opium. Arrived at my lodgings I lost not a moment in taking the quantity prescribed – and in an hour, Oh heavens! What a revulsion, what a resurrection, from its lowest depths of the inner spirit! What an apocalypse of the world within me! That my pains had vanished, was now a trifle in my eyes; this negative effect was swallowed up in the immensity of these positive effects which had opened before me, in the abyss of divine enjoyment thus suddenly revealed. Here was a panacea for all human woes; here was the secret of happiness, about which philosophers had disputed for so many ages, at once discovered; happiness might now be bought for a penny and carried in the waistcoat-pocket; portable ecstasies might be corked up in a pint-bottle. Peace of mind sent in the mail.

De Quincey's consumption of opium was enormous, especially at times of stress, such as when Kate Wordsworth died. Coleridge railed against him for giving such rapturous descriptions: 'Oh, may the God to whom I look for mercy through Christ, show mercy on the author of the *Confessions of an [English] Opium-Eater*, if, as I have too strong reason to believe, his book has been the occasion of seducing others into this withering vice through wantonness.'

De Quincey became well aware of opium's debit column: 'These changes in my dreams were accompanied by deep-seated anxiety and funereal melancholy ... I seemed every night to descend – not metaphorically, but literally to descend – into chasms and sunless abysses, depths below depths, from which it seemed hopeless that I could ever re-ascend ... The state of gloom which attended these gorgeous spectacles, amounting at last to utter darkness ... cannot be approached by words.' In his later years De Quincey managed to decrease his dependence. He died aged seventy-four.

Other notable literary opium addicts include the Reverend George Crabbe (1754–1832), apothecary and clergyman, best known for his work *The Village*; and Francis Thompson (1859–1907), English poet and failed medical student at Manchester, who became addicted at the age of twenty-one when his mother gave him a copy of De Quincey's *Confessions*.

John Keats (1795–1821) was not addicted to opium, but he certainly used it on occasions. After his brother Tom's death from tuberculosis, Keats became depressed and poetically unproductive. In March 1819, to lift his spirits, he went to play cricket and was hit in the eye by the ball. His friend Charles Armitage Brown gave him opium for the pain. Keats remembered only the application of a leech, but the next day, as he later described in a letter to his other brother George, he wrote, 'I am in a sort of temper indolent and supremely careless ... Neither Poetry, not Ambition, nor Love have any alertness of countenance as they pass by me: they seem rather like figures on a Greek vase ...' These side-effects are more likely to be attributable to opium than a leech!

Keats wrote *Ode to a Nightingale* in May 1819, six weeks after his cricket injury, and its imagery is obvious. Brown describes the circumstances in his memoirs:

> In the spring of 1819 a nightingale had built her nest near my house. Keats felt a tranquil and continuous joy in her song; and one morning he took his chair from the breakfast-table to the grass-plot under a plum tree, where he sat for two or three hours. When he came into the house, I perceived he had some scraps of paper in his hand, and these he was quietly thrusting behind the books. On enquiry, I found those scraps, four or five in number, contained his poetic feeling on the song of our nightingale.

> My heart aches, and a drowsy numbness pains
> My sense, as though of hemlock I had drunk,
> Or emptied some dull opiate to the drains
> One minute past, and Lethe-wards had sunk.

In 1820 Brown discovered that Keats was secretly taking laudanum, and extracted a promise from the poet that he would take no more without Brown's knowledge. Keats did not keep his promise: it is known that before leaving England for Italy in September, Keats obtained a bottle of laudanum. At that time the drug was freely available – besides which Keats was a qualified apothecary and could prescribe it for himself. Joseph Severn, who accompanied Keats on his journey, wrote, 'The hardest point between us is that cursed bottle of Opium'. Keats was determined to take opium the moment he felt his illness worsening, to ease his misery and, no doubt, bring him permanent release.[4]

Illustrious drug takers indeed! No wonder it was widely believed that opiates facilitated creativity. In the vast majority of cases opium would have been self-administered initially for medical reasons, notably sleeplessness, headache, and depression. By degrees medical use changed into social or recreational use, though non-medical use was rarely openly admitted. Coleridge and De Quincey were fond of accusing the other of taking opium for pleasure, while they themselves took it for medicinal purposes.

Byron had taken laudanum on occasions; Shelley used it as a prop in times of stress, of which there were many. Branwell Brontë obtained his supplies from Bessy Hardacre's drug store opposite the Bull, where he obtained his other release. Following four years of colic caused by gall stones, Sir Walter Scott was taking two hundred drops of laudanum and six grains of opium a day when he wrote *The Bride of Lammermoor*. Dickens took opium occasionally towards the end of his life, incorporating the drug's effects into his unfinished novel, *The Mystery of Edwin Drood*. Wilkie Collins was expansive in his praise: 'Who was the man who invented laudanum? I thank him from the bottom of my heart'. He wrote *The Moonstone* under the influence of opium. For Elizabeth Barrett Browning 'sleep only came to her in a red hood of poppies'. Dante Gabriel Rossetti, Pre-Raphaelite artist and poet, was addicted to chloral, laudanum and alcohol, the abuse of which produced depression and paranoid illness. His wife and model, Elizabeth Siddal, is thought by some to have killed herself with an overdose of laudanum.

## *A blueprint for genius*

For those who aspire to genius, but who are not enthusiastic about contracting tuberculosis or becoming dependent on opium, are there other ways in which latent creative processes may be made actual? Study of the lives of famous people – especially pathography, the study of their illnesses – might help identify other constitutional or environmental factors which facilitate talent, creativity and genius. Tuberculosis apart, theories which attempt to connect illness with creativity have had a frosty reception from academics. Protagonists, usually retired doctors whiling away the autumn of their lives, are apt to focus on a genius, identify a disease from which he suffered, and naively infer a cause-and-effect relationship. As frequently as the physicians lament the historian's lacunae on the relevance of illness, the historian deplores the physician's lack of breadth and social context.

Take syphilis, for instance. The reduced virulence of this disease, and its transformation from killer to parasite, has encouraged some to cite it as a major factor in the inexorable degeneration of the human race. Paradoxically, others look upon syphilis as a stimulant of intellectual and creative energy. The two opposite potentials combine to produce 'the archetypal cripple endowed with superior intelligence'. Léon Daudet wrote, 'Syphilis makes a great poet of a maid's son, a satyr of a peaceful bourgeois, an astronomer or a conqueror of a sailor.' Matters are made no clearer by the pitfalls of posthumous diagnosis: even if Van Gogh *was* mad *and* a genius, how can anyone be sure that his insanity was caused by syphilis? And, short of such certitude, is it not completely spurious to contend that the spirochaete is a facilitator of creativity? Thomas Mann, author and accepted genius, observed, 'Great artists are great invalids', and although two of his greatest works, *Doctor Faustus* and *The Magic Mountain* were studies of neurosyphilis and tuberculosis respectively, he himself did not suffer from either disease and lived a life of robust good health, dying aged eighty.

But before we examine possible links between illness and genius, it is sensible to define one's terms. In 1903, Cattell wrote his paper, *A Statistical Study of Eminent Men*, in which he listed the top 1,000. Cattell was at pains to distinguish between genius, greatness and mere eminence. George Washington was a great man, but hardly a genius. Napoleon III was neither great nor a genius, but he was eminent. The only scientific instrument Cattell used to draw up his list was a ruler. He measured the entries of those persons who appeared in at least three of six national biographical dictionaries (two English, two French, one German and one American). The top ten, the most eminent persons in history (up to 1903), were, in order, Napoleon Bonaparte, Shakespeare, Mohammed, Voltaire, Bacon, Aristotle, Goethe, Caesar, Luther and Plato.

Two books which sought a blueprint for genius were Francis Galton's *Hereditary Genius* (1892) and Havelock Ellis's *Study of British Genius* (1904),[5] volumes teeming with quasi-scholarship.

Galton investigated the family trees of 'the most illustrious Commanders, men of Literature and of Science, Poets, Painters and Musicians of whom history speaks' and compared them with the physical attributes in the families of 'Oarsmen and Wrestlers'. Galton demonstrated to his own satisfaction that famous men were more likely to have famous relatives. This association he attributed to hereditary influences, being quite oblivious to the influences of nepotism and privilege. For Galton genius was a matter of breeding, a sentiment which befits the Father of Eugenics.[6]

Unlike Galton, Ellis was more receptive to environmental influences, and mooted a variety of medical conditions associated with genius. Hobbes, Keats, Newton and Charles Wesley were premature babies. Bentham, Burke, Constable and Dickens were sickly and delicate infants who yet grew into healthy and vigorous adults. Erasmus Darwin, Kingsley, Lamb, and Priestley stammered, whilst Dr Johnson, Kingsley and J.S. Mill twitched. According to Ellis the most common medical condition to afflict British genius was gout, the disease which martyred Milton, Harvey, Sydenham, Newton, Gibbon, Fielding, Dr Johnson, John Hunter, John Wesley, Charles Darwin, the Pitts and the Bacons.

## *Madness and genius*

The notion that genius and madness are first cousins is one rooted in history. Plato thought that there were two forms of delirium: insanity and inspiration. But it is not enough merely to list ten or twenty geniuses and then scour biographies for evidence of mental illness. While it is sometimes difficult for physicians to agree about *post hoc* diagnoses of *physical* diseases, it is often wellnigh impossible to get psychiatrists to agree about diagnoses of *emotional* diseases. After all, tuberculosis is tuberculosis, but neurosis is not psychosis, and depression is not lunacy. Difficulties in agreeing psychiatric definitions have spawned a voluminous crank literature purporting to prove the link between creativity and mental illness. Not all of it is worthless, as we shall see, but a large proportion of it is high on cant and low on science.

For Ellis, mental illness ran gout a close second in its association with genius, citing Barry, Clare, Collins, Cowper, Gillray, Pugin, Romney and Smart as decidedly insane. Kretschmer, in his *Psychology of Men of Genius* (1931),[7] agreeing with Schopenhauer that 'Genius is nearer to madness than to the average intellect', adds Jean-Jacques Rousseau, Nietzsche, Galton (!), Newton, Tasso, Maupassant, Van Gogh, Dostoevsky, Schumann, Strindberg and Wolf to his list of mad geniuses.

Two of the most unintentionally amusing books written to prove the close association of madness and genius were published in the same year, one by an Englishman, the other by an Italian. Nisbet wrote *The Insanity of Genius* in 1891, but his conclusions are totally devalued by his woolly concepts of lunacy, his lack of critical judgment and his gross overinclusiveness.[8] Yes, Cowper *was* a depressive who tried to cut his throat, Charles Lamb *did* spend six weeks in a lunatic asylum, and Rousseau *was* a paranoid schizophrenic; but Dr Johnson's hypochondriasis did not equate with lunacy, and just because he was known as 'mad Shelley' at Eton does not mean that the poet actually was insane. Equally, Lady Caroline Lamb was not necessarily intending a psychiatric diagnosis when she described Byron as 'mad, bad, and dangerous to know'. And Milton's 'tyranny and total lack of humour' hardly constitutes madness – especially considering that he had to contend with blindness *and* gout.

There are innumerable other examples of Nisbet's cavalier approach to the diagnosis of madness. He says of Coleridge: 'To the medical expert, eccentricity in life and sudden death are eloquent indications of nerve disorder.' He quotes De Quincey's description of Dorothy Wordsworth as proof of a strain of insanity in the Wordsworth blood: ' "Her eyes were not soft, nor were they fierce or bold; but they were wild and startling, and hurried in their motion." She became a confirmed invalid and gradually fell into imbecility.' According to Nisbet, Balzac was unbalanced because his father took to his bed one day, stayed there for twenty years, and then got up as if nothing had happened; and Mendelssohn became unhinged because his grandfather was a stammering hunchback.

1891 also saw the publication of *The Man of Genius* by Cesare Lombroso, a professor of legal medicine at Turin, an engaging but scientifically worthless pot-pourri of anecdotes of the famous and infamous, by which he sought to demonstrate a causal relationship between insanity and genius.[9] He had a deft answer to cynics who cited sane geniuses: 'It is certain that there have been men of genius presenting a complete equilibrium of the intellectual faculties; but they have presented defects of affectivity and feeling; though no one may have perceived it, or, rather, recorded it ... If Richelieu had not on one single occasion been caught in an epileptic fit, who would ever have guessed it?' Who indeed?

Lombroso takes a broad view of 'mental degeneracy': sometimes it is revealed by short stature, sometimes tall. Among midget geniuses could be numbered Aristotle, Plato, Spinoza, Mozart, Beethoven, Keats, Blake (barely five feet), Browning and Mendelssohn. 'Albertus

Magnus [*who?*] was of such small size that the Pope, having allowed him to kiss his foot, commanded him to stand up, under the impression he was still kneeling.'

Lombroso wrote, 'The list of great men who have committed suicide is almost endless', and then goes on to name eighteen, including Hegesippus, Claenthes, Stilpo, Creech and Haydon. Chateaubriand, Cowper and Rousseau 'on several occasions *nearly* put an end to their lives'. Obsessionalism is a frequently observed common denominator of madness and brilliance.

> When Johnson walked along the streets of London he was compelled to touch every post he passed; if he omitted one he had to return. He always went in or out of a door or passage in such a way that either his right or his left foot (Boswell was not certain which) should be the first to cross the threshold … Napoleon could not pass through a street, even at the head of his army, without counting and adding up the rows of windows.

With great reluctance and almost palpable disappointment, Lombroso brings himself to consider sane geniuses. His list is short: Galileo, Leonardo da Vinci, Voltaire, Machiavelli, Michelangelo and Charles Darwin. But all is not lost – with sufficient scrutiny personality defects are bound to surface. In the case of Michelangelo, Lombroso cites 'his complete indifference to women … He never used the female living model, though he made use of corpses'. And, according to his daughter, Darwin 'had a difficulty in pronouncing some letters, especially *w*'. Lombroso adds triumphantly, 'Like Skoda, Rockitanski and Socrates, he [Darwin] had a short stub nose, and his ears were large and long'.

What objective evidence exists for the putative link between psychiatric disorder and creativity, genius, call it what you will? Most of the evidence, especially that provided by Lombroso, Ellis and Nisbet is too anecdotal to be useful. Of the four mad English poets of the eighteenth century – Collins, Smart, Cowper and Clare – Smart is the only one whose poetry is thought to have improved in periods of insanity, and reverted back to the mediocre on recovery. When sane, Smart's poetry was thought to be so bad that Dr Johnson, when asked whether Derrick or Smart was the better poet, replied, 'Sir, there is no settling the point of precedency between a louse and a flea.' Literary critics deem themselves able to distinguish between his sane poetry (*The Hop-Garden*) and his mad poetry (*A Song to David*), but these are very subjective judgements and often hotly debated.

A more scientific approach is to identify famous artists and writers and meet with them to discuss any relevant psychiatric illnesses they may have suffered. Such a study in 1989 selected forty-seven famous British poets, playwrights, novelists and artists – unfortunately (though, perhaps, understandably) they are not identified, and so we have no way of knowing whether there would have been a consensus about the quality of their work, and their claim to fame.[10] Nevertheless, nearly 40 per cent had suffered from an affective disorder, usually depression – especially poets, who were more likely to have received drug treatment or psychotherapy. Painters and sculptors suffered significantly less from mood disorders, and writers who were not creative (e.g., biographers) gave no history at all of either high or low moods. Intense creativity was often associated with periods of elation, euphoria, self-confidence and rapidity of thought (hypomania). It was not clear to what extent alcohol and drugs initiated or sustained these creative periods.

This research gives some credence to the notion that 'no great genius is without a touch of madness', a school of thought which cites, in fairly recent times, Van Gogh, Kafka, Munch, Pound, Hemingway, O'Neill, Plath and Woolf. An American study showed that creativity was associated with an increased likelihood of schizophrenia, manic depression, personality disorders and alcoholism.[11] But others remain unconvinced and argue that the true connection is not between creativity and mental illness, but creativity and mental health, and cite Shakespeare, Einstein, William James, Jung and Bohr to make their case.

Speaking personally, and as a psychiatrist aware of the pitfalls in differentiating normality from abnormality, I believe that the case for the close association of madness (psychosis) and genius is overstated. Schumann tried to drown himself in the Rhine and later died in a mental hospital; Van Gogh cut off his ear and sent it to a prostitute; Virginia Woolf was schizophrenic, heard voices, and drowned herself. All three were suffering from severe mental illness. All three were geniuses. But that does not constitute a causal relationship.

## *The archetypal mad scientist*

Isaac Newton (1642–1727) was a colossus, one of history's finest intellects. And yet he was also mad: merely peculiar in early life (he once threatened to burn his parents to death) but quite raving in middle age. He was once described as being 'covetous of praise and impatient of contradiction'. Even John Locke, a firm friend, found Newton paranoid, 'a little too apt to raise in himself suspicions where there is no ground'. Today he would be diagnosed as neurotic, being oversensitive, moody and avoiding the company of others. He rarely initiated conversation and seldom laughed.

In the years 1692–3, when Newton was fifty years old, his mental symptoms worsened considerably. He became deeply depressed and profoundly paranoid. In 1693 he wrote to Samuel Pepys, 'I am extremely troubled at the embroilment I am in, and have neither ate nor slept well this twelve months, nor have I my former consistency of mind ... I am now sensible that I must withdraw from your acquaintance, and see neither you nor the rest of my friends any more, if I may but leave them quietly.' In a letter to Locke, he wrote, '... being of the opinion that you endeavoured to embroil me with women and by other means I was so much affected with it as that when one told me that you were sickly and would not live, I answered t'were better you were dead. I desire you to forgive me for this uncharitableness.'

Both Pepys and Locke recognized that Newton was not well, and made allowances. He recovered his wits and in 1703 was elected President of the Royal Society, being re-elected annually for the next twenty-four years. In 1705 he was knighted by Queen Anne and widely regarded as the most famous man of his age. (He was number 14 on Cattell's list.) Many explanations have been proffered for his mental illness: delayed shock at the death of his mother; failure to be appointed Provost of King's College, Cambridge; the loss of papers in a fire, supposedly caused by a dog tipping over a candle; and simple exhaustion from working too hard on his *Principia*. One of the most recent explanations was mercury poisoning from his experiments in alchemy. In his attempts to turn base metals into gold, Newton would heat ores and salts, breathing in the fumes and even tasting the resultant brew. Recent analysis of samples of Newton's hair adds credence to this hypothesis: raised levels of mercury and lead were found.[12]

## *Epilepsy*

Epilepsy has had a mixed press over the centuries: some civilizations consider that it is visited upon those that the gods wish to reward; others that it is a sign of divine wrath. In some societies epileptics are regarded with a degree of sanctity; in others they are ostracized or cast out as evil and dangerous. Still others view the *falling sickness* as facilitating intelligence, creativity and genius.

Epilepsy is not a single disease, but a group of diseases whose common causation is abnormal electrical discharges in the brain, but whose clinical manifestations are often quite dissimilar, and dependent upon which part of the brain is affected. *Grand mal* epilepsy is the most widely known, whereby a person loses consciousness, has convulsions or fits, often bites his tongue or passes urine, and 'comes round' remembering little of what has occurred. *Petit mal* epilepsy, or 'absence attacks' occur when a person 'blanks out' for a number of seconds, but 'comes round' without falling to the ground or experiencing convulsions. *Psychomotor* epilepsy consists of vague trance-like or hallucinatory states.

Most cases of epilepsy are *idiopathic*, meaning that no readily identifiable cause can be found. The remainder are caused by a wide variety of conditions which affect the smooth working of the brain, including head injuries, tumours and poisons.

Those who have sought to link epilepsy with creativity or genius have too often uncritically accepted the diagnosis of epilepsy. When fits or convulsions are recorded by ancient physicians, the case for epilepsy is strengthened, but one must be sceptical about the diagnosis in other cases. J. Ernest Bryant wrote a book in 1953 called *Genius and Epilepsy: Brief Sketches of Twenty Great Men Who Had Both*.[13] It might be contended that if only 20 examples could be found in 2,000 years then the association between genius and epilepsy can hardly be a strong one, and may be nothing more than coincidence. Doubts about the veracity of the diagnosis further serves to weaken the putative link.

St Paul is included in Bryant's list of epileptics because the apostle said of himself, 'Ye did me no wrong, but ye knew that because of an infirmity of the flesh I preached the gospel to you on that former occasion.' (Galatians 4:13). The 'infirmity of the flesh' is taken to signify epilepsy. Even if this was the case, and St Paul was accepted as being an epileptic, can he be considered a genius?

The diagnosis of epilepsy in Alexander the Great is just as conjectural: 'But he lost speech, and, falling into a swoon, had scarce any sense or pulse left. But in no long time his health and strength returned.' Perhaps he fainted, or was just overcome with emotion. Few would quarrel with the epithet 'genius' applied to Alexander. Or to Julius Caesar in whom the diagnosis of epilepsy appears well-founded, and whose disability is documented by Plutarch. In Caligula the diagnosis is also generally accepted – Suetonius says that, as a boy, the future Roman Emperor suffered from 'Falling Sickness' – but the description of 'genius' is grotesquely inapt.

In view of its association with sanctity, it is perhaps appropriate that the founders of two of the great religions of the world – Buddha and Mohammed – were thought to suffer from epilepsy. Less illustrious, but still noteworthy, is the epileptic label given to Petrarch, Pascal, Molière, Byron, Flaubert and Swinburne. Dostoyevsky suffered from epilepsy and gave the disease to five of his characters, most notably Prince Myshkin in *The Idiot*. His description of epilepsy should be prescribed reading for all medical students.

### *Sensory loss: deafness*

No one espouses a direct causal link between being deaf and being creative: rather, the social isolation attending deafness is regarded as focusing the power of the creative mind. And yet, in three of the most illustrious deaf – an artist, a writer and a musician – their genius antedated their deafness.[14]

The Spanish painter, Goya, became suddenly and totally deaf at the age of forty-seven. He had already established his reputation and had recently been appointed court painter to Charles IV. Many attribute Goya's deafness to syphilis – certainly it cannot be ruled out since the artist had many mistresses, including one he shared with Godoy, the Spanish Prime Minister. But the suddenness of onset probably rules out pox as a cause of Goya's deafness. Others think that Goya became deaf as a result of lead poisoning, an ingredient of the paint which he applied to his canvases with a frenzied impetuosity. The consequent brain damage resulted in his deafness and changed his personality from the 'world's happiest being' in his youth, to the sombreness and malignancy of his middle age – a metamorphosis amply illustrated in the change from his earlier, highly coloured subjects, to the increasing despair depicted in his later 'black pictures'. He hung his masterpiece, *Saturn Eating his own Children*, in his dining-room!

Jonathan Swift died in 1745, aged seventy-eight, the year before Goya was born. Poet, satirist and Dean of St Patrick's Cathedral, Dublin, and best known for *Gulliver's Travels*, Swift will long be remembered for his amorous correspondence with the two spinsters Vanessa and Stella. Swift suffered from bilateral Ménière's disease, a cruel affliction which visits upon the victim a triad of incapacitating symptoms;: tinnitus (ringing in the ears), giddiness and deafness. As Swift relates, 'I got my giddiness in 1690 (at the age of 23) by eating 100 golden pippins at a time at Richmond. Four years later at a place 20 miles further on in Surrey I got my deafness; and these two friends have visited me one or other every year since; and being old acquaintances have often sought fit to come together.' Initially his deafness was episodic: 'When the deafness comes on, I can hear with neither ear, except it be a woman with a treble or a man with a counter tenor.' Poor Swift was subjected to constant purges and bleedings, despite protesting that his affliction was in his head and not his bowel or blood. It is likely that deafness turned Swift, as it did Goya, into a gloomy pessimist: his increasing paranoia (a common symptom in the deaf) and misanthropy are well depicted in *Gulliver's Travels*.

Beethoven first refers to his deafness in his will, written when he was only thirty-two years old:

> But only think that during the last six years I have been in a wretched condition; rendered more by unintelligent Physicians, deceived from year to year with hopes of improvement, and then finally forced to the prospect of lasting infirmity, which may last for years, or even totally incurable ... Alas, how could I declare the weakness of a sense, which in me ought to be more acute than in others ... I am compelled to live as an exile.

Whilst most of us would sympathize with Milton's reaction to his blindness – 'I am not conscious, either in the more early or in the later periods of my life, of having committed any enormity which might deservedly have marked me out as a fit object for such a calamitous visitation' – blindness to a poet is not the travesty that deafness is to a musician.

How could Beethoven be other than irritable and bad tempered? It is surely fate at her most capricious which makes a master of music stone-deaf. For a long time Beethoven was embarrassed and ashamed of his deafness and begged confidantes to keep his secret: 'In my profession it is a terrible thing'; and again, 'Keep as a great secret what I have told you about my hearing, trust no one, whoever it may be, with it.' As his deafness worsened, he did not share the optimism of his doctors. By forty he was totally deaf and was obliged to lip-read. He talked and laughed inappropriately loud, and sank deeper into melancholia. The only way Beethoven could 'listen' to his music was to pick up the vibrations transmitted via a stick clasped between his teeth and rested on the piano board. The left ear was slightly less affected, and it was to this ear that he directed conversation. Towards the end of his life, at the first performance of his ninth symphony, he had to be turned round to acknowledge the applause of the audience. Like many deaf people Beethoven became withdrawn, insular and paranoid: yet his music did not take on a mantle of unrelieved gloom.

Beethoven died in Vienna in 1827, aged fifty-seven, from cirrhosis of the liver. The cause of his deafness has long been disputed. His last words were reputed to be, 'Applaud friends, the comedy is ended.' According to his wish, an autopsy was performed and the temporal bones (that part of the skull which contains the ear) were placed in the Anatomy Museum of Vienna. Although syphilis has been invoked, it is more likely that Beethoven's deafness was due to otosclerosis, ('a disease in which the patient hears nothing and the physician sees nothing'), an inflexibility of the small bones of the inner ear.

## *Congenital malformations*

The link between *visible* bodily malformations and genius can be postulated as the 'I'll show you!' phenomenon, in which a physical stigma is compensated by intellectual excellence. Such an explanation fits very well in the cases of Pope and Byron, but how much of a factor was Daniel Defoe's lack of external ears or Wilkie Collins' misshapen head?

Mozart has been the focus of many who have attempted to find a physical explanation for his prodigious and precocious talent. Although buried in a mass grave, Mozart's corpse was retrieved from the grave-diggers by the brother of the Viennese anatomist, Joseph Hyrtl. The skull, which remained in the Hyrtl family until 1899, is now in the Mozarteum in Salzburg. Recently it has been subjected to every conceivable measurement in the hope of finding some bony abnormality. And the investigators were not disappointed. 'Trans-illumination [of the skull] shows several areas of thinning in the frontal bone suggesting brain contact that was closer than usual.' Mozart's skull showed premature synostosis of the metopic suture (thankfully abbreviated to PSMS) which probably explains his short stature, straight forehead, marked cheekbones and prominent nose and upper lip – but not why he wrote such beautiful music.[15]

Toulouse-Lautrec, a physical freak with short legs and deformed head, submerged himself in 'paint, drink and love', and became an alcoholic and syphilitic.

## *Byron, the 'lame brat'*

No one contests that Byron was lame, but much heat has been generated about the correct diagnosis *and which foot was affected.* The matter remains unresolved and continues to be highly contentious.

George Gordon Byron was born in London in January 1788 into a family of diminished circumstances. His father had spent two wives' fortunes and later died in penury in Valenciennes. His mother retired to Aberdeen and sent George, her 'lame brat' (to which he is reputed to have replied, 'I was born so, mother.') to the local grammar school. When he was ten years old his great-uncle, 'the wicked Lord Byron', died, leaving George the family title and fortune. At fifteen he fell hopelessly in love with a distant relative, Mary Ann Chaworth, but his passion was hurtfully unrequited: Byron overheard her say, 'Do you think I could care for that lame boy?'

As evidence of the family's improved social standing, Byron was sent to Harrow and then, briefly, to Cambridge University. His first book of verses was published when he was twenty, and by the age of twenty-four he had made his maiden speech in the House of Lords. Later that same year, 1812, *Childe Harold* was published and Byron became famous.

After his brief love affair with Lady Caroline Lamb, Byron married Anne Isabella Milbanke, a rich heiress. Their extravagant life styles soon meant that the couple were in deep financial difficulties. The birth of a daughter, Ada, in 1815 was not sufficient to cement a crumbling marriage, and Anne sought a separation, citing her husband's numerous infidelities and his insanity. (The allegations regarding Byron's incest with his half sister, Augusta Leigh, and the later birth of a daughter were not made public until 1869 when Harriet Beecher Stowe, author of *Uncle Tom's Cabin*, published a book in which she purported to give details told to her by Anne.) Byron decided to quit England for good in April 1816.

The confusion about Byron's lameness is well illustrated by the fact that Thomas Moore, his first biographer, maintained it was the right foot which was affected; Gentleman Jackson, his boxing instructor, thought it was the left; John Galt, another biographer, simply could not make up his mind. Byron's mother always said it was the right – and mothers usually know best! One might have thought that the matter would have been settled by Trelawny who examined Byron's body after his death, in April 1824, at the age of thirty-six, probably as a result of malaria. In his *Recollections of the Last Days of Shelley and Byron*, Trelawny writes:

> He [Byron's valet] led me up a narrow stair into a small room, with nothing in it but a coffin standing on tressles. No word was spoken by either of us; he withdrew the black pall and the white shroud, and there lay the embalmed body of the Pilgrim – more beautiful in death than in life ... I asked Fletcher to bring me a glass of water. On his leaving the room, to confirm or remove my doubts as to the cause of his lameness, I uncovered the Pilgrim's feet, and was answered – the great mystery was solved. Both his feet were clubbed and his legs were withered to the knee – the form and features of an Apollo, with the feet and legs of a sylvan satyr ... His deformity was always uppermost in his thoughts, and influenced every act of his life.

Trelawny's post-mortem examination has been taken as the

definitive account of Byron's deformity. However there is one small but significant inconsistency. Byron's coffin had been hermetically sealed on 25 April and Trelawny did not arrive in Missolonghi until the 26th! Charitably, it has been said that Trelawny described Byron's feet not as they were but as he expected to find them.

What effect did Byron's deformity have on his personality and his literary output? It is certain that Byron regarded his lameness as the enduring tragedy of his life: he suffered humiliation and timidity, and was prone to explosive outbursts of anger when anybody referred to his leg. It also meant he had to endure the endless tortures of so-called 'corrective' boots. He was a man of contrasts: able to be kind and generous, yet, to mask his sense of inferiority, he could be deeply hurtful to others – he scorned Keats as a poet, calling him Jack Keats or Ketch, writer of 'drivelling idiotism'. He could also be insufferably vain, and at one time took to curling his hair. Restriction on physical exercise as a child developed in him a love of reading. He affected to despise dancing. Macaulay called his lameness 'the bad fairy's bundle'. Clare Clairmont wrote in her diary of Byron's 'desire, hatred, revenge, a proneness to mischief, spoliation and cruelty'.

The success of *Childe Harold*, the flattery that followed, his wonderful good looks, his social position and wealth, all combined to make him a source of fascination to women. Yet this was no compensation: he vented his spleen in scathing satires and it is easy to regard this as a catharsis for internalized self-hatred. What capricious malevolence visited such an infirmity upon such a beautiful person?

Malice, self-pity and melancholy suffused his poetry. *On My Thirty-Third Birthday* has the telling lines,

> Through life's dull road, so dim and dirty
> I have dragged to thirty-three.

In the first scene of the drama *The Deformed Transformed* there is a depiction of his childhood:

> Bertha: Out, hunchback!
> Arnold: I was born so, mother![16]

## *Rachitic Mr Pope*

Byron was obsessed by his lameness but managed yet to be a focus of the romantic movement. Pope's physical deformities soured his very existence.

Alexander Pope was born in 1688 and, although largely self-taught, he became arguably the most famous poet of his day. He is best remembered today for such maxims as 'To err is human, to forgive divine', 'Fools rush in where angels fear to tread', and 'A little learning is a dang'rous thing'. Rickets had wrecked havoc upon Pope's frame: his spine was bent forward and sideways, and he compared himself to a spider. He needed a special high chair in order to eat at a table. Sir Joshua Reynolds described Pope as 'almost four feet six inches high, very humped back and deformed'. Pope himself referred to 'that long disease, my life'. His thin legs were wrapped in three pairs of stockings to keep him warm: a maid had to put them on for him because he was too weak to dress himself. Added to his skeletal problems were insomnia, myopia and migraine. Truly, Pope's cup of physical deformities runneth over, and it is little wonder that his physical afflictions coloured his outlook on life.

Depression was inevitable: '[I have] a dejection of spirits that has totally taken away everything, if ever I had anything, which could be called vivacity or cheerfulness.' Other academics and poets heaped plaudits upon his insubstantial frame: Samuel Johnson in his own time, and Byron afterwards. Dr Johnson, in his biography of Pope, describes his 'remarkable gentleness and sweetness of disposition', but those who were the focus of his vindictive barbs would not have agreed. His deformities made him ultra-sensitive to slights, and bitter and vindictive to anyone who criticized him. He yearned for romance, was pathologically vain, and had an ever-lengthening list of enemies. Kindness alternated unpredictably with vindictiveness and insincerity: 'His only weapon was wit sharpened on the whetstone of malice.'

His relationship with Lady Mary Montagu (see the chapter on smallpox) was a case in point: Pope had tried to make passionate love to her and she had reacted by laughing, a slight few could forgive, least of all Pope. He publicly denounced her personal hygiene with allusions to her dirty underlinen. In another vicious broadside against Lord and Lady Wortley Montagu, Pope wrote,

> Avidien [Lord Wortley Montagu] or his Wife (no matter which),
> For him you'll call a dog, and her a bitch.

Lady Wortley Montagu responded in poetic kind, showing in verse how 'the wicked wasp of Twickenham' with his 'wretched little carcase' had produced a 'crooked mind ... accursed through the land'. He denounced a multitude of his enemies in the *Dunciad*, but again his victims retaliated:

> Meagre and wan and steeple-crown'd,
> His visage long and shoulders round;
> His crippled corpse two spindled-pegs
> Support, instead of human legs;
> His shrivelled skin is of dusky grain,
> A cricket's voice and monkey's brain.

Besides his rachitic frame, Pope had to contend with tuberculosis, migraine, asthma, and ultimately, heart failure. He became dependent upon and indebted to his doctors:

> Weak tho' I am of limb, and short of sight,
> Far from a Lynx, and not a Giant quite,
> I'll do what Mead and Cheselden advise,
> To keep these limbs, and to preserve these eyes

Less poetically, he wrote to a friend: 'I am in the condition of an old fellow of Threescore, with a Complication of Diseases upon me; A constant Headake; ruined Tone of the Stomach; the Piles; a Vomiting & Looseness; & an Excess of Wind.' Some detect a self-deprecating style in a man who signed himself Bob Short and wrote *The Club of Little Men*, but posterity remembers him as an evil and vindictive dwarf who relished his reputation and boasted that he was 'proud to see Men, not afraid of God, afraid of me'.[17]

# 6 BONES, STONES AND GROANS

## *A history of gout*

Gout is a comical disease to those who have never suffered its agonies. A picture is evoked of an overweight and overindulgent eighteenth-century aristocrat screaming in pain, his heavily bandaged leg resting on a foot stool. After all, there is something faintly ludicrous about an affliction of the *big toe*, when set against serious and life-threatening maladies of vital organs. Such a dismissively callous attitude to gout victims – conceptualizing it as a retributive disease of the well-to-do – was encouraged by the many scurrilous

The exquisite agony of gout illustrated by James Gillray (1799)

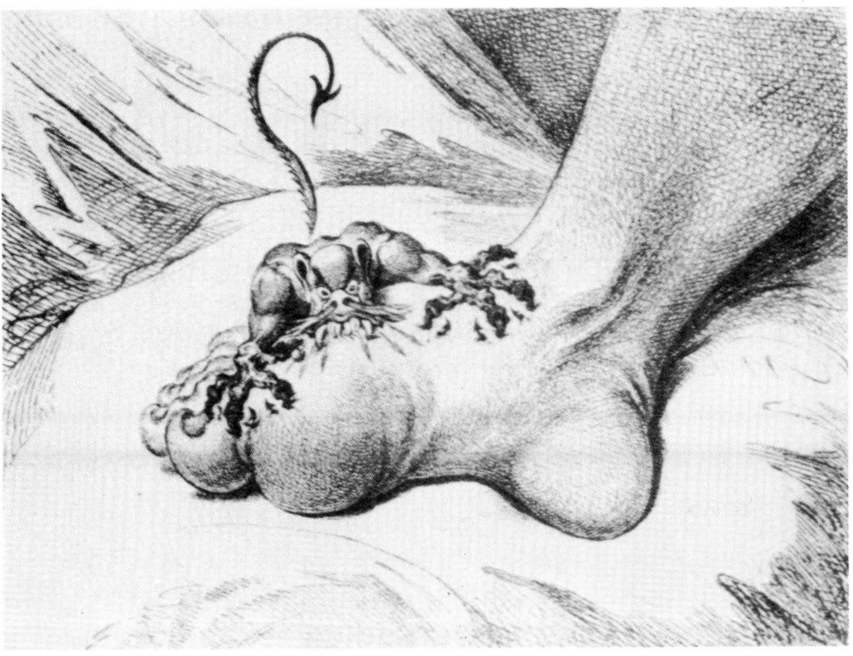

cartoons depicting the Prince Regent (later King George IV), the premier sufferer of his time, getting no more than his just deserves for his wanton lifestyle. The predilection for the great and wealthy – those who could afford vast quantities of red meat washed down with liberal amounts of sweet Mediterranean wine – earned for gout, the Latin description *Morbus Dominorum*. Indeed, some went so far as to claim that one could not consider oneself a *true* aristocrat unless one was crippled with gout.[1]

And yet to those afflicted with this malady the pain of gout defies description. It is a torture exceeding hell's fire. Indeed, it has been suggested that John Milton's gout inspired his description of Hell in *Paradise Lost*, and he is said to have been able to find blindness tolerable if it had not visited in the company of the gout. Shakespeare, in *Cymbeline*, cited Nature's permanent cure: 'By the one sure physician, Death'.[2] Agrippa, the Roman Consul, sought such a physician and committed suicide rather than endure the agonies of a fourth attack. One anonymous sufferer conveyed his agony in a graphic analogy: 'Put your toe in a vice and turn the handle as tight as possible: that is the pain of rheumatism. Give the handle one full turn more: that is the agony of gout.' An even more painful evocation was given by Sydney Smith (1771–1845) when he exclaimed, 'Oh! when I have the gout, I feel as if I was walking on my eyeballs.' Ironically Smith's suffering could so easily have been dramatically eased by colchicine, a unique substance known to the ancients, lost to later generations, and only relatively recently rediscovered. But more of that later.

Since gout usually affected the rich, and overwhelmingly men, and since these were usually members of royalty or the governing classes, it will be apparent that this disease of the big toe has had a disproportionate effect on human history. In 1681 Sir William Temple put it thus: 'I have seen the Councils of a great countrie grow bold or timorous, and the pulse of Government beat high or low, according to the fits of gout or ill health of the Governors.'

The term *gout* is derived from the Latin *gutta*, a drop, and reflects an early belief that the disease was caused by a poison, falling drop by drop into the joint. Hippocrates described *podagra*, *cheiagra*, or *gonogra*, depending on whether the toe, wrist or knee was affected. Gout is a visible disease: it shows itself in red and swollen and exquisitely painful joints. The joints fairly bulge with a chalky concretion, which we now know to be made of uric acid crystals. Such collections of uric acid need not be confined to the joints: they can often be seen as 'tophi' and squeezed out of swellings in the earlobes. Gout also runs in families. Its association with the good life, and its exacerbation by overindulgence in food and wine, was known

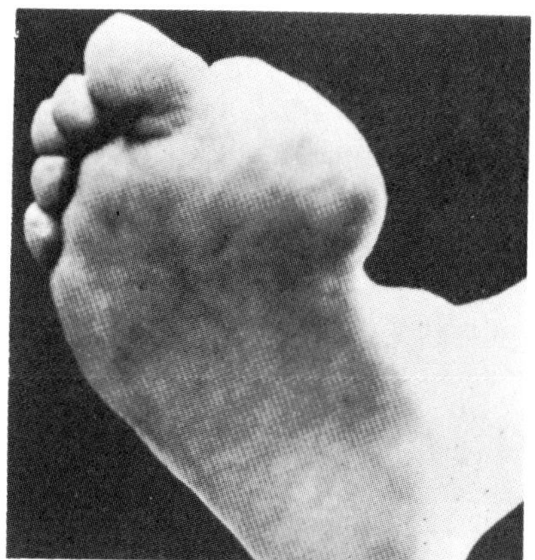

Deformity of the big toe caused by gout

to the Greeks. Paradoxically, alcohol, the premier precipitant of gout, could also ameliorate its effects: 'If you drink wine you get the gout; if you do not drink wine – the gout gets you.' The hereditary and alcoholic aetiologies were entwined by a French physician, when he observed that, 'Gout is the afternoon of the pleasant day enjoyed by the sufferer's grandfather.' If the grandfather's pleasure was obtained on a spring morning or an autumnal afternoon, then this would have incorporated the known seasonal incidence of gouty exacerbations.

Gout is an ancient disease and many of the heroes of Greek mythology are cited as suffering its agonies, including Priam, Achilles and Oedipus. Hippocrates (*c.* 5th century BC) quoted three famous sexually related aphorisms in regard to gout:

> Eunuchs do not take the gout
>
> A woman does not take the gout unless her menses [periods] be stopped
>
> A young man does not take the gout until he indulges in coitus

From the first of these aphorisms it is easy to appreciate that castration came to be viewed longingly by chronic sufferers as a means of permanent cure!

Gout claimed its victims from all periods and in all countries: Henry VII of England had to postpone his wedding to Elizabeth of York, being in the throes of an attack; the Italian Medici family suffered inordinately, one having the disease forever associated with his name, 'Piero il Gottoso' (Peter the Gouty, 1416–69). Charles V, Holy Roman Emperor (1500–58), and the most powerful man in the world, died 'sicke and frustrated of the goute before the High Altar of his chapel in the Escorial'. Charles's son, Philip II of Spain, who married Mary Tudor of England, looked upon his gout as God's retribution for his shortfall of heretics: he henceforth vowed to redouble his efforts to bring heretics to book and so lessen his articular agonies by instituting the Spanish Inquisition. The strategy did not work, since Philip continued to suffer as much as his heretical victims. God moves in a mysterious way.

The loss of the American colonies was due less to the madness of George III (which was totally non-contributory) than to the gout of Pitt, his chief minister. Had colchicine been available to Pitt, as it was to the Greeks, things might have been different. According to this scenario the loss of America can be lain at the *feet* of Thomas Sydenham, known as the English Hippocrates. It was Sydenham's influence, and his aversion to purgatives, that effectively proscribed the use of colchicine for generations of gout sufferers. Sydenham, himself a victim, positively connoted his affliction by declaring 'few fools have the gout'. He expanded upon the benefits of gout as follows:

> But what is a consolation to me, and may be so to other gouty persons of small fortunes and slender abilities, is that kings, great princes, generals, admirals, philosophers and several other great men have thus lived and died. In short it may, in a more especial manner, be affirmed of this disease that it destroys more rich than poor persons, and more wise men than fools, which seems to demonstrate the justice and strict impartiality of Providence, who abundantly supplied those that want some of the conveniences of life with other advantages, and tempers its profusion to others with equal mixture of evil.

According to Sydenham those folk able to live well must philosophically endure the caprice of fate.

Colchicine, an extract of the autumn crocus, was named from its provenance in Colchis in Asia Minor. It was used in ancient times as a constituent of purgative mixtures. Alexander of Thalles described the intense relief experienced in his gouty patients when prescribed colchicine. The problem was that colchicine, the active ingredient, was just one constituent of a purgative mixture. Further, colchicine was a toxic poison if taken in excessive doses, producing severe gastric symptoms of diarrhoea, and even death. The result was that its use declined, despite the documented relief colchicine had given countless Greeks and Romans, and despite the fact that its side-effects could be dramatically ameliorated by mixing it with white of egg and bread crumbs. (Leonhart Fuchs, in 1542, noticed another practical use: it also killed fleas.) But it was Sydenham and his esteemed reputation who proscribed the use of purgatives, and thereby colchicine.

Matters were not rectified until 1780 with the appearance of *L'eau d'Husson*, a patent medicine with a secret ingredient, later found to be colchicine. The beneficial effects of Husson's mixture were quickly and widely appreciated. In 1814 the active ingredient was identified as colchicine by Dr James Want. In 1817, King George IV, the foremost sufferer in the land, who was ingesting vast quantities of laudanum without relief, declared to his physicians, 'Gentlemen, I have taken your half measures long enough to please you ... From now on I shall take colchicine to please myself.'

The two protagonists of American independence, Pitt and Benjamin Franklin, were both sufferers from gout. The rediscovery of colchicine prompted Wallace Graham to reflect on its possible influence on the course of history. 'It would seem a misfortune for England that colchicine was not more widely recognised at the time. It is interesting to speculate whether or not the use of this drug by Pitt's physicians might have prevented the Boston tea party and the Battle of Bunker Hill.'

The incidence of gout has declined precipitously over the last century, probably due to more sensible attitudes towards overindulgence in food and drink.

## *Bladder stones: a chronicle of human misery*

In the days before aneasthetics and antisepsis, surgery was a dangerous business, and surgeons were not highly esteemed. Any major operation usually augured death, and it was small wonder that most people would opt to tolerate intense pain rather than submit themselves to the surgeon's knife.

A bladder stone is an unusual condition nowadays, but it was once a common source of chronic pain and ill-health in both adults and children. Symptoms included pain and bleeding on passing water – which the poor sufferer did very frequently. Surgical removal of the stone (lithotomy) was an extremely hazardous procedure, whether the surgeon chose to cut down through the front of the lower abdomen or approach via the perineum, that region between the genitalia and the anus. The death rate could be reduced somewhat by the swiftness with which the surgeon could remove the stone from the bladder: William Cheselden (1688–1752), the most celebrated English lithotomist of his day could be finished in a little less than sixty seconds, thereby lessening the chances of death from prolonged blood loss and shock.

Cheselden's method of extraction was little different from that used by the ancient Greeks and Romans. Essentially, it consisted of getting the patient into the lithotomy position, tied and pinned down by force if necessary. The forefinger of the left hand would be inserted into the anus; the right hand would push down on the front of the bladder. In this way the stone would be seen to bulge into the

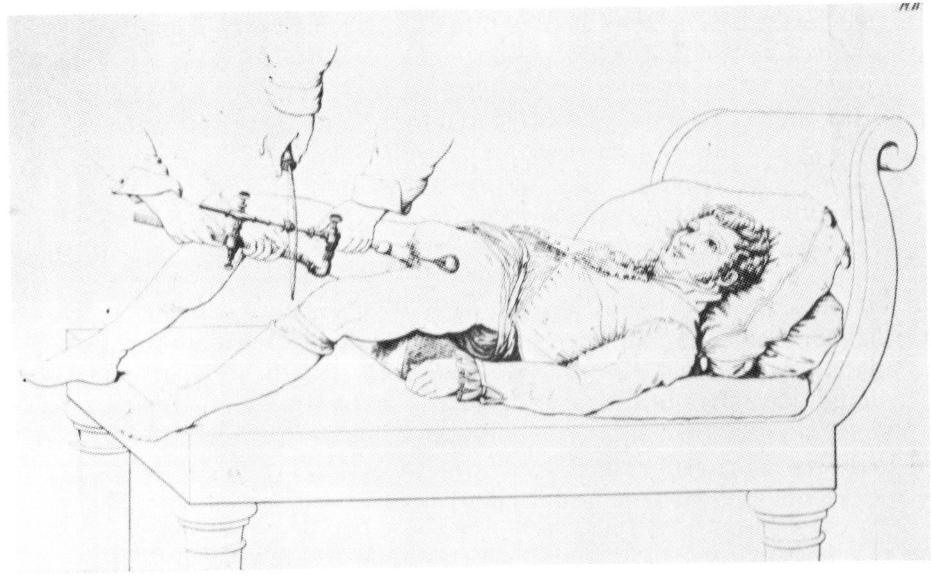

An unanaesthetised patient enduring 'cutting for the stone'

perineum and could be extracted by cutting down upon it with a knife. Unfortunately there was a very real danger of cutting into some essential structures – especially since, as was often the case, the surgeon's knowledge of anatomy was rudimentary. It was not unusual, therefore, for a patient who was 'fortunate' enough to survive the blood loss or infection, to be afflicted by permanent faecal and urinary incontinence and impotence.

A lithotomist's was a precarious career, fame and income being directly dependent upon one's post-operative mortality rate. One of the most successful, and one of the most unlikely, was an unqualified Frenchman whose name has been immortalized in a nursery rhyme: Frère Jacques. In 1690, when he was thirty-nine years old, he donned a monk's habit (although he had never taken holy orders) and apprenticed himself to an itinerant Italian surgeon who specialized in lithotomies. Refused a licence to practise in France, Frère Jacques nevertheless wheedled his way into the court of Louis XIV at Fontainebleau, where he successfully extracted the stone from the bladder of a cobbler. The king was so impressed that Frère Jacques was given his licence to practice. After a brief period of fame a series of disasters threatened his reputation: twenty-five out of his sixty patients died. Autopsies showed that he had slashed through the rectum, the bladder, the vagina, and major blood vessels.

Frère Jacques fled and used his time to learn the essentials of anatomy. Slowly he was restored to royal favour and in 1701 operated on thirty-eight patients at Versailles without a single death. One prospective patient, Marechal de Lorges, took the precaution of observing Frère Jacques operate successfully on twenty-two pauper patients before he would submit to the knife. The Marechal died soon after his operation.[3]

## *Samuel Pepys survives the cutting of his stone*

On 26 March 1658 Samuel Pepys' pain became so intolerable that he had no other option than surgical removal of his bladder stone. Many of us imagine that surgical patients in those pre-anaesthetic days would have induced relative anaesthesia by becoming insensibly drunk. Some did, but not all. Pepys took a draught of liquorice, marshmallow, cinnamon, milk, rose water and white of eggs.

An anatomical illustration of 'cutting for the stone'. Note the proximity of vital structures, including the prostate and bowel

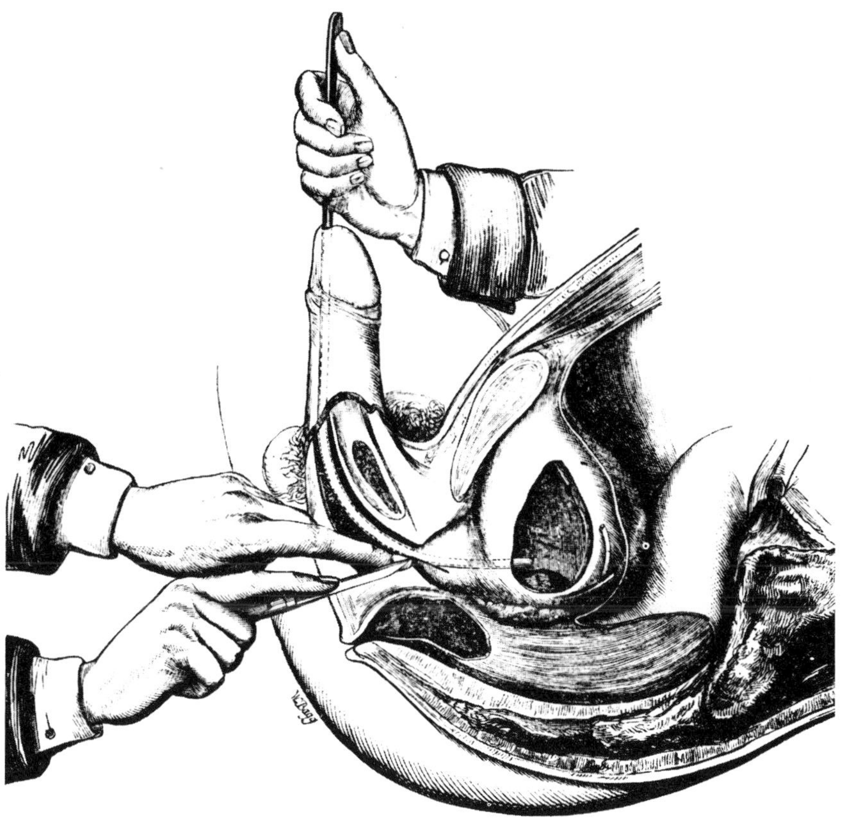

Unfortunately he left no first-hand description of the operation since he did not begin his famous diary until 1660. But the fact that he started his diary at all testifies to the fact that he survived his ordeal. The stone was the size of a tennis ball and weighed two ounces. Each year thereafter, on the anniversary of his operation, he celebrated by having friends to dinner. In 1660 he wrote: 'This day it is two years since it pleased God that I was cut of the stone at Mrs Turner's in Salisbury Court, and did resolve while I live to keep it a festival, as I did last year at my house, and for ever to have Mrs Turner and her company with me.' The celebration of 1663 included fricassee of rabbits and chickens, a leg of boiled mutton, three carps, a side of lamb, roasted pigeons, four lobsters, three tarts, a lamprey pie and a dish of anchovies, all washed down with 'good wine of several sorts'.

In 1664, he had a special case made to house his precious specimen, at the cost of twenty-five shillings: he had always lamented the fact that his mother, who had voided her stone, promptly threw it on the fire. In 1665 he could not decide whether his continuing good health was due to his hare's foot or his taking a daily turpentine pill.

It seems possible that Pepys may have become a bit of a bore about his operation. In 1667 he visited the Lord Treasurer who was very ill. 'I had taken my stone with me on purpose, and Sir Philip Warwicke carried it in to him to see, but he was not in a condition to talk with me about it, poor man.'[4]

### *Other famous martyrs to the stone*

Kidney and bladder stones were never respecters of rank, fame or social class. In a ten-year period from 1862 to 1872, Henry Thompson, an English surgeon, operated on two royal sufferers, one successfully, the other not.[5]

In 1862, Leopold I of Belgium, Queen Victoria's uncle, visited England. Whilst in London he had a relapse of the urinary symptoms which had dogged him for years. After his return to Brussels, and following many painful explorative examinations of the bladder, Leopold sent to England for Henry Thompson. An insight into the anxiety engendered in medical men who are called upon to treat royalty can be gleaned from Thompson's letter to his wife: 'I slept only 1½ hours last night, between 5 and 6 and a half a.m. I took too much coffee and couldn't sleep, and then I got thinking about my case and I got horribly anxious about it in the night. No one knows how anxious, but those who are placed in like circumstances.'

Conquering his nerves, Thompson operated on the King on 1 June. The method he used was to pass an instrument called a lithotrite through the penis into the bladder. A wide variety of lithotrites were developed which attempted by many ingenious ways to grasp the stone, crush it, and have the small fragments voided in the urine. (The principle of the lithotrite was sometimes used by patients upon themselves in order to avoid surgery: one man introduced a long nail through the penis into the bladder, pushed down the stone on to its pointed end, and proceeded to fragment the stone by hitting it with a blacksmith's hammer; another used a long thin blade and managed to saw the stone into smaller pieces over a nine-month period; yet another lassoed the stone with a brass wire and used a spike-ended drill operated by a bow.)

Thompson located the stone which was duly crushed. All went well and a much-relieved Thompson collected his fee of £3,000. Queen Victoria knighted him. It is thought that the post-operative course went so smoothly because Thompson had used a brand new set of instruments, freshly unwrapped, which had not been thoroughly matted with germs from the bladders of countless previous patients.

Thompson's second royal patient was not so lucky. Emperor Napoleon III, nephew of Napoleon Bonaparte, suffered so terribly from the pain of his bladder stone at the Battle of Sedan that he needed twice daily catheterization, and finally surrendered to his Prussian enemies. He and the Empress Eugénie subsequently travelled to England to begin their exile at Camden Place in Chislehurst. Napoleon's urinary symptoms worsened and Sir Henry was called. Ultimately the Emperor consented to an operation. A lithotrite was passed into the bladder and the stone was crushed. Four days later Napoleon had to endure a further operation to crush more stone fragments. Three days later still, with a third operation imminent, Napoleon III ended his suffering, dying in a coma brought about by kidney failure. He was finally laid to rest at Farnborough Abbey. Historians can only conjecture how the map of Europe and the course of European history might have been altered had Napoleon III defeated the Germans at Sedan. Inevitably parallels are drawn with his uncle, Napoleon Bonaparte, fatefully compromised by the agony of haemorrhoids at the Battle of Waterloo. Napoleon Bonaparte also suffered from painful and frequent passing of urine. When he was exiled on St Helena he would often be seen leaning with head against a wall or tree passing urine in small, painful dribbles.

Another famous victim of the stone was Robert Walpole (1676–1745), the first British Prime Minister. Never the picture of health, Walpole was once described by Lady Mary Wortley Montagu as 'The Potent Knight whose Belly goes At Least a Yard before his Nose'. He often passed bloody urine and was prescribed Jurin's lixivium, a secret concoction intended to dissolve bladder stones. As his symptoms worsened, Walpole, who had elected not to be cut, quaffed large amounts of the lixivium, washed down with liberal quantities of opium. On 4 November 1744 a surgeon extracted from the penis 'a Stone exceeding the Dimensions of the largest Kidney-Bean'. He later passed large clots of blood from the bladder containing twenty-six pieces of stone, some as big as the large one passed that morning, and some 'streaked with Yellow Veins, resembling in some measure Mosaic Pavement'.

Walpole died in great pain on 18 March 1745. In a letter to his son Horace one suspects that he regretted putting so much faith in dissolving medicines: 'This lixivium has blown me up. It has tore me to pieces ... That it may be short is all I desire. Give me more opium ... Dear Horace, if one must die, 'tis hard to die in pain.'

### *Fanny Burney's mastectomy*

A vivid description of the horrors of pre-anaesthetic surgery is given by Fanny Burney (1752–1840), author of the famous novel *Evelina*, in a letter written to her sister in 1811 about her operation for removal of her breast.

In the summer of 1810 Fanny Burney, living at the time in France, first noticed a pain in her right breast. Like many of us she hoped that if she took no notice then the pain would eventually ease. This strategy turned out to be a 'false confidence' and she finally agreed to be medically examined. Antoine Dubois, who was obstetrician to the Empress and residing in the Tuilleries awaiting the birth of Napoleon's son, managed to spare the time to examine Fanny Burney whilst his famous patient took a *promenade*. Dubois said nothing to Fanny but plenty to her husband. She was later informed 'that a small operation would be necessary to avert evil consequences'. She reacted by being 'rather confounded & stupefied than affrighted'.

Because of his commitments to the Empress, Dubois could take things no further, and the services of Dominique-Jean Larry, famous army surgeon, were urgently sought. Larry, in turn, brought in François Ribe, anatomist and surgeon. Fanny was 'obliged to submit' to an examination, after which she received an optimistic prognosis. Sadly, premature!

A later examination found the situation 'changed for the worse' and an operation became inevitable. With 'tears in his eyes' Larry proposed to call in Dubois who 'pronounced my doom'. Dubois told her she would suffer greatly; Ribe told her not to withhold her emotions. To lessen her anticipatory anxiety, the doctors agreed that the patient would be given only four hours notice of her operation. 'I therefore made my Will.'

'After sentence was thus passed, I was in hourly expectation of a summons to execution; judge, then, my surprise to be suffered to go on full 3 Weeks in the same state!' (She later discovered that the delay was caused by Dubois' belief that the cancer was inoperable, that she was destined to a 'frightful death', and that an operation would 'but accelerate my dissolution'.) Finally a messenger arrived from Larry giving her two hours notice of the operation and asking her to be sure that her husband was out of the house at the time. 'I finished my breakfast, & – not with much appetite, you will believe! forced down a crust of bread.' She then busied herself preparing the salon for her operation. 'The sight of the immense quantity of bandages, compresses, spunges, Lint – Made me a little sick.' Then came word of a two-hour delay!

Finally, and without being announced, 'seven men in black' entered, five doctors and two students. Dubois desired her to mount the bedstead, and ordered out the nurses and maids. Dubois' tone later softened and he 'spoke soothingly'; Larry was 'pale as ashes'. Dubois then placed a handkerchief over the patient's face. 'It was transparent, however, & I saw, through it, ... the glitter of polished Steel.' A silent consultation ensued and Fanny discerned through the handkerchief that Dubois intended the whole of the breast to be removed.

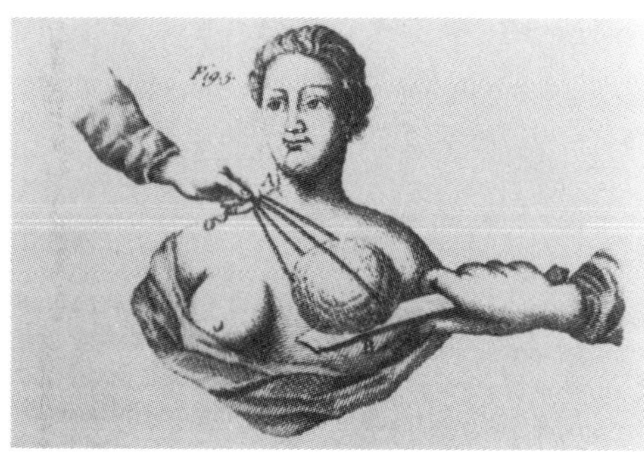

An early illustration of breast surgery before the advent of anaesthetics

The letter describes the rest of the operation.

> When the dreadful steel was plunged into the breast – cutting through veins, arteries, flesh, nerves – I needed no injunction not to restrain my cries. I began a scream that lasted unintermittingly during the whole time of the incision – & I almost marvel that it rings not in my Ears still, so excruciating was the agony ... the air that suddenly rushed into those delicate parts felt like a mass of minute but sharp and forked poniards ... But when again I felt the instrument – describing a curve –

cutting against the grain, then indeed I thought I must have expired. I attempted no more to open my Eyes – they felt as if hermettically shut, and so firmly closed, that the Eyelids seemed indented into the Cheeks. The instrument this second time withdrawn, I concluded the operation over – Oh no! presently the terrible cutting was renewed – & worse than ever, to separate the bottom, the foundation of this dreadful gland from the parts to which it adhered, I felt the knife rackling against the breast bone – scraping it! This performed, while I yet remained in utterly speechless torture, I heard the Voice of Mr Larry, in a tone nearly tragic, desire every one present to pronounce if anything more remained to be done. The general voice was Yes ... Mr Dubois pointed to some further requisition – & again began the scraping! – and, after this, Dr Moreau thought he discerned a peccant attom. My dearest, Esther, not for Days, not for Weeks, but for Months I could not speak of this terrible business without nearly again going through it! I could not *think* of it with impunity ...'

Fanny Burney's ordeal lasted twenty minutes. Later she allowed herself some justified self-congratulation: 'I bore it with all the courage I could exert, & never moved, nor stopt them, nor resisted, nor remonstrated, nor spoke – except once or twice during the dressings, to say '*Ah Messieurs! que je vous plains*!' [Gentlemen! I pity you!]'

Fanny Burney died twenty-nine years later at the age of eighty-eight, a fact that casts grave doubts on the validity of the diagnosis of cancer. After the operation Larry set off with Napoleon on the long march to, and back from, Moscow.[6]

# 7 A THERAPEUTIC INTERLUDE

At about this halfway point in the book, it may be instructive to consider the therapeutic agents available to ancient and medieval physicians. Most doctors prior to the seventeenth century ascribed to the humoural theory of diseases, first expounded by the ancient Greeks. According to this, the body was made up of four humours: blood, phlegm, black bile and yellow bile. Disease was simply a manifestation of an imbalance of humours, and successful treatment merely necessitated excess humours having to be drained away or deficient humours topped up. To this end, physicians employed a variety of strategies, including purging, bleeding and blistering, or, more usually, a combination of all three.[1]

## *Purging*

A purge was a method of emptying the bowels and has been used by physicians since ancient times to treat a bewildering array of symptoms and diseases – including diarrhoea! A purge can be given orally, or rectally as an enema or clyster (the terms being used synonymously). Purging is an ancient practice, though, intriguingly, no mention is made of enemas in either the Bible or the Talmud. The Greeks got the enema habit from the Egyptians: Herodotus, in the 5th century, records that the Egyptians 'purge themselves every month, three days successively'. According to Pliny the Elder, the Egyptians probably got the idea from watching a bird called an ibis, with its beak in its anus, blowing Nile water up its rectum. Herodotus also noted that the relatives of Egyptians who could not afford to be properly embalmed, often opted for a 'bargain basement' procedure consisting of powerful chemicals introduced into the rectum to dissolve the internal organs.

Enema solutions usually consisted of three parts: the vehicle (water, beer or milk), the emollient (oil or honey) and various drugs used for their supposed specificity of action. In earlier times, the

Self-administered enema apparatus

Self-administered enema apparatus

solutions were poured into an animal's bladder attached to a tube which was then introduced into the rectum. Guy de Chauliac, writing in the fourteenth century, describes how it was done: 'The patient when he is to have it administered holds himself bent forward on his knees, with his belt on and his mouth open. And after he has taken it, let his body be rubbed, and let him turn on to the painful part, and let him hold [i.e., retain] the clyster for an hour or two, or even as long as possible.' Vartomans, who practised in the sixteenth century, used to suspend his patients from a rope attached to their feet, for greater penetration.

For those to whom the prospect of baring the bottom was anathema, apparatus was devised to enable self-administration. Ambroise Paré catered for these with an instrument 'with which one may give a clyster to himself by putting the pipe into his fundament'.

Throughout the sixteenth and seventeenth centuries enema apparatus was constantly being refined. Syringes were widely used to introduce the solutions. Holy water enemata were used successfully to exorcize devils from possessed nuns, and tobacco smoke was sometimes used to resuscitate persons who had apparently drowned. A variation invented by Juke consisted of a tapering funnel, six feet in length, the narrow end of which went into the rectum and the other end of which was hung on the back of the door!

As can be imagined, the French took to purging with much greater enthusiasm than the coy English. When Louis XI had a stroke in 1480 he was given an enema and recovered. Henceforth, the procedure became popular throughout the country and was even used on sick pets, especially dogs. The rich could buy a four-legged stool from the middle of which projected a vertical tube to be inserted (carefully) into the rectum.

## *Cupping*

The principle of dry cupping is straightforward enough. Firstly, a glass or other form of cup is heated to remove some of the air inside. It is then pressed firmly on to the skin. The partial vacuum draws the skin into the cup and produces a swelling. Wet cupping entails abrading the skin with a scarifier before applying the cup, with the result that the cup fills with blood. Both methods probably produce any alleviation of pain by counter-irritation, substituting one discomfort for another. The Amerindians used buffalo horn, sucking the air from a hole in its tip, then plugging the end.

Like purging, cupping was used for a wide variety of ailments. Hippocrates used dry and wet cupping for menstrual disorders;

Hot cupping applied to the buttocks to help ease the pain of sciatica

Aretaeus for prolapse of the uterus, kidney stone and epilepsy. Maitre Henri de Mondeville, surgeon to King Phillipe of France, wrote about the indications for cupping in a book published in the fourteenth century: '[Apply the cup] near the navel to bring back a displaced uterus; over the navel itself to reduce a hernia or stop excessive menstruation in girls; over the liver if the right nostril is bleeding; over the spleen if the left nostril is bleeding; on both liver and spleen if both nostrils are bleeding.'

People who applied cups had to be very careful not to burn their patient. Sometimes, to expel the air, a lighted piece of paper was placed in the cup, but this carried the risk of scorching the skin with hot ash.

George Orwell, author of *Animal Farm* and *1984*, was cupped for pneumonia in Paris in 1929: 'They only put on six glasses, but after doing so they scarified the blisters and applied the glasses again. Each glass now drew out about a dessertspoonful of dark-coloured blood. As I lay down again, humiliated, disgusted and frightened by the thing that they had done to me, I reflected that now at least they would leave me alone.' (It was not to be: the doctors later applied a mustard poultice strapped tightly to his chest.)

## *Leeching*

Leeches are a variety of worm that sinks its jaws into a victim and feeds off the blood. Virtually the whole of the inside of a leech is stomach and it can swell enormously to accommodate a large blood meal. When the leech has gorged its fill, it simply falls off, but, because of the anticoagulant it has injected, the victim's blood continues to flow freely.

An officer from the Arakan wrote in 1943:

> Leeches are far worse than the Japs. I have them in my trousers and in my boots. They attach themselves to a vein where they remain until they become so bloated with blood that they drop off, or until one spots them and forces them away with a burning cigarette. They are quite painless and are therefore not noticed easily. I have actually had one on my nose. But the trouble about them is that even when they have gone the blood keeps flowing and one gets a sort of nervous complex in the damp jungle, feeling that every twig or bit of leaf that attaches itself is a leech.

One drawback identified by Pliny in *Historica Naturalis* was the possibility of a fatal infection ensuing if the leech's head remained buried in the skin. To obviate this possibility, Pliny recommended cutting through the body of the leech as it fed: 'The consequence is that the blood oozes forth through a syphon as it were, and the head, gradually contracting as the animal dies, is not left behind in the wound.'

Many physicians, Galen included, gave advice on the steps to be taken if a leech was inadvertently swallowed. One remedy was to drench the animal in a mixture of vinegar and urine. Writing in 1895, Dr Granger, a surgeon in Her Majesty's Indian Service, wrote,

> On going outside the fort I found an old Pathan greybeard waiting to see me ... Eleven days ago he was drinking from a rain-water tank and felt something stick in his throat ... I introduced a polypus forceps into the lower part of the pharynx where a body, distinctly moving, was felt ... With considerable force I managed to remove it. It was a leech between two-and-a-half and three inches in length with a body the size of a Lee-Metford bullet. I quote this case as a typical example of the carelessness of natives of the class from which we enlist our Sepoys.[2]

Marcel Proust (1871–1922), in *Remembrance of Things Past*, evokes the horror of treatment with leeches: 'Cottard, to her [Francoise's] disappointment, gave the preference, though without much hope, to leeches. When, a few hours later, I went into my grandmother's room, fastened to her neck, her temples, her ears, the tiny black reptiles were writhing among her bloodstained locks, as on the head of Medusa.'

Avicenna wrote on the proper application of leeches.

> They should be squeezed to make them eject the contents of their stomachs. If feasible they should be given a little lamb's blood by way of nourishment. The slime and debris should be cleansed from their bodies with a sponge. The place of application must be shaved, washed and rubbed until it is red. To ensure that they will not crawl into the gullet, nose or anus, one must draw a thread through the tail. When the leeches are full sprinkle a little salt over them, or pepper, or snuff, or ashes. Do not use leeches again if they have been applied to a case of typhoid fever, cholera or smallpox.

Leeches were extensively used for centuries (and are experiencing somewhat of a renaissance in our own times to reduce bruising). It was reckoned that there was no disease that would not benefit from the application of leeches to the vessels of the anus, particularly cases of nose bleeds, or patients coughing or vomiting up blood.

Leeches were big business in France in the nineteenth century, and

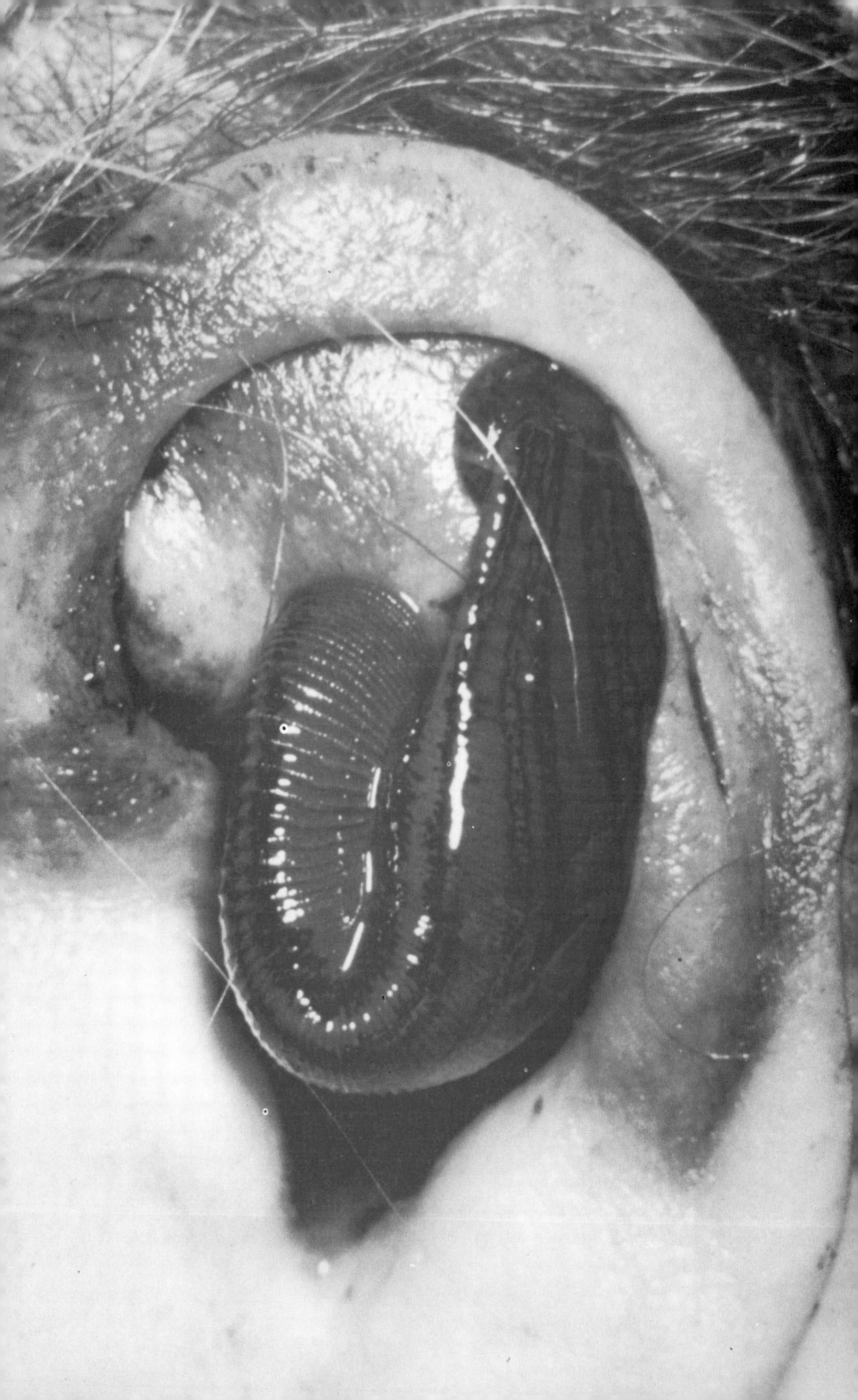

A seton on the back of the neck used to treat a weeping eye

*Opposite:* The inspiration for Alien? A leech sucking blood from a patient's ear

a profitable export earner. In 1824, five million were shipped to England.

## *Counter-irritants*

The theory of counter-irritation was to produce an area of inflammation on the skin through which the noxious humours would drain. One of the commonly used blistering agents was cantharides, a powdered form of blister beetle (Spanish fly) applied to the skin.

Another method of producing counter-irritation was by using a seton. This involved threading a length of twine, silk or horse hair through the skin and leaving it to discharge indefinitely. The nape of the neck was a common site for the insertion of setons, especially in treating eye complaints. Setons threaded through the scrotum were supposed to alleviate testicular complaints. An 'Issue' used the same principle of counter-irritation, substituting for the thread a small foreign body, such as a pea.

One of the most straightforward ways of producing counter-irritation was by cautery – simply to burn the patient with a hot iron! Aretaeus treated epilepsy by burning through the scalp down to the skull, to produce an eschar, or artificial sore. Cautery was applied to the soles of the feet to cure apoplexy.

Blisters were used on many royal patients: William, Duke of Gloucester, only surviving child of Queen Anne was blistered for smallpox, but died, bringing to an end the Stuart line; the exiled James II endured great suffering from blisters applied to treat his stroke; George III was regularly blistered on his shaven head.

But the most famous royal patient to have to endure inadequacies of medieval medicine was King Charles II, whose final agonies have been recorded in the minutest detail. The King awoke on Monday, 2 February 1685, and went, as usual to his private closet. He was noticed to be deathly pale – it was obvious to all that something was very wrong. Suddenly the King had a violent convulsion and fell into the arms of an attendant.

The King was put into bed and immediately sixteen ounces of blood was taken off from his right arm. More blood was removed by deep scarification of the skin. He was given a strong antimonial emetic to induce vomiting, followed by a powerful purge. His scalp was shaved and blisters and cautery applied. A succession of mixtures was then administered to adjust the humoural imbalance: white hellebore to encourage sneezing; a draught of mallow roots, sweet almond kernels, melon seeds and barley water; a gargle of bark of elm; and a plaster of pitch and pigeon dung was applied to the royal

Cautery with a hot iron as a form of counter irritation

feet. The next day the King was a little better, but relapsed on the Wednesday. 'Spirit of human skull' was given, 'a sure harbinger of impending dissolution'. The King's condition steadily deteriorated: Sir Walter Raleigh's cordial was given as a cardiac tonic, followed by Goa stone, quinine bark, and Oriental bezoar stone – a sort of gall stone from the stomach of an eastern goat. Charles submitted to these frantic medical assaults with resignation and good humour, apologizing to the assembled company for taking so long to die. Death finally released him on the Friday morning after a final twelve-ounce bleed.[3]

# 8 DISEASES OF THOSE WHO GOVERN

## 1 The Royals

Royal maladies have figured prominently in the annals of medical history since ancient times, not only because illnesses suffered by kings could have profound effects on the countries they ruled, but also because, surrounded as they were by literates, the minutest details of these illnesses were likely to be recorded for posterity.

### *Tutankhamun and the feminine pharaohs*

A statue of Tutankhamun shows the young Pharaoh with prominent breasts (gynaecomastia). Smenkhkare, Tutankhamun's predecessor, had such large breasts that a depiction of him was long taken by experts to be of Nefertiti. In a colossal statue of Akhenaten found at the temple of Karnak, the Pharaoh is shown as having well-developed breasts, wide hips and no external genitalia. Despite this depiction, Akhenaten managed to sire six daughters by Queen Nefertiti, though some experts contest his paternity. A headless statue of Akhenaten's father, Amenophis III, in the Metropolitan Museum of Art in New York, clearly shows gynaecomastia.

Experts have long debated the blood relationship between these four pharaohs of the Eighteenth Dynasty. It is now clear that Smenkhkare and Tutankhamun were full brothers, that their father was probably Amenophis III, and Akhenaten their putative uncle. Some have conjectured that Akhenaten is shown without genitals because he had been castrated; others suggest, totally implausibly, that she was a woman masquerading as a man. Medical explanations for such feminine features have included a pituitary tumour causing eunuchoidism, or liver failure brought about by schistosomiasis, a disease common in Egypt then as now.

Another explanation, which takes into account the incestuous nature of pharaonic matings, is that the gynaecomastia was an inherited abnormality due to prolonged inbreeding. Perhaps, it is argued, emasculation was the price to be paid by successive generations when genetic variation becomes secondary to the

The pharaoh Akhenaton showing him with enlarged breasts, feminine hips and without male genitalia

principle of 'keeping power in the family', a tradition indulged in by royals until very recent times.[1] It is telling that both Smenkhkare and Tutankhamun, despite being married to beautiful young princesses for many years (actually, their half-sisters), failed to produce offspring. Most art historians are convinced that pharaonic femininity was merely a transitory sculptural style, and that there is no need to invoke a medical cause. But such an explanation is unlikely to appeal to a twentieth-century physician intent upon making a 4,000 year retrospective diagnosis![2]

### *A most royal malady*

Queen Victoria, the most powerful monarch of her day, carried within her the seed of catastrophe – the gene responsible for the bleeding disease haemophilia. By means of this genetic blight, it can be argued that Victoria brought about the Russian Revolution – indirectly and inadvertently, of course.

In the general population the haemophilia gene is rare and its pernicious effects are kept in check by assortative mating. Haemophilia is caused by a 'sex-linked' gene, which means that although the disease affects males, it can be carried through successive generations by females who appear perfectly healthy, but who are able to transmit the gene to their sons. Queen Victoria was just such a 'carrier'. Her defective gene was probably a mutation of her father's X chromosome: Edward, Duke of Kent, married late in life in an attempt to ensure the Hanoverian succession after the tragic death of Princess Charlotte in childbirth, and it is established that elderly fathers have a much increased likelihood of passing on genetic mutations to their children.

Queen Victoria and Prince Albert had nine children. One, possibly two, of their four sons was a haemophiliac; two, possibly three, of their five daughters were carriers. These daughters, through marriage, passed the gene into the European royal families.

Leopold, Duke of Albany and youngest of Victoria's sons, was a haemophiliac who, though sickly as a child, survived long enough to marry and sire children. It was Leopold whose birth was assisted by chloroform administered by John Snow (see page 44). Many (men, doubtless) who thought painless childbirth unnatural, were quick to find a link between the anaesthetic and haemophilia. Leopold's daughter was a carrier and his grandson a haemophiliac who bled to death after a motor accident. Leopold died, aged thirty-one, of a brain haemorrhage following a fall which caused a minor blow to the head.

The two definite 'carrier-daughters' were Princess Alice and Princess Beatrice. It was Alice's daughter, Alix, who married the future Tsar Nicholas II, so taking the gene into the Romanov line. Her son, the Tsarevich Alexis, was a haemophiliac. His mother, desperate to try anything which might be able to help Alexis, fell under the influence of the monk, Rasputin, who claimed to have hypnotic powers which would ameliorate the effects of the disease. Alexis' initial improvement meant that his mother came to depend upon Rasputin more and more. Soon the monk was advising the royal family on more than medical matters. The increasing power of Rasputin is cited as one of the factors leading up to the Russian Revolution and the murder of the Tsar and his family at Ekaterinburg in 1918.

Beatrice's daughter, Victoria Eugenie, married Alfonso, King of Spain, and bore him five sons, three of them haemophiliac. Of these, Alfonso and Gonzalo were the last two, definitely identified, haemophiliac descendants of Queen Victoria. Alfonso, who always blamed his mother for giving him haemophilia, died in 1938 in Miami when the night-club singer who was driving him swerved and crashed into a telegraph pole. He died of haemorrhage, aged thirty-one and childless.[3]

## *Mental and moral heredity in royalty*

Frederick Woods was a doctor at the Harvard Medical School who made a special study of European royalty. From biographical sources he graded 832 kings and queens on scales of intelligence and morality.[4] Intellectually, the majority of both men and women fell in the middle band (as one would expect), and numbers tailed off towards both the 'imbecile' (grades 1 and 2) and genius ends (grades 9 and 10). There is a progression from Philip, the imbecilic son of Charles III (1), through King William IV (3), to King William III (9). Geniuses are very scarce, but include Frederick the Great and William the Silent. As for the ladies: Anne, the second wife of William the Silent is in the moronic range, and Joanna the Mad, scores only 2. One may wonder what Caroline of Anspach (8) found to talk about with King George II (3).

Although morality is an even more difficult concept to quantify than intelligence, this did not deter Dr Woods. He reserved the lowest three grades for the 'distinctly vicious, depraved, licentious, dissipated, cruel or extremely unprincipled'. George IV scores a mere (2), whereas Albert, husband of Queen Victoria, scores a resounding (10). Catherine II is definitely depraved, but happily Victoria comes in with the same score as Albert.

What is the point of all this and where is the science? It would appear that the intelligent line of Hanover stayed put in Germany and the dullard branch of the family crossed the Channel to become King George I of England, reminding one of the apocryphal history examination question, 'Name the four Georges and give reasons.' This sorry clan came to an end with William IV, the Sailor King, whose sole service to his country was to die without legitimate heirs, thereby allowing the succession of Victoria. Woods diplomatically resisted the temptation to grade the children of Victoria and Albert.

## *Madness, the right royal malady*

Mad monarchs stretch back to biblical times. Nebuchadnezzar, King of Kings, let power go to his head. The Bible tells us how this king of Babylon imagined himself turned into a wolf, imitating the behaviour of that beast, howling, gnawing at flesh and avoiding all human contact.

The prophet Samuel deliberately chose Saul as King of Israel because of his melancholia and paranoia, his homicidal and suicidal tendencies. When, despite these vicissitudes, Saul made a success of the kingship, Samuel, intensely jealous, anointed David king in his stead. In a fit of despair Saul committed suicide by throwing himself on to his own spear.

Warrior kings gain their thrones by force of arms, and it is only human that they should wish to found a ruling dynasty, and be succeeded by their sons. But it is mysterious that because a man is the son of a king, he is assumed to be the best person to succeed to his father's throne – especially when that prince is obviously insane. It is even more mysterious why his subjects would tolerate such a patently illogical and risky process. Lunatic princes who were the products of kingly dalliances, and whose mothers were not even invited into the royal bed, were doubly undeserving to rule over others.

Madness in royalty assumes a unique importance because it is so frequently allied to despotism. 'The greater the power in the hands of a fool, the more disastrous is likely to be the use he makes of it.' Esquirol, the famous nineteenth-century French psychiatrist once stated that one out of sixty members of royal households was insane, compared with one in eight hundred ordinary men.[5]

Royal madness reached virtually epidemic proportions in the reigns of the Julio-Claudian emperors, though the founder, Julius Caesar, seems relatively untainted. The most charitable consensus is that Tiberius was a paranoid psychopath and Claudius was a high-grade imbecile, but Caligula (Gaius) and Nero were definitely unhinged – though a vocal minority maintains that the homicidal behaviour of Caligula amounted to nothing more than 'an exaggerated form of those weaknesses which were characteristic of the age in which he lived: he was prodigal, immoral, pleasure-loving and cruel'.

Gaius, the product of a consanguineous marriage, was born in AD 12 and given the name 'Caligula' by the Roman soldiers because of the miniature military boots he used to wear. He succeeded Tiberius in AD 37, accelerating the latter's departure by suffocation. Tiberius had been well aware of the murderous potential of his heir and proclaimed that he was 'bringing up a serpent for the Roman people'. In the year of his accession, Caligula became seriously ill and, although he recovered, henceforth he went in constant fear of assassination. Caligula's reign has been documented by Suetonius (unfortunately that part of Tacitus's *Annals* dealing with Caligula has been lost). The author recounts stories of Caligula's habitual incest with his sisters, his homosexuality, and his transvestism. He thrived on torture and execution on a massive scale, and he openly gloried in his power to have anyone decapitated at a nod of his head. Although Caligula came to consider himself a god (and commanded that his horse Incitatus should be made a Consul), he did not believe himself omnipotent – and with good reason, for in AD 41 he was murdered along with his fourth wife, Caesonia, and his infant daughter. Medical historians would probably agree that Caligula suffered from schizophrenia and epilepsy.

Claudius succeeded Caligula at the age of sixty and ruled for fourteen years before being poisoned by his wife-niece Agrippina. Despite Robert Graves's portrayal of Claudius as a wise and learned ruler, others have characterized him as a drunk and a debauchee whose blood lust was almost the equal of Caligula's.

When Nero's father Domitius Aenobarbus was congratulated on the birth of his son he observed, 'From Agrippina [Caligula's sister who was later to marry Claudius] and me only a monster and a scourge of humanity can come forth.' And thus it came to pass. Among many others, Nero poisoned his brother, had his mother Agrippina assassinated, and put to death two wives, Octavia and Poppaea, the latter by kicking her in the stomach when she was pregnant. He put Rome to the torch but managed to blame the Christians, whom he proceeded to torture and kill in their thousands. When his offer of marriage was turned down by Antonia, Claudius's daughter, he had her put to death, marrying instead Statilia Messallina, after he had ensured her widowhood by murdering her husband. Eventually the legions rose up against such tyranny, and Nero resorted to suicide in AD 68.[6]

## *The Spanish Habsburgs*

In more recent times, although pharaonic marriages between brother and sister no longer take place, consanguineous marriages persist: the greatest honour for a Habsburg princess was to marry a member of the House of Habsburg. Papal dispensations were obligingly granted for Habsburg marriages which would have resulted in the prompt excommunication of those of lesser rank. Not only were the results a disaster for the royal families, they were an even greater disaster for the countries over whom they reigned.

The history of the Spanish royal family is an object lesson in the close association of consanguineous marriages and mental instability. The most serious consequences of marriages between close relatives are the emergence of genetic stigmata – both physical and mental – which would ordinarily have been flushed out by assortative, random mating. Early on, the Habsburgs brought forth a galaxy of luminaries, but as the generations passed, the effects of inbreeding became more and more apparent. It started with the marriage of Ferdinand of Aragon and his cousin Isabella of Castile, a union which produced *Juana la Loca*, Jane the Mad, their third child, in 1479. A union was arranged between Juana and the Habsburg, Philip the Fair, son of Maximilian I, and in 1496, at the age of seventeen, the bride-to-be was duly shipped off to the Netherlands. Juana's royal standing took on a new significance after the deaths of her elder brother and sister, making her heiress-presumptive of Aragon and Castile, as well as wife of the future Habsburg emperor. But Isabella was wary of her daughter's competence to reign and her anxieties seemed well-founded when Juana sunk into a prolonged state of mental apathy following her husband's return to the Netherlands after a visit to his Spanish in-laws. The forsaken wife languished in Spain, increasingly and overtly unstable, before being summoned to rejoin her husband in 1504.

By scrutinizing the many portraits of Maximilian I, it is easy to discern the source of the Habsburg jaw, lip and nose, features which became even more pronounced in Charles V (1500–58), the son of Juana and Philip. His protruding jaw (prognathism), flattened forehead and humped nose are plainly to be seen in portraits and busts. Charles became King of Spain in 1516 and Holy Roman Emperor in 1518. The gross protrusion of his lower jaw caused his mouth to hang open, making it difficult for him to chew food; and his large tongue gave him problems with articulation. Despite the appearance of stupidity, Charles was an able ruler. He also displayed a sense of humour when he shrugged off a remark made by a Spanish peasant, 'Your Majesty, shut your mouth, the flies in this country are very insolent!'

When, in September 1506, Philip the Fair unexpectedly died, Juana withdrew further from all social contacts, finally losing her reason completely. For a long while she refused to accept her husband's death and would stay close to his coffin, refusing permission for his burial. When he was finally placed in his vault, Juana visited him dressed as a nun and, ordering the coffin to be opened, she fell about the corpse in a frenzy of kisses. This macabre spectacle was repeated many times over the next several weeks. Ferdinand set about finding a place for his mad daughter to live. He chose Tordesillas where Juana was to be confined for the rest of her life. Mad she may have been, but she was still potential breeding stock: Henry VII of England proposed marriage, whether sane or insane, just so long as she could bear children!

The title, King of Spain, passed to Juana's son, Charles, later to be Emperor Charles V. This was not universally popular, and a breakaway faction insisted that Juana herself accede to the Spanish throne: this she did in one of her rare lucid intervals. But it could not last, and Juana soon reverted to madness. Henceforth, from 1531 to

1555 Juana was dead to all but her 'jailers' at the Tordesillas, and alone with her delusions. 'The close of her life was very tragic. She had sunk into the state of a beast. When she was not in a condition of frenzy, of which the chief objects were the wicked women of her suite and the ghost of the black cat, she refused to leave her bed, which received all the excretions of her body. She vegetated in her foul den.' Gangrenous sores began to appear on her body, exacerbated by days of immobility. She died in great pain, aged seventy-six. Juana was a queen who had never ascended the throne, but whose legacy of insanity was to flow in the veins of her descendants.

Whilst sane for the most part, Juana's son, the Emperor Charles V, nevertheless shared his family's macabre obsession with death. As his own end drew nearer, he was in the habit of practising his funeral obsequies each night in his private chapel. The choir would sing the mass, conducted by Charles sitting in his coffin. The rehearsal over, everyone would go back to their beds.

Charles V married his cousin, Isabella, a union which produced Philip II (he of the Spanish armada). Philip, never the equal of his father, pledged his troth to his niece, his cousin and his aunt in a series of political marriages. Papal dispensations were easily come by, especially since the popes were often appointed by, or relatives of, Habsburg monarchs. Philip inherited his full quota of Habsburg stigmata: protruding jaw, asthma, gout, dropsy, epilepsy and melancholia. Philip II's son, Don Carlos (about whom more later) was physically deformed and mentally degenerate, and ended up, like his grandmother, safely under lock and key, dying in mysterious circumstances. Don Carlos's brother, Philip III, was 'weak, sickly, and scrofulous', and *his* son, Philip IV, weaker still, until *his* son, Carlos II finally did for the Spanish Habsburgs. Continuing the Habsburgs' penchant for genetic catastrophe, Carlos II's mother was also his first cousin, and he

Widespread facial destruction in congenital syphilis

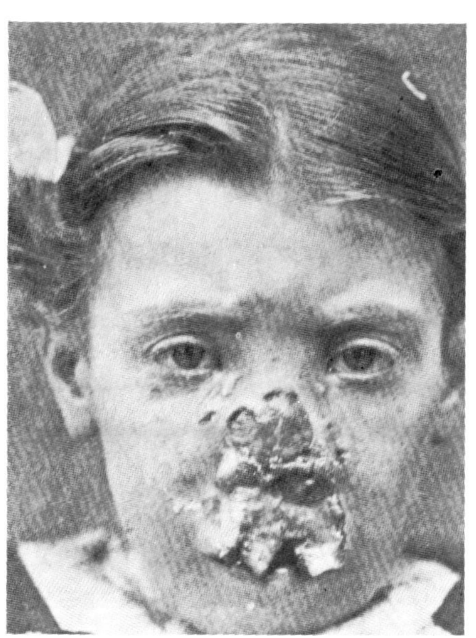

was further burdened by congenital syphilis. He came to the throne at the age of four, the distillate of genetic disadvantage: feeble-minded, impotent, stone deaf and epileptic. He was often in the habit of opening the coffins of his ancestors, and peering inside. He died, aged thirty-nine, his queen applying freshly killed pigeons to his head to prevent vertigo. *Sic transit gloria Habsburgs*: four generations of incest.

## *Don Carlos*

The greatest tragedy of Juana's line was played out by her great-grandson, Don Carlos. Much apocrypha attends his life, especially his childhood. It is said that his deep-seated malice displayed itself early in his life in the way he used to bite the nipples of his nurses; that he did not speak a word until he was five; and that the first word he exclaimed was 'No!' A speech impediment persisted until his tongue-tie was cut when he was twenty-one.

He was brought up by aunts and tutors since his father, Philip II, was away in England, married to Mary Tudor. In adolescence, Don Carlos began to develop traits of character which did not wholly please his grandfather, the Emperor Charles V. At the age of twelve he was described thus: 'His head is disproportionately large to the size of his body. He is physically weak and displays a tendency to great cruelty. I am told that when live hares or other animals are brought to him out hunting, he enjoys roasting them alive. Someone made him a present of a large tortoise, which bit his finger one day, whereupon he bit off its head … In short he is of an incredible pride, stubborn of will, and quickly roused to anger.' After Charles V's death in 1558, what few constraints there were upon Don Carlos disappeared, and his dark, sadistic personality developed unchecked. In 1559 Don Carlos attended an *auto-da-fé*, a ten-hour orgy of death in which heretics were burnt alive before a vast and enthusiastic crowd. Don Carlos was noted to enjoy the spectacle greatly.

Mary Tudor having died, Philip II married for the third time. His bride was Elizabeth of Valois, the beautiful sixteen-year-old daughter of Henri II of France. The pity which Elizabeth felt for her stepson has been grotesquely misinterpreted as love, most notably by Schiller in his play *Don Carlos*, later a Verdi opera. Whatever the reason, the father-son relationship gradually deteriorated into one of open hostility, and Don Carlos sank into the Habsburg melancholia and pre-occupation with death. In 1564, aged nineteen, he dictated his will, but did not die. Indeed, the royal families of Europe regarded him as a possible bridegroom: a description of him, sent to

Maximilian who was looking for a husband for his eldest daughter, has come down to us: 'He is neither tall nor well developed, and one shoulder is a little higher than the other; the chest falls in, and there is a slight rise visible at the bottom of the back; he cannot use his right side so well as his left; he has a thin weak voice and speaks with difficulty, he cannot pronounce the 'r' or 'l' properly ... he speaks out what he thinks and feels without reserve, and if anyone offends him they do not come off easily.' The report ends, 'Don Carlos is a feeble, sickly man, but the son of a powerful monarch.'

Another description was even less flattering. 'The Prince is of very low stature, ugly and of disagreeable countenance; he is melancholy in temper ... sometimes [he suffers] with delirium, which he seems to have inherited from his grandfather and great-grandmother.' Don Carlos used to roam the streets at night, forcing his attentions on women unfortunate enough to cross his path. Once, when someone threw water over him, he ordered the house to be burnt and its inhabitants murdered. In another fit of fury, when sent a pair of boots which were too small, he ordered that the boots be cut up into pieces, cooked and fed to the shoemaker. Don Carlos frequently exploded into paroxysms of rage at the slightest contradiction, and he was widely regarded as mad, people speaking openly of their fears for the succession.

For such a physically unattractive and behaviourally unpredictable young man as Don Carlos, it may seem surprising how many looked to him as a possible marriage partner: Margaret, daughter of Catherine de Medici (aged seven); Mary, Queen of Scots, recently widowed; Grand Duchess Anna, daughter of Maximilian; even Dona Juana, his own aunt, and ten years older than him. Elizabeth of England pretended to be interested! But his hotheaded and indiscriminate violence to those around him continued to cause the gravest concern. Like all heirs-apparent he was dissatisfied with the minor responsibilities entrusted to him by his father, and grew increasingly resentful of Philip, especially in the latter's prevarication about finalizing his son's marriage to Anna, Don Carlos's preferred bride.

Filial dislike turned to hatred, and Don Carlos conceived a plan to escape from his father's presence and make for Italy. It was supposed to be a secret but spies kept the King informed of his son's intentions. Late one night in January 1568, the King, accompanied by his body guards, burst into Don Carlos's bedroom, confiscated his weapons and ordered that the windows be nailed up. Henceforth the Prince was to be a prisoner. Don Carlos, humiliated by such ignominious treatment, attempted to starve himself to death, but failed. He even swallowed his ring because someone had told him that a diamond was a potent poison. By June Don Carlos was feverish and sinking fast: he died in July, aged twenty-three. Philip has long been suspected of murdering this 'lame, epileptic semi-imbecile and a raving homicidal maniac'.[7]

## *The insanity of King George III*

George III, known to his subjects as 'Farmer' George, was a long time on the British throne, and for much of that time he was mad. Many of the country's maladies were attributed to the insanity of its monarch, both during his lifetime and subsequently, including the humiliating loss of the American colonies. Recent medical research has cast George in a more kindly light, since it has become apparent that his madness was not of his making, but the fault of Mary Queen of Scots, who lived some two centuries before. It is now posited that George III was an innocent victim of a pernicious gene which, through generations of inter-marriage, had been given the opportunity to flourish, causing mayhem on an individual, familial, national and international scale.

The course of George III's bouts of illness have been minutely documented in state papers, official correspondence and in the medical notes of the doctors called upon to treat him. In all, the King suffered five attacks of madness, the first in 1788 when he was fifty years-old. The attack started in June with severe abdominal pain, which was diagnosed as a problem with the gall bladder. Over the next several months the king's health deteriorated: he complained of headache, insomnia and became increasingly restless. Periods of great excitement were interspersed with periods of lucidity and calm. In early November the King became stuporous and the doctors feared for his life.

One of the doctors called to treat the King was Francis Willis, owner of a private madhouse, a man qualified both as a doctor and a cleric. It mattered not to Willis that his patient was the British monarch – Willis treated him as he would any other, by bundling him into a strait jacket or restraint chair for the slightest show of insubordination. The good doctor used to boast that he 'broke in [patients], as horses in a menage'. The King had to submit to vomits, purges, bleeding, blistering, cupping and the application of leeches. If George was not paranoid before, he soon became terrified at the very sight of Willis.[8] The King's illness was used as an excuse to attempt to unseat the Prime Minister, William Pitt, and bring down the government. Willis was deferred to by the most powerful men in the land, his opinion being constantly sought about the King's chances of recovery.

Plans were far advanced for the King's son, later (much later!) to be George IV, to be proclaimed Regent, when, as if through spite, the King's mind cleared. Although George's recovery caused widespread relief and celebration, a profound unease lingered among those who were party to the full details of the King's illness. Most worrying were the mental symptoms. Those closest to the monarch contemplated with horror the prospect of a lunatic king, and sought Willis's reassurance that recovery was complete and relapse impossible.

Anxiety in the King's party lessened year by year as George continued to enjoy good health. Twelve years were to pass before the first relapse in 1801, when George once more showed temporary signs of insanity. A second short relapse in 1804 was followed by another six years of mental health. Then, in 1810, the King suffered his fourth attack, an attack which would last the remaining ten years of his life. During this final decade, although the illness waxed and waned, its course was inexorably downhill, through blindness, deafness and emotional lability into mindless senility, his silent and solitary existence overseen by Dr Willis's sons, Robert Darling and John. The Prince of Wales became Regent in 1811, finally replacing the old King's men with his own.

The madness of George III had a profound effect on the history of Great Britain and on the history of psychiatry. When the most important man in the land becomes insane, it inevitably brings the subject into the public arena: suddenly it was respectable to be mad, and the number of those diagnosed insane rose precipitously. But there was little interest shown in the intricacies of psychiatric diagnosis: after all, madness was madness. The most widely accepted retro-diagnosis made on George III was 'manic depressive psychosis', which merely medicalized the king's alternating episodes of mania (excitement) and depression. Psychoanalysts have tried their hand at identifying possible causes of his breakdown. One prime candidate was the vitriolic filial relationships of the Hanoverians, each succeeding son attempting to out-loathe his father's loathing for his own father. But apart from this family failing, George III was an unusual Hanoverian: well-liked, even-tempered on the whole, and faithful to his wife: it is said of him that as a private citizen he would have been admirable, but as a king he was a disaster.

The doctors of the day, and those subsequently, have tended to ignore the *physical* concomitants of the King's mental illness: each attack was heralded by colicky abdominal pain and followed by weakness of the limbs. These non-specific symptoms take on a new significance when linked with the colour of the King's urine. Examination of the urine was one of the few procedures carried out by nineteenth-century doctors. Very little else was available to help in diagnosis – indeed, since the patient was the King, the doctors were not allowed to speak until spoken to: consequently the doctors were somewhat hampered in elucidating the royal symptoms unless they were spontaneously offered up by the monarch! Whole visits were sometimes spent in silence: 'His Majesty appears to be very quiet this morning, but not having been addressed we know nothing more of His Majesty's condition of mind or body than what is obvious in his external appearances.'

But to return to the colour of the king's urine. This was frequently described as 'dark' or red. This finding, together with the physical symptoms which preceded the insanity, have prompted Richard Hunter and Ida Macalpine to posit a very different cause for George III's madness: porphyria. This rare disease, which is caused by a recessive gene, produces episodes during which the body is unable to metabolize porphyrin, a pigment present in red blood cells, and consequently this substance is excreted in the urine, giving a characteristic dark red colour. The porphyrin acts as a toxin upon the brain, precipitating symptoms of insanity. Tracking back George III's family tree, a number of his ancestors would appear to have had urine which aroused comment by dint of its colour: Mary Queen of Scots; and her son, King James I of England (King James VI of Scotland), who had urine likened to the colour of wine.[9] It has even been proposed that the death in childbirth of Princess Charlotte, George III's granddaughter, was due to an acute attack of porphyria. It is also postulated that the disease, introduced into the House of Brandenburg-Prussia by George I's sister, claimed the life of Frederick the Great. Much weight was given to Hunter and Macalpine's hypothesis when Hanoverian descendants alive today tested positive for porphyrins.[10]

Is George III's reputation rehabilitated by the knowledge that his insanity had a specific genetic cause? Maybe. But porphyria does not explain the loss of the American colonies *since the Stamp Act which sowed the seeds for revolt antedated the king's first attack of insanity by almost a quarter of a century!*

### *Nine million die through surgeon's error*

It was a fact, universally accepted, that Frederick III, who became Emperor of Germany on 9 March 1888, was a man of exceptional qualities: wise, brave, liberal and popular with his subjects. Had he lived as long as his father did before him, or his son after him, Germany would surely have entered a golden age. But it was not to be. On 15 June, just ninety-nine days after his accession, Frederick was dead, and most blamed the incompetence of his English doctor, Morell Mackenzie. Wilhelm II succeeded as Kaiser, his personality as different as it was possible to be from that of his father. Twenty-six years later, in 1914, this psychopath was to plunge the world into war.

Frederick was born in 1831 and married Queen Victoria's eldest daughter in 1858. It was in January 1887, when Frederick was fifty-five years old, and still Crown Prince, that he first complained of hoarseness. When the symptom persisted, Dr Gerhardt, Professor of Clinical Medicine at the University of Berlin, examined Frederick's larynx (voice box) and found a nodule on the left vocal cord. Gerhardt failed to snare or excise the nodule, and finally resorted to cautery. After thirteen unsuccessful attempts to burn away the lesion, Gerhardt began to consider that his royal patient was suffering from cancer, albeit at an early stage. When the hoarseness did not remit, Professor von Bergmann, surgeon at Berlin University, was called in to give a second opinion. He diagnosed cancer and advised surgery: splitting the larynx from the front of the neck and removing the tumour before it could spread to adjacent structures.

There was one major problem: neither Gerhardt nor von Bergmann were laryngologists, and they decided, no doubt for both medical reasons as well as political expediency, to call in an expert before submitting the future Emperor to an operation which would permanently take away his power of speech. Their choice fell upon Morell Mackenzie, an Englishman, who had written a classic text on diseases of the larynx, as well as founding both a London hospital for treating diseases of the throat and the *Journal of Laryngology*.

Before Mackenzie had the chance to examine the Crown Prince, Professor Tobold, a German laryngologist, looked into the royal throat and pronounced it cancerous. The operation was fixed for 21 May; Mackenzie arrived on the 20th. The Englishman examined Frederick, but would not agree that it was cancer until a small piece of the lesion had been looked at under a microscope. Mackenzie's advice was deemed sensible and a biopsy specimen was sent to Professor Rudolf Virchow of Berlin University, the most eminent authority of the day. Virchow could find no evidence of cancer. Mackenzie sent Virchow another specimen. Again, Virchow failed to find any cancer cells. Virchow's report concluded: 'There is nothing present which would be likely to arouse the suspicion of wider and graver disease.'

The tide of opinion turned against the operation, and, greatly relieved, the Crown Prince immediately set off for London to attend the celebrations for Queen Victoria's Jubilee, accompanied by Mackenzie. After the Jubilee, Mackenzie successfully cauterized a recurrence of the growth, and the Crown Prince's natural voice returned. In August 1887 the Queen knighted Mackenzie, and Frederick set out for the Italian Riviera to convalesce.

Within a day of his arrival in Italy an urgent telegram was sent to London summoning Mackenzie. After being examined, Frederick asked, 'Is it cancer?', to which Mackenzie replied, 'I am sorry to say, sir, that it looks very much like it,' but added the important rider, 'it is impossible to be certain.' Frederick's condition fluctuated greatly over the next three months, and in February 1888 it was necessary to perform a tracheostomy (whereby a tube is inserted into the larynx below the voice box) in order to assist breathing. Mackenzie had turned away from a diagnosis of cancer: 'In my opinion, the clinical symptoms have always been entirely compatible with non-malignant disease, *and the microscopic signs have been in harmony with this view.*'

On 9 March the Emperor died and the Crown Prince succeeded him as Frederick III. Ninety-nine days later, on 15 June, Frederick followed his father to the grave.

Bismarck, the German Chancellor, demanded a report. Mackenzie wrote, 'It is my opinion that the disease from which the Emperor Frederick III died was cancer ... Whether the disease was originally cancerous or assumed a malignant character some months after its first appearance, it is impossible to state.' A hurried post-mortem examination showed widespread destruction of the larynx.

Recriminations followed thick and fast. The opening salvo was fired by Gerhardt on behalf of the German doctors, in a pamphlet attacking Mackenzie's incompetence. Gerhardt even accused Mackenzie of deliberately taking the first biopsy specimen from the right, healthy, vocal cord. Mackenzie counter-attacked, pouring scorn and derision on his German colleagues, and stating, quite justifiably, that none of the biopsy specimens examined by Virchow contained evidence of cancer. Virchow, equally justifiably, stated that he had only reported on the tissues which he was sent, and was not responsible if the cancerous portions of the lesion were not included in the specimens. Mackenzie's rejoinder was considered intemperate by the British medical establishment, and he was censured by the Royal College of Surgeons. He died in 1892, aged fifty-four.

It has always fascinated the 'What if ...?' school of history to wonder what would have happened if Frederick had been operated upon when the growth was at an early stage. True, the future Emperor would have been unable to talk, but he would have been alive, and the 1914–18 war, started by his son, would never have taken the lives of millions. Was it incompetence on Mackenzie's part? Did he vacillate because his patient was a king and not a commoner?

We shall never know, but one intriguing hypothesis has recently been mooted: perhaps the original lesion was not due to cancer, but to syphilis; and perhaps Mackenzie suspected its syphilitic origin and remained silent in deference to the royal dignity of 'Frederick the Noble'?[11]

## 2 Leaders

Historians rarely pay much heed to medical matters: battles and wars are won by superior force, better tactics or good fortune, and the health or illnesses of the protagonists are usually regarded as an irrelevance. A cursory consideration of the First World War will show just how short-sighted and restricted is this outlook. Statesmen and senior ranks in the armed forces are usually elderly: with age comes maturity – but also impending senility. Growing up in the 1950s, I could never conceive that the men who governed the country could possibly make mistakes: they were just too wise and too well advised – otherwise how else would they be in positions of power and influence? Teenagers today, well aware of the shortcomings of the famous and powerful, would scoff at such naivety.

But let us go back to World War I. Historians are beginning to question the wisdom of decisions made by the likes of Sir Douglas Haig and Sir John French, which resulted in such great loss of life, and to consider the part played by illness, both physical and psychological.[12] Victory at the Marne was in no small measure due to the cardiac and renal infirmities of General von Moltke, the 66-year-old Commander of the German Army, who simply 'lost his nerve' and retreated. In the closing years of the war, General Erich Ludendorff decided that German victory would only come as a result of one last decisive battle on the Western Front. In March 1918, when all initially appeared to be going well, Ludendorff became suddenly overtly anxious, issuing orders and counter-orders, and, in a state of 'hysterical paralysis', desperately sought an armistice. After the war he built altars to Thor and Odin in his garden. In 1926 Ludendorff was diagnosed as having a toxic goitre, which adequately explains his restless energy, his nervous tension and his physical exhaustion. Ludendorff could claim with some justice that the outcome of the war could have been very different if he had had his thyroid gland surgically removed in 1914.[13]

## *George Washington*

Illness can severely compromise the judgement and actions of soldiers and statesmen: George Washington was both. Yet he died in retirement in his sixty-eighth year, barely forty-eight hours after contracting a sore throat.

At the age of nineteen, Washington caught smallpox, which left his face permanently scarred. He was also a martyr to malaria. After America's victory in the War of Independence – a victory due, in no small part, to Cornwallis's surrender to Washington at Yorktown – it was natural that the American people would look to Washington to be their first president. He was elected unanimously. He took to his new office with alacrity – too much so in the belief of many, for he seemed to ape the King of England, driving about in a coach-and-four, with outriders in livery, and his wife being addressed as 'Lady Washington'. Somewhat reluctantly, Washington accepted a second term of office, but when the time came, he adamantly refused a third term, deciding instead to retire to his Mount Vernon home in March 1797 and devote himself to managing his estates.

His retirement was not destined to be a long one. On 12 December 1799, Washington returned home wet and chilled after a day in the saddle. The next evening he suffered a rigor and had the greatest difficulty in breathing and speaking. His symptoms were not relieved by bleeding, so a cloth soaked in sal volatile was wrapped around his throat, and his feet were bathed in hot water. Dr Craik diagnosed quinsy, applied a blister to the throat, and bled the patient a second time. Craik was joined by two other doctors, Elisha Cullen Dick and Gustavus Richard Brown. Dick wished to ease Washington's breathing by performing a tracheostomy, but he was overruled. Dick could see little point in further blood letting, saying that Washington needed 'all his strength; bleeding will diminish it' – but again he was overruled. Washington, always a realist, checked his will and addressed his doctors: 'I feel myself going. I thank you for your attention. You had better not take any more trouble about me, but let me go off quietly. I cannot last long.' On the evening of the 14th, Washington lapsed into unconsciousness.

What was the nature of this quinsy (an abscess close to the tonsil) which carried off the most eminent American of his day? Some have mooted diphtheria but this is an unlikely diagnosis in a man of Washington's age. It is likely that it was a streptococcal infection, from the same family of bacteria which causes scarlet fever.

## *President Grover Cleveland*

Grover Cleveland (1837–1908), destined to become President of the United States, was born in New Jersey. When he was sixteen years old, his father died following acute appendicitis, and Cleveland was forced to find a job as a teacher in the New York State Institution for the Blind. He later moved to Buffalo, studied assiduously, and was admitted to the New York bar at the age of twenty-two. When the Civil War broke out Cleveland just as assiduously avoided enlisting: in 1863, when the Conscription Act was passed, he hired a Polish sailor to enlist in his place. In the same year Cleveland was appointed district attorney in Buffalo, later becoming Governor of New York, and finally contested the Presidency as a Democrat in 1884, which he won despite publicly admitting that he had contributed financially to the support of a child, the son of an attractive widow, ten years earlier.

Cleveland failed to get re-elected in 1888, but, after a brief return to the practice of law, he was successful in the presidential campaign of 1892. He was immediately plunged into an economic crisis which threatened calamity: Grover Cleveland was widely regarded as the only man with strength and determination enough to see the country through such a dire crisis. It was at that precise time that the President was diagnosed as suffering from cancer.

In June 1893, Dr R. O'Reilly took a biopsy specimen from the back of Cleveland's throat. It was a tumour the size of a quarter and had already spread to invade the bone of the upper jaw. Dr Joseph Bryant, an eminent surgeon, was consulted, and stated unequivocally that were the growth in *his* mouth, he would have it removed at once. Cleveland agreed to an operation, but insisted, in view of the parlous state of the economy, on absolute secrecy. On the evening of 30 June, the President boarded the yacht *Oneida* at Pier A in New York harbour, to meet in secret with his retinue of eminent surgeons and dentists. The next morning the yacht steamed slowly up the East River. The saloon was turned into an operating theatre and the President anaesthetized. Dr Hasbrouk, the dentist, extracted two molar teeth, after which Dr Bryant excised the growth. In just over thirty minutes the operation was over: Bryant had removed most of the left upper jaw but had left the orbit, the bony cavity containing the eye, intact. All the work had been performed from inside the mouth, so there were no external tell-tale facial scars.

Four days later, when the *Oneida* dropped anchor in Buzzards Bay, Cape Cod, Cleveland felt well enough to disembark and walk to Gay Gables, his summer home. Although people who came into close

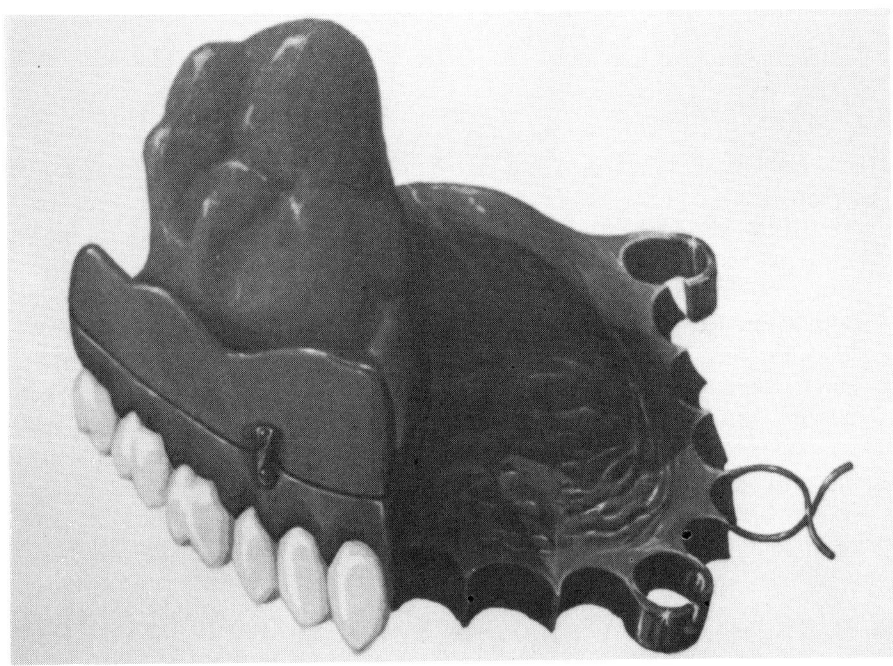

A prosthetic jaw and teeth used to restore facial contour after surgery to remove a cancerous growth. Such a prosthesis was fashioned for President Cleveland

contact with the President were aware of something wrong with his mouth, no one appreciated the seriousness of the operation which Cleveland had survived. By 1 September the President was deemed well enough to resume his normal duties, having been fitted with a prosthetic jaw of vulcanized rubber which made his features and voice normal.

The secret of the President's operation was kept for nearly two months. The news was finally broken in the *Philadelphia Press* to an incredulous public. It was widely assumed that the leak sprang from Dr Hasbrouk, but the identity of the informant is largely academic: the important thing was that secrecy had been maintained when it mattered most.[14]

## *Woodrow Wilson*

Wilson (1856–1924) was born in Virginia in 1856, went to college in North Carolina and then graduated from Princeton in 1879. In the same year he entered law school, qualifying three years later. From then on Wilson was regarded as a political scientist of the first rank, being elected President of Princeton in 1902.

On a May morning in 1906 Wilson woke to find that he was unable to see out of his left eye. He was diagnosed as suffering from 'hardening of the arteries', although still only fifty years old. Despite the fact that his eyesight never fully recovered and that he was left with some residual problems in his limbs, Wilson continued hard at work. In 1910 he was approached to run for Governor of New Jersey and won handsomely for the Democrats. He became the natural choice for the presidential candidacy in 1912. When elected he told his cabinet, 'While I am not ill, my health is not exceptionally good, and I have signed a protocol of peace with my doctor. I must be good.'

Although his work load continued to tax his health, he felt fit enough to fight for a second term. Shortly after his second inauguration in 1917, Wilson was ordered to bed by his doctor. With the entry of America into World War I, his weariness increased and he began to appear visibly gaunt, and rely more and more on his second wife, Edith. With victory in war came physical exhaustion, exacerbated by worry and insomnia. Problems to do with the peace conference and the establishment of a League of Nations bore down upon him, until, quite suddenly in Paris on 3 April 1919, he became seriously ill with a high fever. It can be reasonably assumed that Wilson had suffered another stroke, which made him act in a most peculiar manner: among other things, he became convinced that every Frenchman was a spy. Physically he appeared to make a remarkable recovery, but the change in his personality persisted. Before long, his health declined again, and he appeared on the verge of mental and physical collapse.

On 2 October, Wilson suffered another stroke, which left him paralysed down the left side and semiconscious. For two weeks it was touch and go: one of his doctors declared that he might live five minutes, five months or five years. All this was withheld from the American public who, in the absence of medical fact, were left to medical conjecture. For all practical purposes, Mrs Wilson became the President of the United States: she took over the reins of government, ably assisted by Dr Grayson, and for eighteen months America had little more than a sick, part-time President. Although Wilson's paralysis improved a little, his emotional lability and depression continued. He even became delusional at times.

In April 1920, Wilson met with his cabinet for the first time in six months. Each was announced as he entered the room so that Wilson would be spared the embarrassment of not recognizing him. As one cabinet member observed, 'It was enough to make one weep to look at him. One of his arms was useless ... His voice was weak and strained ... The President seemed at first to have some difficulty in fixing his mind on what we were discussing ... Finally Mrs Wilson came in, looking rather disturbed, and suggested we had better go.'

In the vital last months of his Presidency, when important issues concerning the peace treaty were being hammered out, Wilson was a lame duck. The Senate rejected the Treaty of Versailles. Despite this, Wilson's egocentricity made him seek the Democratic nomination for a *third* time in 1920. When he failed, he is reported to have 'unleashed a tornado of masterful profanity', an indication that his power of speech was not totally lost.

### *Franklin Roosevelt*

Roosevelt (1884–1945) gained the White House by the sheer force of his personality. In 1921, he was struck down with poliomyelitis (infantile paralysis) and never walked normally again. But he refused to be cowed by this cruel disease and became all the more determined to succeed to the very highest office. Some say, perhaps fancifully, that America elected Roosevelt its 32nd President, in 1932, in order that a crippled president should lead a crippled country back to renewed health.

Before his illness, Roosevelt struck a fine athletic figure, enjoying sport and all forms of physical exertion. Although a member of a vastly wealthy family, Roosevelt elected to enter politics as a Democrat. He was elected to the New York Senate in 1910.

He contracted poliomyelitis whilst on holiday on Campobello Island in August 1921. After a spurt of violent exercise and an ice-cold swim, Roosevelt developed a fever, followed by pains and loss of movement in the legs. William Keen, a celebrated octogenarian physician, who happened to be on holiday in the area, was called in. He misdiagnosed thrombosis (clot) of the spinal cord. Eight days later he proferred his bill for $600, and added that it might be an inflammation rather than a thrombosis. (Keen, when at the height of his powers, had formed part of the surgical team who operated to remove President Cleveland's tumour.) The first mention of poliomyelitis was by Dr Robert Lovett almost two weeks after the fateful swim. Roosevelt refused to give in to his paralysis: he rejected his mother's advice to live out the life of a country gentleman, preferring instead to heed his wife Eleanor and her entreaties for him to return to public life as soon as possible.

In 1924, Roosevelt accepted the Democratic nomination for the governorship of New York as a stepping-stone to the presidency. As 1932 approached, and with it the election for President, Roosevelt was forced to parry suggestions that his paralysis was due to syphilis or due to an inflammation of the brain. He won the election in 1932 – and the next in 1936. But the strain of this second term began to take its toll. One aide observed in 1937, 'He looks all of fifteen years older since he was inaugurated.' In 1940 Roosevelt embarked upon his controversial third term during which time America entered the Second World War. Roosevelt travelled widely in his efforts to defeat the axis powers, growing daily more hypertensive. By the time he started his fourth term in January 1945, his health had become a cause of great concern. By March 1945, Roosevelt's systolic blood pressure was almost twice normal levels. The President suffered his fatal seizure on 12 April 1945.

All great men should have autopsies if only to stifle diagnostic speculation or accusations of medical malpractice. Some contend that Roosevelt *did* have an autopsy, but that the findings were not disclosed for fear of embarrassment that a misdiagnosis had been made of a potentially curable condition. One physician had noted that prior to 1943, Roosevelt had a pigmented naevus over his left eyebrow. When, at a later time, the physician saw that the naevus was no longer present, he concluded, reasonably, that it had been surgically removed. Perhaps it had been a malignant melanoma, a virulent form of skin cancer which spreads rapidly to other organs in the body? In 1949 surgeons from Walter Reed Hospital, Washington DC, presented a scientific paper on the treatment of malignant melanoma. All the slides and specimens they showed, except one, had a serial number. The exception was a slide of cancerous brain which bore the date 14 April 1945, the day Roosevelt's body arrived in Washington from Warm Springs.

Critics blame Roosevelt for accepting the fourth term, accusing him of being manifestly unfit to hold office. His doctors were bound to secrecy by the Hippocratic Oath not to reveal the extent of his poor health; his colleagues kept their own counsel for motives of self-serving ambition. Political opponents pointed to his cadaveric appearance, the head that was too heavy for his shoulders, the deathly pallor, trembling hands, dulled eyes and the blue, blue lips. Could such a man seriously be thought capable of leading his country? Did his illness make him agree commitments to Stalin at Yalta which would not have been conceded by a healthy man? 'The ills of the post-war world have been laid at Roosevelt's grave.' His poor judgement can be gauged by his remark he made about Stalin: 'I think that if I give him everything I possibly can and ask for nothing from him in return, *noblesse oblige*, he won't try to annex anything and will work with me for a world of democracy and peace.'

Wilson and Roosevelt were sick men whose ill-health compromised their performance at vital times in the history of America and the world. One has to balance political maturity with potential invalidity of mind and body. The incompetence of sick men in high office can often be successfully camouflaged in times of peace; in times of war, when alertness and the ability to make quick decisions are imperatives, illness rarely goes unnoticed or forgiven. As Zola said about the bladder stones of Napoleon III, 'A grain of sand in a man's flesh, and empires totter and fall.'

## *Three post-war presidents*

The association between stress and coronary heart disease has been known for centuries. John Hunter, the famous Scottish surgeon, used to lament 'My life is at the mercy of any rascal who cares to take it.' Hunter died of a heart attack following a row with a surgical colleague at St George's Hospital, London. Given the link, it is hardly surprising to see that deaths from heart attacks are correlated with high stress jobs. And none come more highly stressed than the presidency of the United States.[15]

President Eisenhower suffered his chest pains following a frustrating day on the golf course on 24 September 1955. He had given up cigarettes six years before but was still partial to hamburgers and raw onions. Eisenhower returned to his presidential duties after only two months away. It was a quiet time with few decisions of moment to be taken: happily the Soviet Union did not take the opportunity to launch a nuclear attack on America! Eisenhower began to show signs of depression and commented, 'My future life must be carefully regulated to avoid excessive fatigue.' Even had he wanted to forego a second term in office, the Republican party, bereft of an alternative candidate, would have inevitably drafted in the old war horse for a further turn of duty. But Eisenhower's heart was not the only organ causing concern: in June 1956 the President suffered a relapse of his regional ileitis for which he had to have abdominal surgery. He made an uneventful recovery.

The next time Eisenhower fell ill was a much more serious affair. On 25 November 1957 he felt giddy. He dropped his pen and was unable to pick it up again. Worse, he found it difficult to talk. His doctors were guilty of minimizing the seriousness of his symptoms and of reassuring him of a quick and uneventful recovery. The doctors called it an arterial spasm affecting the blood supply to the brain, an inexcusable euphemism for a stroke. It was fortunate that Eisenhower was able to be back to his presidential duties within weeks. Eisenhower managed to live out his second term and experienced profound disappointment at Nixon's defeat by Kennedy in 1960. Doubtless, if the constitution had allowed it, this ailing general would have fought to serve his country for a third time, with all the grave risks entailed when an ill man dons the mantle of the world's most powerful office.

## *Crisis in Camelot*

The leadership of the free world passed from Eisenhower to John F. Kennedy: young, handsome and seemingly healthy. He won the Democratic nomination against Lyndon Johnson, in part because the latter had had a well publicized coronary heart attack back in 1955.

The Kennedys, the closest America has come to a royal family, are an object lesson about how riches can assure neither happiness nor health. Even when he occupied the White House, rumours were rife that President Kennedy suffered from Addison's disease, a condition in which the adrenal glands fail to secrete sufficient steroids. Kennedy and his doctors remained tight-lipped, apparently believing that the health of the most powerful man in the world was his own affair. Eisenhower was always prepared to be frank and open about his medical problems. Not so Kennedy, who was inclined to make political capital by recounting that his back problems were caused by a football injury at Harvard and exacerbated by being rammed by a Japanese destroyer in the Second World War. His back pain was helped by a corset and frequent injections of local anaesthetic. But there were a number of clues which pointed to the added diagnosis of Addison's – for those who had eyes to see.

In a medical paper written in 1955 on the effect of adrenal disease in surgical operations, Dr Nicholas reported on three patients. The third case cited was a man of thirty-seven, who was stated to suffer from Addison's disease but to be well-controlled with replacement steroids, and who underwent an operation on 21 October 1954 at Cornhill Medical College to correct an old wartime injury to his lower spine. Despite Addison's disease, the operation on this patient was uneventful, and he returned four months later to have the metal plate removed from his back. Such was the extent of the information given by Nicholas.

In the *New York Times*, dated 21 October 1954, the following news item appeared: 'Senator John F. Kennedy, Democrat of Massachusetts, is scheduled to undergo surgery today'. It went on to detail the wartime spinal injury. In February 1955, the same paper reported that Kennedy had entered hospital for the removal of the metal plate.

Now it is most improbable that two men, both thirty-seven, would enter the same hospital for the same operation on the same day, and then both return at exactly the same time, four months later, to have their metal plates removed. The likelihood is that Nicholas's third patient was the future President and that Kennedy *did* suffer from Addison's disease. None of the late President's doctors have ever challenged the mathematics of two and two making four. It is quite likely that Kennedy's Addison's disease was well-controlled and had no adverse effect on his performance as President. White House observers, having read up the literature on Addison's disease, and aware that replacement steroids were required to compensate for any shortfall, became 'experts' in assessing any signs of overdose by carefully checking for any evidence of facial puffiness. But if steroids are given in excess of need, a puffy face is the least of their problems: patients can also suffer from a variety of physical and mental symptoms, including a degree of euphoria which can cause an inappropriate friendliness and an unrealistic optimism which might not sit well with world leadership. Perhaps such optimism coloured his judgment about the Bay of Pigs, the Cuban Missile Crisis, or played a part in his ignoring the advice of those who told him that Dallas was not a safe place to visit.

It was Kennedy's assassination in November 1963 that brought Lyndon Johnson to the Oval Office eight years after his heart attack. Good sense made Johnson limit himself to the single term.[16]

## *Winston Churchill*

Winston Churchill (1874–1965) believed, erroneously, that he was destined to live only as long as his father: forty-six years. Consequently he resolved to live at a frenetic pace, ever striving, ever achieving.

Churchill had far exceeded his father's span when he became Prime Minister in 1940 at the age of sixty-five. Worries about Churchill's health led to the appointment of Lord Moran as his personal physician.[17] Between 1943 and 1945 Churchill suffered recurrent bouts of pneumonia, all of which responded to treatment with sulphonamides. But, inexorably, Churchill's grasp on important issues began to be compromised. Alanbrooke, the Chief of the Imperial General Staff, and no doctor, was nonetheless able to read the signs of Churchill's deteriorating health. In March 1944, Alanbrooke observed, 'He seems quite incapable of concentrating for a few minutes on end, and keeps wandering continuously.' The Polish Ambassador recorded in May 1944, 'Perhaps, however, he has his own reasons for repeating certain things to us over and over again.' Churchill won the war, but not the general election of July 1945. The socialist government of Clement Atlee shifted Churchill and concerns about his health off centre-stage.

Churchill suffered his first stroke whilst playing gin rummy in August 1949. The weakness in his right hand quickly recovered, and the public was told that he had suffered a chill. There was little panic since the great man no longer held high office, though he was still leader of the opposition. How different was the situation at the time of his second ischaemic attack in February 1952. Churchill had again become Prime Minister: before his Cabinet colleagues he was seen rambling, incoherent and palpably confused. A plan by Moran to persuade Churchill to retire and accept membership of the House of Lords failed miserably.

In June 1953 Churchill suffered another stroke whilst attending a dinner for the Italian Prime Minister. Because he could neither speak nor move, the uninitiated believed him to be drunk.[18] Churchill recovered somewhat, but never completely. By the time of the Conservative Party Conference in 1954, Churchill's speech was peppered with mistakes and mispronunciations. He made publicly embarrassing *faux pas*. For one error he had to apologize in the House of Commons. By the time he relinquished the office in April 1955 he was spending most of his days in bed. It is a matter of grave concern that Churchill hung on to office after his stroke in February 1952. His continuance in office after his stroke in June 1953 is a sad reflection of man's conceit.

## *Anthony Eden*

Churchill was succeeded as Prime Minister by Anthony Eden (1897–1977) in April 1955: some say that an obvious invalid was replaced by a clandestine one. Eden never had Churchill's force of character. Physically he always appeared frail where Churchill was robust. In June 1952 Eden, who was Foreign Secretary and Deputy Prime Minister, became jaundiced, probably as a result of gall stones and an inflamed gall bladder. An operation to remove his gall bladder was performed in April 1953 but was not entirely successful. A second and then a third operation were carried out (in America) over the next two months, but Eden's biliary problems were never satisfactorily resolved. He remained vulnerable to intermittent bouts of biliary fever, which sapped his energy and compromised his performance. As Eden was to say himself: '[the] fever attacks are so weakening that nobody could suffer from them and do a good day's work'. Ill-health added to Eden's propensity to be excitable and temperamental. In November 1966, as the Suez crisis was reaching its crescendo, Eden was described as 'sprawled on the front bench [of the House of Commons], head thrown back and mouth agape. The face was grey except when black-ringed caverns surrounded the dying embers of his eyes.'

Eden's problems in coping with the crisis, which was engulfing him, were compounded by the side-effects of the benzedrine he was taking to keep himself awake. His mood lurched from excitement and euphoria to querulousness and depression. It was against this medical background that Eden committed Great Britain, ill-prepared and largely unsupported by world opinion, to invade Egypt and take control of the Suez Canal. The Anglo-French invasion was a fiasco, and Eden was forced by world opinion to order a cease fire, on 6 November 1956, only days into the war. Earlier, Eden had burst into tears when rung up by an angry Eisenhower. Humiliated, the country cried out for blood, and Eden decided to step down in January 1957.

### *Two twentieth-century dictators*

Benito Mussolini contracted syphilis when he was twenty-two years old in 1905, the same year that it became possible to visualize the spirochaete under the microscope, and one year before Wassermann's

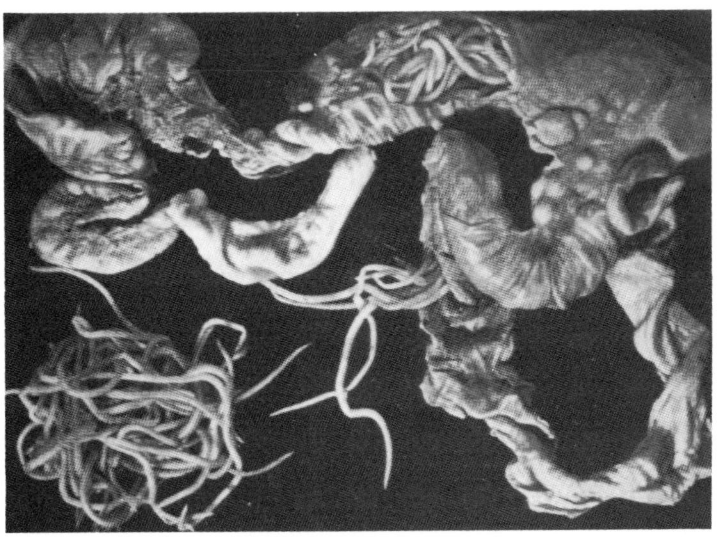

Mass of ascarids in small intestine

diagnostic blood test. In 1939 people began to suspect that Mussolini might be suffering from syphilis of the nervous system. This tentative diagnosis was made on his failing comprehension of English and his generally perceived intellectual decline. Yet two blood samples, tested in England and Germany (the latter in 1943), were negative. But El Duce did suffer from worms! In 1942 Mussolini passed the largest round worm his physician had ever seen: 'a real hypertrophic Fascist ascarid'.

It was virtually inevitable that Adolf Hitler be thought of as a syphilitic. But we must not rush to assume the diagnosis is not without some foundation: Himmler had a dossier which revealed that Hitler contracted syphilis in his youth. Further, Hitler's personal physician, Professor Morell, was physician-in-chief of a venereology clinic in Berlin, but a physician first and foremost. It has been suggested by others that Hitler suffered from Parkinson's disease following Encephalitis Lethargica contracted in the First World War: this condition would adequately explain the tremor in his left arm and leg, his shuffling gait and his stooped stance. Further, the 'oculo-gyric crises' which so often accompany Parkinson's disease would fit well the description, 'His dull blue eyes had a hard, strange look, and during the short greetings they suddenly turned upwards'. Large doses of belladonna, prescribed for Parkinsonian muscular rigidity, could explain Hitler's intermittent confusion, excitement and hallucinations.

# 9 THE MEDICAL DETECTIVE

Some of the most spectacular advances in medicine have come about by accident, a doctor being in the right place at the right time and having the insight to appreciate its significance: Sir Alexander Fleming's discovery of penicillin was just such an example of serendipity. Nowadays the vast majority of medical discoveries are made by teams of doctors and scientists formulating hypotheses and collecting information over long, painstaking years of research. This chapter looks at examples of medical detective work, ancient and modern, where the origin of a disease was elucidated by accurate observation coupled with deductive logic – and, not unusually, a large dollop of good luck.

Mercifully, St Anthony's Fire no longer afflicts mankind. In the Middle Ages this mutilating disease occurred in epidemic proportions, usually in autumn, especially following damp and foggy summers. Sufferers would begin to vomit and complain of burning abdominal pains. Diarrhoea would follow with severe pains in the muscles, convulsions and coma. But the most frightening manifestation was the progressive blackening of the limbs: starting in the fingers and toes – which became cold and intensely painful – gangrene would spread centrally towards the body, causing the limbs to shrivel and fall off. Many who survived were left without arms and legs. Prayers of appeasement were to no avail, and the good suffered along with the bad. The very sight of someone suffering from the disease was enough to induce terror: the only succour was provided by the monks of St Anthony.

It was sometime towards the end of the sixteenth century that men recognized the association between the disease and the weather. Wet summers caused the grain harvest to be blighted with a fungus. The fungus, now known as *Claviceps purpurea*, contained a chemical called ergot which constricts the blood vessels, cutting off the supply to the extremities, and causing gangrene.[1] To prevent St Anthony's Fire, one had only to avoid eating bread made with blighted rye! The discoverer of this simple expedient to avert human misery must forever remain an unsung hero, or heroine.

## *The Devonshire colic*

The name of the individual who saved generations of sufferers from the ravages of St Anthony's fire may not be known to us, but we do know the names of those men we have to thank for finally solving the riddle of the Devonshire colic.

The Devonshire colic was known to the ancient Greeks, though not, of course, by that name. Epidemic abdominal pains followed by paralysis was described by Nikander, a Greek physician and poet, living in the second century BC.

> foam runs from his lip
> A feeble cough tries, it in vain to expel
> He belches so much and his belly does swell
> ...
> Meanwhile there comes a stuporous chill
> His feeble limbs droop and all motion is still,
> His strength is now spent and unless one soon aids
> The sick man descends to the Stygian shades.

Another Greek physician, Paul of Aegina (629–90), describes an epidemic in which many had convulsions, and many died.

The connection with Devon was made by John Huxham in his description of a disease which occurred in that county in the autumn of 1724.

> An enormous Vomiting soon followed, for the most Part of exceeding green Bile, sometimes black with a greater quantity of Phlegm ... The Belly became extremely bound, neither answering to the most drastic Purges or sharpest Clysters, the latter coming off without Wind or Stool, the former being soon vomited. But the tragedy was not yet over ... a most excruciating Pain now seized the whole spine of the Back, soon affecting the arms, and altogether destroyed the Motions of the Hands ... Some totally lost the Use of their Hands.

Huxham then adds two very significant observations: 'Sometimes the tormenting Pains would cease for a few Days, and then return with equal Vehemence, especially on taking the least Cold, or drinking Beer, or Cyder' and, 'Children were not so severely tormented by it as the Adult.'

The next piece in the jigsaw was provided by Théodore Tronchin (1709–81), physician and friend to Voltaire, Rousseau and Diderot. In 1757 he published a paper about the effects of poisons on the body, including lead. Tronchin drew attention to the extreme colic and paralysis that often followed treatments for arthritis and gonorrhoea which contained Sugar of Lead. He also found these same symptoms commonly afflicted those working with leaden glass. Additional evidence adduced to implicate lead included the occurrence of symptoms after people drank water stored in leaden cisterns, or Rhinish or Moselle wine which had been adulterated by sugar of lead to increase the sparkle and alter the flavour.

Huxham had linked Devonshire colic to cider; Tronchin had drawn attention to the symptoms of lead poisoning; it fell to Sir George Baker (1722–1809) to *prove* that the lead in cider was the cause of Devonshire colic. George Baker, a native of Devon, was educated at Eton and Cambridge, and became a royal physician and President of the Royal College of Physicians. His elegant series of experiments were to put the link between lead and colic beyond doubt, though he was vilified as a 'traitor' by the farmers and brewers of Devon!

Baker set about putting theory to the rigours of experimental verification. He decided that common things were common, and that the key to the mystery of the colic was likely to be 'immediate and obvious' and not 'remote and obscure'. Baker was alerted to the effects of lead by Dr Wall of Worcester who wrote, 'The counties of Hereford, Gloucester and Worcester, are not, as far as I know, subject to the colic ... there is no lead used in any part of the apparatus for grinding or pressing the apples, or fermenting the liquor. I knew a farmer, who, wanting casks, filled a large leaden cistern with new cyder, and kept it there, till he could procure hogsheads sufficient to contain the liquor. The consequence was, that all who drank of it, were affected by it as lead workers usually are. We had eleven of them, at one time, in our infirmary.'

Now Baker knew that the farmers of Devon used lead-lined presses. He first tested cider from Exeter and found it to contain lead. Cider from Hereford tested negative. Devonshire farmers were incensed – until they removed the lead from their presses and were never again troubled by Devonshire colic.[2]

In the later twentieth century lead remains a cause for concern. Although its use in the making of paint has been proscribed, it is still emitted from the exhausts of cars, producing, some believe, subtle but long-lasting effects upon the brains of children.

## *Diabetes, 'the pissing evil'*

The history of diabetes well illustrates the slow accumulation of knowledge about a disease. It is a disease of great antiquity: in the Ebers papyrus (approximately 1500 BC), Egyptian physicians give a prescription to 'drive away the passing of too much urine'.

Voiding large amounts of urine (polyuria) and the attendant thirst are the two most striking symptoms of diabetes, the name being derived from the Greek word for 'a syphon'. Aretaeus the Cappadocian, in the second century, described the 'melting of the flesh and limbs into urine'. He goes on, 'Moreover, life is disgusting and painful; thirst unquenchable; excessive drinking which, however, is disproportionate to the large quantity of urine, for more urine is passed; and one cannot stop them from either drinking or making water.' Somewhat surprisingly, it was not until the seventeenth century that it was first recorded that the urine of diabetics tasted sweet. This 'discovery' was made by an English physician, Thomas Willis (1621–75), and has led to the name *diabetes mellitus* to distinguish its taste from the other disease characterized by polyuria, *diabetes insipidus*. Willis succinctly depicts diabetes as the disease in which patients 'piss a great deal more than they drink', and goes on to observe that the urine 'is so wonderfully sweet, or hath an honied taste'. It was another Englishman, Matthew Dobson, who, in 1776 correctly identified the sweet taste as that of sugar. Dobson described in great detail his diabetic patient Peter Dickonson, thirty-three years-old, who was admitted to the public hospital in Liverpool in 1772. He passed twenty-eight pints of urine in twenty-four hours, his body becoming, 'wasted, dry and hard'. Dobson collected Dickonson's urine and evaporated it over a flame, producing a 'white cake', which was found to smell and taste of sugar.

It was more than a hundred years later that the next great step was taken in the elucidation of diabetes. In 1889, Minkowski and von Mering removed the pancreas of a dog to settle an argument as to whether the animal would survive. Their surprise discovery, repeated in experiments on other dogs, was that 'after complete removal of the organ [the pancreas], the dogs became diabetic'. Large quantities of glucose appeared in the urine and the blood. Most of the dogs died within a week of operation. The implication was clear: the pancreas was essential to life and had a profound effect on the metabolism of sugar. In 1900, Eugene Opie, an American working at Johns Hopkins Hospital in Baltimore, noted that when autopsy slides were made of pancreatic tissue taken from a seventeen-year-old girl who had died of diabetes, specific areas, known as the islets of Langerhans, had degenerated. Could these areas be responsible, in healthy individuals, for producing a substance which prevented diabetes?

The answer to this question was provided by the Canadians, Frederick Banting and Charles Best. Their experiment was simplicity itself: make an extract of dogs' pancreases and inject it into one which is diabetic – if the levels of sugar in the diabetic animal's urine and blood decreases, then it is a reasonable assumption that something in the extract is essential to the normal metabolism of glucose. Banting and Best's theory was proved to be correct, and the essential constituent – now known as insulin – was shown to be secreted by the islets of Langerhans in the pancreases of normal animals and humans. It was now just a matter of time before insulin from animals was used to save the lives of human diabetics. The Nobel Prize for Medicine in 1923 was shared between Banting and Macleod (the professor who ran the laboratory in which Banting worked). Poor Best, a second-year medical student, got profound thanks and was doubtless able to include his achievement in his curriculum vitae. Banting, who was knighted in 1934, died in a flying accident in 1944.[3]

## *Kuru*

A medical quiz once asked the connection between a human disease of New Guinea and a cattle disease in England: the answer was kuru, the grotesquely-named 'laughing' disease.

Although an island, New Guinea is large enough for Indian tribes to live remote from the white man and his so-called civilization. The Fore Indians, a veritable throwback to the Stone Age, were only discovered in 1936. They were short, suspicious and aggressive towards strangers.

In 1949, as is the custom of the white man, Papua New Guinea was given over to be ruled by Australians, who set about exploring and exploiting the interior. A patrol office was established at Okapa, deep in Fore territory, and an Australian named J. R. MacArthur was put in charge. In 1953, MacArthur recorded in his diary that he had seen a small girl sitting at a fire, her head jerking from side to side, her face twisted into involuntary spasms (the origin of the name 'laughing' disease). He was told that she was the victim of sorcery and would soon die. He subsequently found many more cases – usually women and children – who shivered, shook, became paralysed and died. They were victims of kuru.

It would have been reasonable for MacArthur to accept that kuru was a form of hysteria in susceptible females, and yet, on closer observation, early physical signs might be detected: a clumsiness perhaps or an unsteadiness when walking. The natives frequently denied or minimized the presence of kuru, since the disease meant certain death in a very public and undignified way. Counter-spells by friends and relatives never worked, and this was taken to signify that the enemy's magic was stronger. *Tukabo*, the ritual killing of a putative sorcerer, also failed to lift the spell. When males contracted the disease they usually opted to die of starvation than to die of shame. Many chose suicide rather than contemplate mute paralysis and incontinence.

In 1955, another Australian, Dr Vincent Zigas, slowly came to the conclusion that kuru was a physical illness, and not a psychological or hysterical one. He gathered together a group of sufferers and flew them to Melbourne, submitting them to every possible test he could think of. To no avail: all the tests came back negative. In 1957, Zigas was joined by D. Carleton Gajdusek, a Harvard research scientist who had become intrigued with kuru and was determined to solve its mysteries. Gajdusek had decided that kuru was a degenerative disease of the central nervous system and he set about finding the causative agent: gene, toxin or germ. After studying hundreds of cases in great detail it became clear to Zigas and Gajdusek that people could not catch the disease by being in the company of kuru victims: they concluded that kuru was not contagious.

It was logical to think of a poison producing such symptoms, but extensive analysis of food, soil and blood, failed to identify anything. Besides which, when natives moved out of the area, the susceptibility to kuru went with them, even when they changed their diet completely. In desperation the doctors plied the Indians with antibiotics, vitamins, steroids – but nothing they did altered the downhill course of the disease. Next Gajdusek tried a sociological approach and asked the Fore Indians about the changes in kuru over time. To his great surprise and disbelief, he was told that kuru was a relatively recent disease and that it had only become a serious problem within living memory. Old men could remember times when there was no kuru. Gajdusek's next surprise was to find that kuru was geographically contained within an area roughly thirty-five by twenty-five miles. Neighbouring tribes who intermarried with the Fore suffered from kuru; other tribes who had little or nothing to do with the Fore appeared immune. Further, *no white man had ever contracted kuru*.

It was natural on the available evidence that a genetic cause would be implicated. Since females had a much greater susceptibility and mortality, and because the surviving men were moving further afield to look for new wives, the Australian government passed a law prohibiting free movement of Fore males, for fear that, by some genetic mechanism, they would spread kuru throughout New Guinea. A fact that did not fit in with a genetic explanation was the appearance of the disease in a woman who had married into the Fore and subsequently developed kuru: genetics would explain the children contracting kuru, but not the mother! Perhaps the genetic causation was a false trail after all.

In 1959, W.J. Hadlow, a veterinary surgeon, wrote a letter to *The*

*Lancet* remarking on the similarity between kuru and scrapie, a disease of sheep. The interesting thing about scrapie was that it could be brought about in a sheep which had been injected with a suspension of brain tissue from a diseased animal. The problem was that the second sheep might take up to two or three years to show signs of disease. Gajdusek felt he had little choice but to test the new hypothesis with respect to kuru. In 1962, he obtained brain tissue from kuru victims after death and injected it into chimpanzees. He then settled down to a very long wait. After three years his patience was rewarded when the animals began to develop the symptoms of kuru. It was now clear that the disease was caused by a virus with an incredibly long incubation period.

But why only the Fore? And why predominantly women and children? The answers were provided by two anthropologists, Robert and Shirley Glasse. Indeed, kuru was a recent disease, which started just fifty years before in Uwami, and whose subsequent progress *mirrored the spread of cannibalism*. The Fore had become cannibals around 1915, and protocol laid down that the dead body had to putrefy before being baked. By custom, the men did not partake of the feast, leaving the meal for the women and children to enjoy. It was they who tucked into brain teeming with kuru virus.

There was a bonus for Gajdusek. Besides injecting the mashed brains of kuru victims into chimpanzees, he also injected brains obtained from people who had died from Jacob-Creutzfeld disease, a rare disorder which causes premature senility. These chimpanzees also fell ill, demonstrating that a second slow virus was at work. Gajdusek conjectured that perhaps a Fore victim of Jacob-Creutzfeld disease had been eaten, and the virus had subsequently become altered into one able to cause kuru. Gajdusek got the Nobel Prize in 1976, and kuru has been consigned to the history books.[4]

But brain disease caused by viruses with long incubation periods (perhaps years, even decades) continues to cause concern. Anxieties about Mad Cow Disease centre on the possible transfer of a viral disease from cows to humans.

Recently another aspect of virally induced brain disease surfaced. In the early 1980s Human Growth Hormone, given to correct short stature in children, was made from the pooled pituitary gland extracts of human corpses. Could some of these posthumous donors have suffered from Jacob-Creutzfeld disease and be responsible for the spread of a brain disease with a long incubation period? Despite government reassurances, only time will tell.

## *Huntington's chorea*

Huntington's chorea represents Fate at its most capricious and vindictive. The disease runs in families but does not manifest itself until the person reaches his thirties or forties, when there is an insidious worsening of the two principal symptoms: dementia and chorea. The dementia causes a rapid decline in mental powers, whilst the chorea produces involuntary movements of the body, especially the limbs, head and face. There is an inexorable decline to helplessness and death within ten to fifteen years.

Huntington's chorea is a genetic disease passed from generation to generation, affecting roughly half the offspring, males and females equally. The tragedy of Huntington's Chorea stems from its late onset. It is not a disease which kills children or adolescents: rather, it lies in wait until the victims have matured, married and had children of their own, thereby ensuring that the killer gene is passed on to the next generation. Slowly, very slowly, the patient, now in his early thirties, realizes that he is heir to the same disease which took away his father or mother's intelligence and self-respect in the prime of their life, the butt of cruel jokes and jibes. A parent, when he or she finally realizes the fatal inheritance, is frequently overwhelmed with guilt for having passed it on to beloved children.

Huntington's chorea is predominantly a disease of the white races, the greatest number of sufferers being found in the New England states, from whence it has spread westwards across America. The high incidence of the disease in America finds its origin in an earlier westward migration from England. By painstaking historical research it has been established that in 1630 three young men from the village of Bures St Mary in Suffolk, set off to start a new life in the American colonies. The three were members of a group of emigres headed by Herbert Pelham, a staunch Puritan fleeing the excesses of King Charles I. After a three-month voyage they landed in Salem, Massachusetts.

The three men got off to a bad start, each getting into trouble in their adopted country. Their family lines were also blighted: no fewer than seven of the daughters or granddaughters were regarded as witches, most famously Elizabeth Knapp and Mercy Disborough, the latter undergoing the traditional water trial in 1692. Unequivocal evidence of Huntington's chorea appears in the fifth generation, but its existence before that time is strongly suggested by this description of Elizabeth Knapp's involuntary behaviour:

> [she carries] herselfe in a strange and unwonted manner, sometimes she

> would give sudden shriekes and then would burst forth into immoderate and extravagant laughter ... as sometimes shee fell onto ye ground with it ... Shee was violent in bodily motions, leapings, strainings and strange agitations ... [she] began by drawing her tongue out of her mouth most frightfully to an extraordinary length and greatnesse, and many amazing postures of her bodye.

No wonder Elizabeth Knapp was thought possessed by the Devil himself.

Further research has shown that the three men were in fact half-brothers, sons of 'the base Mary Haste' of Bures St Mary. A relative of the Haste family is recorded as having been convicted of witchcraft in England: her name was Anne Disborough, an ancestor of Mercy.

So when did the Huntington family acquire the disease to which they gave their name? They didn't. George Huntington was the *doctor* who, in 1872, wrote about the hereditary form of chorea which he came across as a general practitioner in Long Island: he was physician to the Mulfoot family, one of whom was a great-granddaughter of Mary Haste. The inhabitants of Long Island used to call the disease 'that disorder'. In 1910, George Huntington recalled visits as a boy with his doctor father: 'Driving with my father through a wooded road leading from East Hampton to Amagansett, we suddenly came across two women, both bowing, twisting and grimacing. I stared in wonderment, almost in fear.'

Today, ninety years on, Huntington's chorea is still a fearful disease, spoken about in whispers, if at all. But genetic research is changing the outlook for the future. A blood test is now available which will accurately predict the chances that an individual will develop the disease as one grows older, enabling informed choices to be made. This has eased the burden for those whose blood test has been negative, but has done little to improve the lot of future victims. Intriguingly, some of those at risk have decided not to have the test, preferring not to know. A family with which I was involved with recently had two teenage children, whose father was in a pitiable state of dementia and chorea. Both opted to have the test. Statistically speaking, one should have tested positive, one negative. There was a seemingly interminable wait for the results. Then the results came through: *both tested negative*. My own sense of joy and relief was barely containable.[5]

# 10 THE THREE MOSQUITEERS – MANSON, ROSS AND REED

## 1 FILARIASIS

*Filariasis is a group of diseases – the best known being elephantiasis – which are caused by minute thread-like worms (nematodes), spread from person to person by the bites of* Culex, Aëdes *and* Anopheles *mosquitoes. The worms lodge in the lymph glands causing blockage and grotesque swellings. During the late evening and early morning the worms are found in the blood stream in huge numbers. Effective drug treatment is now available.*

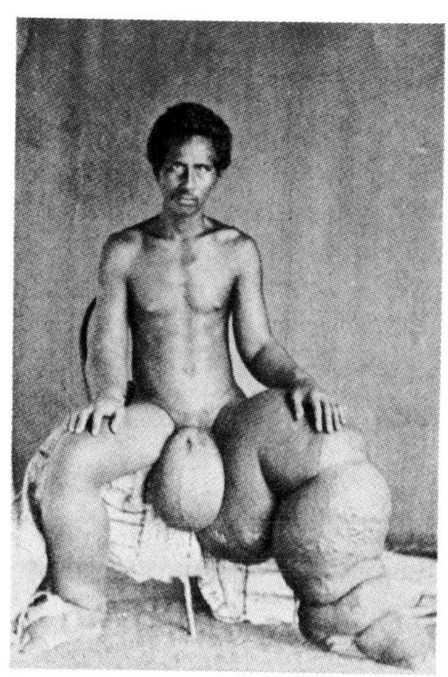

Gross swellings in elephantiasis

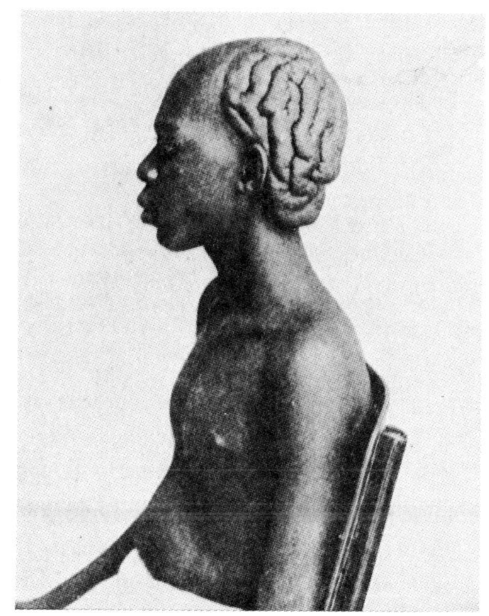

Elephantiasis of the scalp

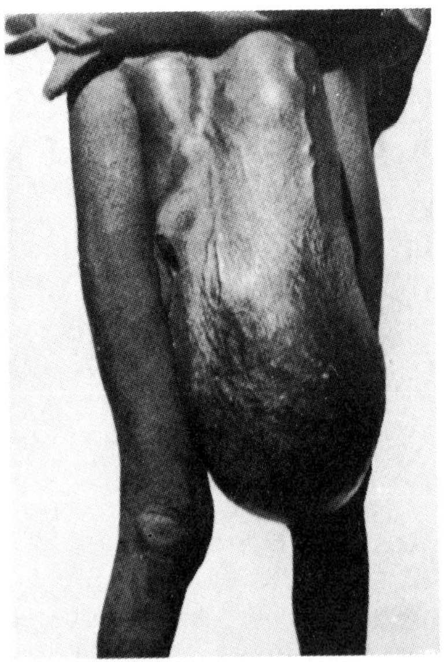

Elephantiasis of the scrotum

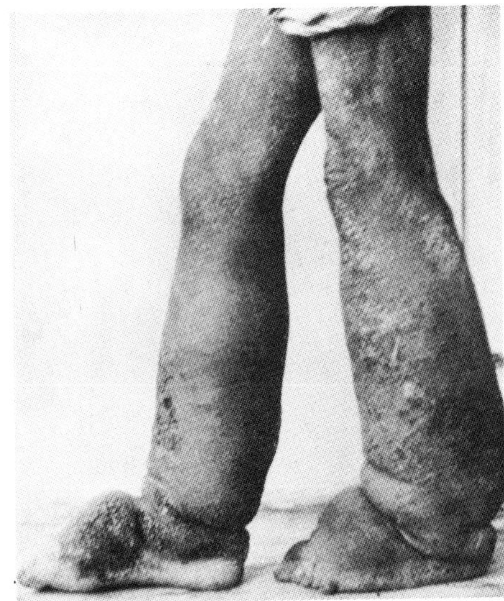

Elephantiasis of the legs

The importance of elephantiasis in this chapter is the fact that it was the first disease to be shown to be dependent for its spread upon mosquitoes. This was shown to be the case by the careful researches of the Scot, Sir Patrick Manson. This chapter is about the work of three men, Manson, Ross and Reed, and their elucidation of the causes of three diseases, filariasis, malaria and yellow fever.[1]

## 2 MALARIA

*Malaria is still the greatest of the killer diseases. It is* not *confined to the tropics, though its greatest incidence is between 45°N and 40°S, being spread by the bite of the female anopheles mosquito, which introduces the malarial parasites into the blood stream. Four parasites can cause malaria –* Plasmodium vivax, *the most common, causes tertian fever, often with a relapsing course at intervals of weeks or months. Malignant tertian fever (blackwater fever) is caused by* Plasmodium falciparum. *The four types of parasite are distinguishable from one another under the microscope.*

*The disease is caught early in childhood and either kills or produces chronic debilitation. Although afebrile varieties are known, the hallmark of malaria is fever, with chills and intense thirst. As the fever recedes, drenching sweats supervene. The periodicity of the fever provides a useful classification: daily (quotidian), every second day (tertian), and every third day (quartan). Sufferers from malaria become chronically debilitated: 'Malaria has the disastrous effect of permitting human existence while precluding the possibility of human health and happiness.' The spleen is usually enlarged and tender.*

*Mosquito control has had only limited success in reducing the prevalence of malaria. In recent times, effective prophylactic drugs have become available, but strains of drug-resistant parasites are increasing. The black races show a relative immunity through the sickle-cell mechanism.*

## *The Roman disease*

At the age of thirty-three, Alexander the Great ruled the world. He was finally felled in Babylon, not by a human enemy, but by the malarial parasite. The Teuton, Alaric, captured Rome in 410 but did not live to enjoy the fruits of his victory – the mosquitoes of the Campagna, the Roman marshes, saw to that. It was always the invaders who suffered most, since indigenous Romans had acquired relative immunity. Roman fever had always posed a very real threat to foreign church dignitaries visiting the Pope, and this was one factor in the decision to move the papal court to Avignon.

Cesare Borgia only recovered from an attack of malaria because his physician tucked him in the carcass of a recently disembowelled mule.[2]

Medical historians agree that malaria was introduced into the New World by Europeans. Negroes were taken from Africa to work as slaves in the Americas because of their relative immunity to the effects of malaria.

## *The disease of the swamps*

The most commonly invoked agency to explain malarial fever was the wrath of God. The Chinese considered it to be the work of three demons, one with a hammer, one with a bucket of water and one with a stove, thereby explaining the three cardinal symptoms of headache, chills and fever.

The association of intermittent fever with swampy, marshy ground was recognized early on. The Greek physician, Hippocrates, commented that those who lived in low, moist, hot areas and drank stagnant marsh water suffered from enlarged spleens. Galen taught that malaria was due to an imbalance of the four humours which could be restored by bleeding and purging. When, finally, Galen's views were challenged some 1,500 years later, there was a revival of interest in the association of the disease with noxious air. *Mal'aria*, Italian for 'bad air', was a term first used by the French physician Jacquier in 1743.

In 1717 Giovanni Maria Lancisi advanced his theory that the disease was caused by microscopic 'bugs' or 'worms' which somehow gained entry into the blood stream. Others suggested poisonous vapours given off by plants; still others suggested spores. In 1879 Edwin Klebs, a German pathologist working in Rome, claimed to have identified the organism responsible: a bacterium found in soil which, when injected into rabbits, produced malaria-like symptoms. Because of Klebs's international reputation, many believed the origin of malaria to have been solved – but such optimism was premature. In 1847, another German, Heinrich Meckel, described a characteristic finding in patients with malaria – the occurrence of round granulated bodies when the blood film was examined under the microscope. At that time no one suspected that these granules were the causative organisms. It was not until 1880 when Alphonse Laveran, a French physician, showed that Meckel's granular bodies were living organisms, that the true cause of malaria became apparent.

## *Laveran's pigmented bodies*[3]

Laveran worked as a doctor in Algeria in the late 1870s. He noticed, as others had before him, that when the blood of malaria victims was examined under the microscope, countless small black particles could be clearly seen. At autopsy it was not unusual for whole organs to be so coloured. Back in 1858 this pigment had been identified as a form of haemoglobin, the substance which transports oxygen in the red blood cells. It became clear that the pigment was a characteristic finding in malaria and was produced at the same time as the fever.

The normal way in which a blood sample was examined entailed smearing it as a thin film on a glass slide, allowing it to dry, and staining it with dyes in order that the various constituents would appear in different colours. Any live organism was well and truly dead by the time the pathologist focused upon it under his microscope. Laveran occupies his place in the Malarial Hall of Fame simply because he began to look at fresh, liquid and unstained blood specimens. Seeing things *au naturel*, he noticed that the pigment was *inside* a clear 'envelope', sometimes crescent-shaped, sometimes round. Laveran believed these to be the actual parasites which caused malaria, but he was unable to prove it. Then, on 5 November 1880, he saw something new. Something moved! Something was wriggling about! It was alive! The pigmented granules were dancing about on the microscope slide! 'I was astonished to observe that at the periphery of this body was a series of fine, transparent filaments that moved very actively and beyond question were *alive*.' Laveran conjectured that the symptoms of malaria were linked to the life cycle of this dancing parasite, and that the reason these living organisms had not been seen before was because they had been killed by the process of preparing the blood film. Laveran, realizing the significance of what he had seen, immediately wrote to the Academy of Medicine in Paris to stake his claim. He called the filaments *flagellae* and observed that they would detach themselves from the crescents and spheres and swim off at high speed. (The organism itself was later allocated to the family of unicellular animals called *Plasmodium*.)

What Laveran regarded as a giant step forward in the study of malaria – the identification of the very organism which causes the disease – was not so regarded by other workers. Laveran's live organisms remained stubbornly invisible to other researchers, especially Italians. Some even thought him deluded, in a similar fashion to the man who reported seeing canals on Mars. When William Osler, the most famous doctor of the day, failed to see Laveran's organism, all appeared lost. The malaria establishment opted instead to attribute the disease to the bacterium discovered in swampy water the year before by Klebs and Tommasi-Crudeli, which they confidently christened *Bacillus malariae*

But Laveran, for the greater glory of Truth (and France), refused to be cowed. He set about convincing his sceptics by the simple expedient of practical demonstrations. He would assemble his microscope, prepare a fresh sample of malarial blood, and actually point out the organisms to sceptical colleagues. It was an effective, if slow, strategy. After all, it is difficult to refuse to believe the testimony of one's own eyes. Or so one would think. Patriotic blindness sometimes proved to be a more powerful force than scientific truth. Laveran visited Marchiafava and Celli, two other famous Italian malariologists, but they refused to examine fresh specimens and consequently continued not to observe the parasite. When, two years later, they finally switched to fresh samples they immediately detected the organism and rushed into print, *without any mention of Laveran's visit two years before*. Convincing themselves that they were looking at an organism different from Laveran's, Marchiafava and Celli named it *Plasmodium malariae*. The partisan problems which were to dog progress in malarial research had started early.

Laveran had to wait a long time for the recognition he so richly deserved. It was not until 1887, seven years after its original discovery, that William Osler reported in the *British Medical Journal* that he, too, had now seen the parasite with his own eyes. Truth had triumphed at last: in 1907 Laveran was awarded the Nobel Prize.

### *Manson, Ross and the mosquito*

Having finally agreed upon the causative organism, the next problem was how the malarial parasite got into the blood stream. The story switches to England and Ronald Ross, an arrogant, quarrelsome man, quick to find fault, and quicker still to take offence.

Born in 1857, Ross was the son of a general in the British army, and meekly accepted the choice of career that his father made for him: to become a doctor in the Indian Medical Service. Ronald would have preferred to write romantic poetry, but, from the quality of what he has left us, it is clear that the world owes a debt of gratitude to the general. Initially depressed, it slowly dawned on Ross that the fame he craved might be gained through medicine rather than poetry.

In 1889 he married Rosa Bessie Bloxam, and the newly weds left England for India. Ross made no secret of his dislike of his fellow doctors, and it was inevitable that his attitude would provoke rivalries and jealousies. Ross determined to focus his energies on malaria. Armed with a diploma in public health from the Royal College of London, and barely two months' study of bacteriology at St Bartholomew's Hospital, Ross was woefully ill-equipped for his mission. Yet, through a mixture of ignorance and arrogance, he determined to conquer all adversity. Nine years after Laveran had reported seeing the malarial parasite, and two years after Osler's corroboration, Ross still had doubts, preferring to believe that the putative parasites were nothing more than misshapen blood cells. It was not for another five years, on a visit home to England, that Dr (later Sir) Patrick Manson demonstrated the parasite to Ross. It was at this same time that Manson shared with Ross his theory that the mosquito was responsible for the spread of malaria. Manson, as we have seen, had discovered the role of the mosquito in the spread of elephantiasis in the 1870s, and had speculated in the *British Medical Journal* in 1894 that the same insect might be responsible for the spread of malaria. The two men agreed that it was Ross's destiny to return to India and prove Manson correct.

Manson was not the first to moot the part played by the mosquito in the spread of malaria. In 1717, Giovanni Maria Lancisi, the man who suggested that malaria might be caused by microscopic 'worms',

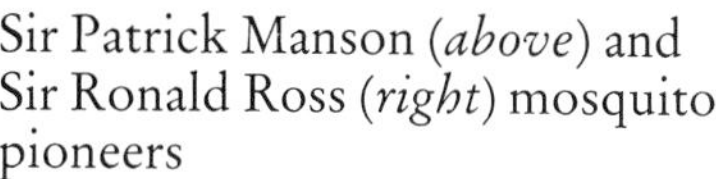

Sir Patrick Manson (*above*) and Sir Ronald Ross (*right*) mosquito pioneers

also suggested the vital role that the mosquito might play in the transmission of the disease. In 1807, an Irish-American doctor, John Crawford, proffered his theory that the mosquito laid her eggs when it bit its victim. Alas, his ideas were held to ridicule. In 1854, Louis Beasuperthuy concluded that both malaria and yellow fever were spread by the bite of mosquitoes who inhabited marshy ground. In 1882 another proponent of the mosquito theory, Dr Albert King, suggested the erection of a finely woven wire screen to encircle Washington DC in order to protect its inhabitants from the mosquitoes of the Potomac Flats.[4] Exactly why so many found the mosquito theory of malaria such anathema is curious, since Sir Patrick Manson, the 'Father of Tropical Medicine', had already shown conclusively that the mosquito spread the microscopic worm responsible for elephantiasis.

Before returning again to India in 1894, taking time off from his novel *The Spirit in the Storm*, Ross wrote a scientific paper entitled *A List of Natural Appearances in the Blood Which Have Been Mistaken for Forms of the Malaria Parasite*, which was published in the *Indian Medical Gazette*: this, barely one year after he had scoffed at those who thought that Laveran's organisms were anything other than misshapen red blood cells! If his paper was intended as self-effacement, drawing attention to a mistake which anyone could have made, it would have shown Ross as a man happy to profit from genuine error. But Ross was never one to concede a mistake of any kind and with retrospective falsification contended that identification of the malarial parasite 'presents little difficulty'. Such an arrogant, self-aggrandizing style was not designed to endear him to his fellow malariologists, most of whom had been working in the field far longer than Ross, and who possessed a much greater knowledge of the subject than he. Ross possessed just one book on malaria, subscribed to no other journal than the *British Medical Journal*, could speak no foreign language other than schoolboy French and was consequently unable to keep abreast with the Italian malarial literature, knew virtually nothing about advances in microscopy, and, most astonishingly, could not tell one mosquito from another (and, therefore, assumed that there were no differences). Setting sail for India, Ross gave himself about a year before his anticipated triumphant return to England, hailed and feted as the person who had proved the mosquito theory of malaria.

Ross joined his regiment in Secunderabad and immediately suffered from the intense heat – temperatures, incidentally, which were much too hot for mosquitoes. His brief was clear: he would find patients suffering from malaria, allow mosquitoes to feed on their blood, kill the insects and dissect them to see what became of Laveran's organism (now called *Plasmodium*). All the while Ross corresponded with Manson, sharing with his mentor his periods of enthusiasm and frustration. In return, Manson would précis relevant scientific papers and encourage him in his quest for the 'Holy Grail'. Manson, who did not subscribe to the theory that the parasite was spread by the *bite* of the mosquito, urged Ross to induce malaria in healthy people who had *drunk water in which mosquitoes had died*. 'The Frenchies and Italians will pooh-pooh it, then adopt it, and then claim it as their own.' He added, 'The malaria germ does not go into the mosquito for nothing, for fun or for the confusion of the pathologist. It has no notion of a practical joke. It is there for a purpose …'

Teacher and pupil had long since decided that the fate of the flagellae, which Laveran had watched breaking away from the spherical plasmodium, was the key to the malarial enigma: Ross was under instructions to focus his attention on what became of the flagellae when they were sucked into the mosquito's gut. Ross reported progress to Manson:

> I said I was going to watch free flagella. With my usual luck I found a beauty in my first specimen and watched it for three solid hours

> exactly, without taking my eye off him ... He riggled [sic] around for 20 minutes ... Then he brought up against a phagocyte [a white blood cell which devours invading organisms] and remained so long I thought the phagocyte had got hold of him. Not a bit; he was not killed or sucked in; but kept poking him in the ribs in different parts of the body. I was astonished; and so, apparently, was the phagocyte. He kept at this for ¼ of an hour, and then went away across two fields [of vision] and went straight at another phagocyte! ... and the phagocyte seemed to rear up and try to get round him, but could not. At last the phagocyte seemed to give up and flattened itself against an air-bubble, the flagellum still poking away at him. After 50 minutes, movement became much slower and I thought the animal was dying – when a very curious thing happened; a third phagocyte came at him with mouth open, but had no sooner got near him when the flagellum left his fallen foe and attacked the new one, holding on and shaking like a snake on a dog. In one minute the third phagocyte turned sharp round and ran off howling!!! – I assure you. I won't swear I heard him howling, but I *saw* him howling. He went right across a whole field, the flagellum holding on to his tail ... This continued for five minutes, the poor phagocyte literally *legging it*, after which the flagellum left him and went away.

So impressed was Ross with the brave adventures of the lone flagellum and the three phagocytes that he determined to write an account 'in the style of "The Three Musketeers" '.

Since his medical duties took up no more than an hour a day, Ross had ample time at Secunderabad to devote to his research. Although Manson had alerted Ross to the mosquito, the older man was well adrift in his theory as to the means by which the insect spread the disease: Manson believed that people caught malaria by swallowing contaminated water in which infected mosquitoes had died. It did not occur to him – as seems so obvious to us in retrospect – that the plasmodium was transmitted in the bite of the mosquito. In 1896, an Italian, Amico Bignami, had debated with Manson through the columns of the medical journals whether it was the insect's bite which was more important or its posthumous pollution of water. If water pollution was the mode of spread, how was it that whole populations who shared the same water supply, did not succumb to the disease? Ross heard of Bignami's ideas and immediately assumed that the Italian was attempting to appropriate Manson's mosquito theory. But Manson *was* correct about another aspect of the spread of malaria when he wrote to Ross, 'Possibly different species of mosquito modify the malaria germ; that the differing degrees of virulence depend on the difference of species of mosquito that has served as alternative host to the parasite.' Up to that point Ross had been using mainly *Aëdes* and *Culex* species, neither of which, as we now know, transmit the malaria parasite.

In September 1895 Ross was posted to Bangalore to help cope with an outbreak of cholera. His enthusiasm for this new disease worried Manson, who played the patriot card: 'Laveran is inclined to take up the mosquito hypothesis and I have no doubt that by next summer the French and Italians will be working at it. So for goodness sake hurry up and save the laurels for old England.'

In April 1897, whilst posted at Sigur Ghat, Ross finally caught the disease which he had studied second-hand for so long. He diagnosed himself by identifying the *Plasmodium* in his own blood, and dosed himself with quinine. In a period of remission he had time to contemplate how he might have contracted the fever: he was very dubious that it came from drinking infected water simply because neither of his two servants was ill, despite drinking the same water. Could it be due to a forgotten mosquito *bite*? He set about collecting the local mosquitoes, including a single example of a type which he descriptively dubbed 'dapple-winged' (actually an anopheles). The 'dapple-winged' mosquito was unique in at least one respect: it tilted at an angle of forty-five degrees, head down, when feeding on humans, whereas the bodies of other species remained parallel to the skin. *Despite two years of collecting mosquitoes, this was the first anopheles that Ross had ever seen.* This was probably because Ross left collection of insects to others – and since the anopheles bred in remoter areas it was only natural that his native servants concentrated on collecting those mosquitoes which bred in more accessible sites.

Again Manson urged Ross to concentrate on the fate of the flagellum. Manson was sure that the flagellum was the key to the mystery. Ross was instructed to find out where the flagellum went when it was sucked up by the mosquito in its blood meal, and which species of mosquito was responsible for the spread of malaria in humans. His efforts to implicate *Aëdes* as the culprit were unsuccessful, but he remained optimistic and in high spirits: 'I must discover America if I continue to sail along this parallel westward far enough.' The intense heat and his continued failure soon made him exasperated. He described revenging insects which 'tormented me at their pleasure' and the screws of his microscope rusting with the sweat of his brow.

In August 1897, Ross's attention was again drawn to the dapple-wing, a number of which had just hatched from larvae in his laboratory. There were ten in all, and Ross gave them their first feed, a blood meal teeming with *Plasmodium*, from Husein Kahn, a malarial patient. He sacrificed two within half an hour, hoping to catch sight of the flagella: he was disappointed. Then two died in the night, and two he spoilt. That left four. Another dissected mosquito showed nothing, and another died. Only two remained. When he dissected the ninth mosquito, years of hard work were finally rewarded. Under the microscope Ross saw pigmented cells in the mosquito's stomach. They looked nothing like the flagella he sought, but equally they resembled nothing he had ever seen before – and the pigment was the same colour as that found in malarial blood. He killed and dissected his last dapple-wing five days after its blood meal and found again the pigmented cells – but they had grown larger. What was the nature of the pigmented cell? What happened next? Ross was in a frenzy of excitement. He was also clean out of anopheles. He was able to show that the pigmented cells did *not* occur in the stomachs of either grey or brindled varieties of mosquito.

Ever fearful that foreigners were hard on his heels, he wrote to the *British Medical Journal* to tell its readers the momentous news. Ross's paper, *On Some Peculiar Pigmented Cells Found in Two Mosquitoes Fed on Malarial Blood* was published in December 1897, together with an endorsement by Manson that Ross 'may have found the extracorporeal phase of malaria'. Dr Thin, a second expert asked by the *BMJ* to comment, was not convinced that the pigmented cells were in any way relevant. Ross paid no attention to Thin and wrote to Manson, 'I really believe the problem is solved, though I don't like to say so ... *I am on it.*' Ross was so convinced that by some means the flagellum changed into the pigmented cell that he was moved to name 20 August 1897, the day of his discovery, 'Mosquito Day', and to express his joy in verse:

> This day relenting God
> Hath placed within my hand
> A wondrous thing: And God
> Be praised. At His command,
>
> Seeking His secret deeds,
> With tears and toiling breath,
> I find thy cunning seeds,
> O million-murdering Death.
>
> I know this little thing
> A myriad men will save,
> O death, where is thy sting?
> Thy victory, O Grave?

It was the high point. Ross was subsequently frustrated in his efforts to continue his work. In September he was posted to Kherwara, a remote place with no malaria and only two other Englishmen. Ross was sure that it was a deliberate act of spite by a jealous superior. His requests to escape were ignored, and for four vital months Ross languished in the wilderness. Finally, in February 1898, he was transferred to Calcutta with instructions to devote his time to malaria research – and kala-azar (a protozoal disease now known to be spread by the bites of sandflies). He was ecstatic! Calcutta literally swarmed with dapple-wings. Unfortunately Indians with malaria were at a premium and Ross hesitated to experiment on Europeans. To eschew such ethical dilemmas, he decided to make do with pigeons and sparrows. He wrote to Manson, 'What an ass I have been not to follow your advice before and work with birds.'

What, Ross asked himself, happened when the fully grown pigmented cells (coccidea) burst in the mosquito's stomach on the seventh day? He managed to prick a coccidium with a needle and watched numerous 'rods' discharged onto the microscope slide. Ross thought of these rods as somewhat similar to spermatozoa and he determined to find where they went in the mosquito's body after leaving its stomach. He describes his success in a long letter to Manson:

> I feel *almost* justified in saying that I have completed the life cycle [of the Plasmodium which produced malaria in birds] ... I am nearly blind and dead with exhaustion!! – but triumphant. Expect one of the most wonderful things.
>
> ... Sometimes the rods were more common in the [mosquito's] head, sometimes in the thorax. I went after mosquito after mosquito spending hours over each, until I was blind and half silly with fatigue. The object was to find if possible a place or structure [in the mosquito's body] where the rods accumulate ... Nothing.
>
> On the 4th, however, after pulling out the head by its roots, some delicate structure dropped out. This proved to be a gland of some sort, consisting of a long duct. I noticed at once that the rods were swarming here ... Looking further, the cells of one whole lobe of the gland were simply packed with them ... Now what was this gland? It appears to lie in front of the thorax close to the head, but breaks so easily in the dissection that I cannot locate it properly. In the second mosquito however there was no doubt that the duct led straight into the head-piece, probably in to the mouth.
>
> In other words it is a thousand to one, it is a *salivary gland* ... Malaria is conveyed from a diseased person or bird to a healthy one by the proper species of mosquito and is inoculated by its bite.

Manson communicated Ross's discovery in July 1898 at a scientific meeting in Edinburgh. It was well received. He warned Ross: 'The fat is thoroughly in the fire now & you may expect now to hear more of yourself than your modesty may care for.' Hardly, since modesty was an attribute Ross did not have in abundance. Ross felt his exile acutely: it was *his* discovery, yet he was stuck thousands of miles away, deaf to the accolades. More ignominious still, Ross was posted to Assam to continue the study of kala-azar. Thus was Ross effectively prevented from following up his work in malaria and going on to prove that the life cycle he had demonstrated in birds applied equally in humans, and that it was the dapple-winged mosquito which was solely responsible. Neither the French nor the Italians would have treated their pioneers in such an inglorious fashion. Was Ross now reaping the revenge of all those colleagues and superior officers whom he had so disdained over the years?

Ross had clearly shown that the mosquito was responsible for the spread of malaria in birds. It was a small step to demonstrate that the same mechanism applied in humans. But this was not to fall to Ross, but to a bunch of thieving Latins, jealous that England, a non-malarial country, had stolen the glory which should rightfully have been Italy's – for did not Italy give the disease its name? Impotently, Ross railed against the obduracy of the British army for not allowing him to complete the job for the glory of England.

In late 1898 Ross had calmed down and was even exchanging pleasantries with the Italians, Bignami and Grassi. But it could not last. Before long Ross was calling Grassi's integrity into question – and not wholly without cause. After Ross's vindication of the mosquito theory in birds, the Italians set themselves two tasks to retrieve their national pride: to prove that the human malarial parasite went through a life cycle similar to that of birds; and to identify the mosquito responsible for the spread of human malaria. The Italians went about these tasks in unseemly haste, simply because they knew that Robert Koch was working on the same problems, and they could not bear the idea that yet another malaria triumph would slip through Italian hands. To make matters worse, the Italian government had put expensive facilities at *Koch*'s disposal when the great man stopped off in Rome after visiting German East Africa. Grassi, never accorded such VIP treatment, was incensed, especially as Koch's preliminary reports from Africa did not even mention the pioneer work of the Italians (nor of Ross, though that was unimportant).

It was his fear that Koch would steal his thunder that prompted Grassi into premature publication of his results. Instead of identifying the specific mosquito, Grassi named three as 'enormously suspect': one *Anopheles* and two *Culex* species. He hedged his bets despite the fact that dapple-wings, an anopheles characteristic, had been already identified by Ross as the species responsible for malaria in birds. *Bignami, in his earlier experiments, equally rushed, had actually exonerated anopheles!* But by the end of 1898 the Italians had finally identified anopheles as the culprit: Grassi was so delighted that he sent a copy of his paper to Koch as a Christmas present, a calculated snub to the German. How 'calculated' was the snub to

Ross has been a topic for debate ever since. In their paper the Italians appeared to give the impression that the life cycle of *Plasmodium* was something new: the only reference to Ross's work was a brief sentence, 'It [the life cycle of *Plasmodium*] finds in large part confirmation in that observed by Ross for proteosoma of birds in the *grey mosquito*'. Scant mention indeed for Ross's pioneering work! No wonder he raged and continued to wage war on the Italians for the rest of his life, lessening his reputation in the process.

Grassi's perfunctory reference to Ross was scientifically unethical and indefensible, and was surely intended to minimize the Englishman's contribution. His indebtedness to Ross was immense: the life cycle of the parasite in birds and the identification of the culprit mosquito was Ross's, and Ross regarded Grassi's work as piracy. It would be a travesty to allot to Ross and Grassi equal renown: after all Ross had carried out the pioneer work in birds; but it was Grassi who had completed the work in humans. One had led, the other followed.

Ross left India in 1899, bitter that ignorant superiors had thwarted his plans to complete his work in humans. Manson helped get him a job as lecturer in the new Liverpool School of Tropical Medicine. He remained four months before setting off to eradicate malaria from Sierra Leone. Ross was always embittered about what he saw as a lack of recognition given to his work: despite a knighthood he was irked that neither the India Medical Service nor the Indian government acknowledged his work. Had not Edward Jenner received £30,000 from Parliament? Ross submitted a similar petition to Lloyd George, then Chancellor of the Exchequer, but it was refused. He tried again when Lloyd George was succeeded by Austin Chamberlain – again unsuccessfully.

Such was the international debate generated by the Ross-Grassi feud, and so polarized was opinion, that it was proposed that *both* Ross *and* Grassi should be awarded the Nobel Prize in 1902. It was left to one man to decide: Robert Koch, no doubt remembering his Christmas present of four years before, advised that Ross should be the sole recipient.

Ross had described part of the life cycle of just one parasite, *Plasmodium relictum*, which infects birds. Four parasites are now known to infect man: *Plasmodium vivax*, the commonest; *Plasmodium ovale*, the rarest; *Plasmodium malariae*, the cause of quartan fever; and *Plasmodium falciparum*, the deadliest. *Plasmodium falciparum* is probably, evolutionarily speaking, the youngest, since successful parasitism should not result in the death of the host.

## *The endless fight against malaria*

It is indeed ironic that blood letting was for so long the treatment of choice in malaria: blood, essential to fight the parasite, was what the patient could least afford to lose! We now know that each rigor and chill represents another wave of mass destruction of red blood cells by the plasmodia. Happily, most patients were too poor to afford the doctor's fee, and so improved their chances of survival as a result.

Quinine has a long history in malarial treatment. It was said that a Spanish soldier in Peru went down with malaria and was abandoned by his comrades. He managed to crawl to the side of a forest pool and drank. He then fell asleep. When he awoke his fever had gone. He remembered that the water had had a bitter taste and noticed that a large tree-trunk, split by lightning, had fallen into the pool. When he chewed the bark, he discovered the source of the bitter taste. The date of this romanticized fiction is not known, but the curative properties of the cinchona bark must have been known before 1630, for it was in that year that Don Juan Lopez de Canizares, Governor of Loxa, was cured of malaria after drinking an infusion made from it. The bark was exported to Europe around 1633.

But why was it called cinchona? According to Sebastino Bado it was named after Señora Ana de Osorio, Countess of Chinchon, the beautiful and charming wife of the Spanish Viceroy to Peru. Sometime after her arrival in Lima in 1629, the Countess fell ill with malaria. The physicians were impotent. Then word reached Don Lopez, who recommended the same treatment which had successfully cured him. It did the trick, the Countess recovered, and the bark became known as the Countess's powder. When she returned to Europe in 1639 she transported a large shipment of bark and distributed it to the poor. In her honour, Linnaeus, the botanist, named the genus of trees 'cinchona', italianizing the original Spanish spelling. Unfortunately, the story is totally untrue. The official diary of the Count of Chinchon was discovered in 1930. Ana died in Spain, three years before her husband was posted to Peru. It was his second wife, Francisca, who accompanied him, and she remained perfectly well throughout their posting abroad.

Because the Jesuit fathers were very active in investigating the curative properties of the bark, it soon became widely known as 'Jesuit's powder'. Its popularity was assured when, in 1649, Cardinal de Lugo, supervisor of the Jesuit pharmacy in Rome, prescribed it for Louis XIV, then the Dauphin, who was suffering from malaria. Anything even nominally Catholic was sure to be rejected in Protestant England, where doubts were cast upon the efficacy of the bark. Matters were not improved by the fact that unscrupulous traders, well aware that most people could not distinguish cinchona bark from any other, substituted other woods which were more easily available and cheaper. To Oliver Cromwell anything which smacked of Popery was deeply suspect and to use Jesuit Bark was an unthinkable heresy. As a result, the Lord Protector died of malaria in 1658.

In England a new substance rivalled the bark. It was the discovery of Robert Talbor who determined to keep the ingredients of his cure a secret. When the last remaining son of Louis XIV fell victim to fever, Charles II sent Talbor to France to administer to the heir. Talbor's treatment worked wonderfully and he was richly rewarded by a grateful monarch, notwithstanding the enmity of the entire French medical establishment. Louis XIV, as was his wont, insisted on knowing Talbor's secret ingredient. The Englishman sold the secret to the king for a very large sum of money, a monopoly for ten years and the promise that the secret would be kept until after Talbor's days. Unfortunately, Talbor died the next year at the age of thirty-nine. Louis ordered publication of the formula: cinchona bark with various additives to disguise its characteristic taste. It was the same ingredient that had saved the king when he was Dauphin.

It was inevitable that efforts would be made to transplant the cinchona tree from its natural home in South America to Europe. The first attempt was made by Charles Marie de La Condamine who had set sail as part of a French scientific expedition. He became particularly interested in studying the cinchona tree which was becoming scarce as a result of the high European demand for the bark. La Condamine resolved to collect cinchona seeds from the trees which grew in Peru. He decided to return home across the Andes, exploring the Amazon from its source to its mouth! He took extraspecial care of his precious seedlings, which he stored in a special box. The journey took eight months. As he was transferring his luggage from a small boat to the ship that was to take him back to Europe, a massive wave carried off the box and with it his precious cinchona seeds.

Another original member of the expedition, Joseph de Jussieu, also scoured the jungle for botanical rarities. He sent to Europe specimens of the cocoa plant, the source of cocaine. He also collected cinchona seeds which he kept in a locked trunk, continuously guarded. After some thirty years in the jungle, Jussieu decided to retire and booked his passage home to France. While waiting for his ship in Buenos Aires, one of his servants, who had assumed his locked trunk contained treasure, stole the specimens of a lifetime. The shock sent Jussieu insane.

Quinine, the active ingredient of cinchona, was finally isolated from the bark by two French chemists, Joseph Pelletier and Joseph Bienaime Caventou in 1820. Unlike Talbor, these men shared the details with their fellow scientists for the benefit of humanity. (Another extracted constituent was quinidine, an invaluable drug in the treatment of heart conditions.) It was not until 1944 that two Americans, Woodward and Doering, working at Harvard, synthesised quinine in the laboratory.[5]

After the discoveries of Ross and Grassi, it was inevitable that such knowledge was used to check the spread of malaria and to bring about its eventual eradication. Attacks upon the mosquito can take many forms. The breeding sites can be drained, preventing the larval forms from developing. Predatory fish can be introduced into lakes which will feed on mosquito larvae. Nets and repellents can prevent the insects biting:

> The Mosquito is little
> But has bugs in her spittle.
> Repellents and spray
> Will keep her away!

– a poster from World War II for American troops fighting in the Pacific.

But the task of eradication is immense and costly. The major problem in any strategy planned against the mosquito is the insect's fecundity. A female mosquito lays, on average, two hundred eggs. If half of these turn out to be females, then within five generations there will be twenty million mosquitoes. As the life cycle is completed in two weeks, and since in tropical countries breeding continues throughout the year, one female could theoretically produce progeny designated by the number twice ten followed by twenty-six noughts! Even if ninety-nine per cent perished, the deficit would be quickly made up. Nevertheless, when battle plans were well thought out and adequately financed, victory, albeit temporary, was won. America succeeded in building the Panama Canal, in no small measure because of its successful assault on the mosquitoes responsible for malaria and yellow fever.

A seemingly major leap forward was taken with the discovery in 1941 of dichloro-diphenyl-trichlorothane (DDT) a potent insecticide, believed to have been harmless to man. Unfortunately, over the years, dangerous side-effects of DDT have become apparent, limiting its widespread use.

The battle against malaria was almost won in this century in India, but now the disease is re-emerging: the number of cases in 1961 fell to fifty thousand; by 1977 it had soared to thirty million. Initial optimism has been replaced with a new realism about the enormity of the task of mosquito eradication. Currently malaria kills two million children every year, and this number is set to rise dramatically as *Plasmodium falciparum* becomes resistant to all known drugs, including chloroquine. The situation is gravest in sub-Saharan Africa, Central and South America, and South east Asia, since there is little commercial interest in combatting a Third World disease. Recently trials have started on a controversial malaria vaccine, a trial of which has recently been approved by the US Food and Drugs Administration. Manuel Patarroyo, a biochemist from Bogota, developed the vaccine in the late 1980s and conducted trials in Latin America. He claimed great success but Britain's Medical Research Council expressed reservations and refused to allow the vaccine to be used in trials in the Gambia. Other scientists have criticized the British decision, and the US army, led by workers at the Walter Reed Institute in Washington, have joined Patarroyo to test the efficacy of the vaccine. Recent results, published in *The Lancet* in March 1993, show the vaccine to be 39 per cent effective overall, but 77 per cent effective in children under 4, and 67 per cent effective in adults over 45, pointing to the feasibility of this type of treatment on a large scale.[6]

An insect and its parasite who have inhabited the planet for millions of years will not go without a fight.

## 3 YELLOW FEVER

*Yellow fever is an infectious tropical disease caused by a virus which is transmitted by the bite of the mosquito* Aëdes aegypti. *In severe cases death may follow fever, jaundice, haemorrhages and delirium. A prophylactic vaccine has been developed.*

### *A most feared disease*

Smallpox and bubonic plague originated in the Old World and caused mass slaughter when transported to the New. The debate about the provenance of syphilis continues to the present day, but there is little dispute that Columbus encountered in Hispaniola a grim and deadly disease, previously unknown in Europe: yellow fever. Despite the colour in its name, this fever's most feared symptom went under a different hue. *El vomito negro* exactly conveys the characteristic feature – the vomiting of black blood.

The disease usually starts with fever and chills and a sense of profound weakness. Small quantities of vomited blood augur ill, and raise the spectre of a diagnosis of yellow fever. Often, after two or three days, the symptoms might remit and the fever subside. Some patients do indeed recover, but many relapse into a second phase of the disease, characterized by profuse bleeding and an intense jaundice. Massive haemorrhages into the stomach provoke vomiting, and blood pours from the nose and gums. Bleeding into the skin produces extensive bruising. A fatal outcome can result.

In the seventeenth century, epidemics of yellow fever were often triggered by the disembarkation of soldiers from Europe. In 1664, on St Lucia, only 89 out of 1,500 soldiers survived. Those who stayed on board also fell victim to this killer disease: indeed, many ships acquired a grim reputation as harbingers of yellow fever, and sailors would refuse to sail in them.

So long as yellow fever remained confined to the tropics, people in more temperate climates could afford to be complacent. This situation changed dramatically in 1668 when the disease landed in New York, running amok and inducing terror in the population. The subsequent cold winter effectively cleared the city of infection, but the disease took firmer hold in the hotter, southern states. Doctors attempting to explain the causation and spread of yellow fever fell into the two traditional camps: contagionists and miasmatists. The former believed that the disease spread from person to person and invoked strict quarantine in order to lessen its pace. A woman fleeing infected Philadelphia, made Milford in Delaware only to have her wagon burnt and herself tarred and feathered. Contagionists looked for a source of the infection and pointed the finger at the West Indies.

Yet there was much that simply did not fit with the contagionist explanation. How was it possible for a mother to tend a sick child, or a husband to sleep with a dying wife, without contracting the disease? And why did yellow fever often attach itself to places rather than people? Sailors would catch it on a particular ship; guests would catch it when staying in a certain hotel. Surely this was because these places were infused with a miasma, a poison in the air. Sometimes tar barrels were set alight on street corners in order to neutralize the pollution. It was common experience that people were more likely to contract the disease at night, especially in low-lying areas – indeed, people living on the upper floors of buildings seemed to have a relative immunity! Further, the disease did not appear to like very dry climates, epidemics often breaking out at times of high humidity.

There was also an intriguing time delay associated with outbreaks of yellow fever. Ships would set sail with a healthy crew, only to have the sailors fall ill with yellow fever some two weeks out to sea.

A compromise theory, whereby miasmatic poisons could attach themselves to objects and thereby spread disease, became the rationale for disinfection of goods and property. Houses, sometimes even whole districts, were put to the torch.

### *Jesse Lazear, medical martyr*

By the turn of the present century people were beginning to become impatient with the lack of progress in identifying the cause of yellow

Walter Reed, yellow fever investigator

fever. A number of doctors cited microscopic organisms, but none of the claimed discoveries withstood rigorous investigation. Dr Sanarelli identified a bacterium, but others showed it to be a common and innocent bystander (in much the same way as some regard the HIV organism today). On the island of Cuba, where yellow fever ran riot, Dr Carlos Finlay of Havana (son of a Scots doctor and French mother) believed he had solved the riddle: yellow fever was spread from one person to another by the bite of a mosquito. He even identified the mosquito responsible: *Culex fasciatus* (now called *Aëdes aegypti*). Unfortunately the good doctor was unable to provide any evidence to substantiate his claim, and was widely regarded as a crank, despite the fact that Sir Patrick Manson had already demonstrated that elephantiasis was spread by mosquito, and Ronald Ross had shown that malaria was transmitted by the same insect.

In 1900, Major Walter Reed of the US Army Medical Corps was posted to Cuba. It was his job to attempt finally to solve the enigma of yellow fever. He headed a commission which included Dr James Carroll. It was Carroll who paid a call on Finlay and was told all about the old doctor's theory. Finlay donated a batch of *Culex* eggs to Carroll, who entrusted them to Dr Jesse Lazear to supervise their hatching. The plan was simple: once the eggs had hatched, female mosquitoes, safe inside a test-tube whose open end would be placed against the skin, would be fed on a patient with yellow fever; the insect would later be offered a meal from a healthy volunteer. One had only to wait patiently to see if the volunteer fell sick with yellow fever. QED.

There was no shortage of 'donors' because the disease was felling hundreds of soldiers in the American garrison. The bigger problem was the ethics of 'recipient' selection, since there was at that time a 70 per cent mortality. Self-induced experimental disease has a long and honourable history in medicine – even if at times the doctors have seemed a trifle irresponsible and naive.[7] In 1789, Dr Nathaniel Potter had gone to bed wrapped in the 'perspirable matter' of a yellow fever victim, and awoke the next day complaining only of the smell. In 1902, Stubbins Ffirth, a medical student, had rubbed black vomit into cuts in his arms, made the material into pills and swallowed them, and inoculated himself with infected blood, urine and sputum: his subsequent survival casts grave doubt on the veracity of the original diagnosis!

Lazear was one of eight volunteers, none of whom fell ill. Finlay's theory looked destined for the rubbish bin of medical history. Despite being disappointed (and relieved!), Carroll and Lazear continued to tempt reluctant mosquitoes to feed off them. Sixteen days later, Carroll succeeded in getting a mosquito to feed: within four days he had gone down with yellow fever. But this single instance proved nothing – after all, Carroll could have caught yellow fever some other way. What was needed was for the same mosquito to be persuaded to bite someone who Lazear could be virtually certain could not have caught the disease by any other means. A trooper from the Seventh Cavalry volunteered, and contracted yellow fever three days later.

Carroll suffered grievously, but survived. He became delirious and experienced acute chest pains. Lazear suffered chronic guilt, assuaged somewhat by the fact that Carroll himself had placed the mosquito on his own arm. The trooper's dose was a much milder one. But then Lazear himself began to feel unwell. The convalescing Carroll took over his care and commented on 'the expression of alarm in his eyes when I last saw him alive'. The nurse recorded, 'the black vomit would spurt from his mouth through the bars of his cot'. Lazear died on the tenth day. But how had he come to be infected in the first place? At the start of his illness he had confided to Carroll that when he was on the hospital wards getting trapped mosquitoes to feed off patients, a mosquito which happened to be flying around the ward had landed on his hand and started feeding. Lazear had not wanted to disturb the insect feeding on his patient's abdomen, and so decided to leave undisturbed the one feeding off himself. This rogue mosquito probably brought about the doctor's death. He died leaving a wife and two children, the younger of whom he had never seen.

Reed, who had been absent in Washington, returned to Cuba and Carroll's deeply felt, but unspoken, accusations of cowardice. Within two weeks Reed was back on the mainland to publicize the commission's findings. He was convinced that the problem was solved, despite the fact that only two out of eleven volunteers had contracted yellow fever. Reed returned again to Cuba and set up Camp Lazear, an outpost of hospital tents, in order to replicate the experiments. Within a short time he was claiming an 80 per cent success rate, though it is doubtful if the volunteers saw it that way!

How could such success rates be explained in view of Finlay's unmitigated failures? The explanation was that the organism, now known to be a virus, once inside the mosquito's body, had to incubate for roughly two weeks before it became infectious: previous attempts to spread the disease had occurred too early, long before the organism had matured inside the mosquito.

All now fell into place: the mosquito flew at night, preferring humid conditions and low-lying areas. It was sensitive to cold and haunted ships and houses. But some still doubted, pointing out that Reed and his colleagues had not been able to demonstrate the causative organism under the microscope. With hindsight, it is little wonder: the micro-organism responsible turned out to be one of the smallest viruses known, and would never be visualized using a light microscope. A highly effective vaccine was developed in 1937.[8]

### *An Old World infection after all?*

After identification, the virus was found to be endemic in Africa, especially in wild monkeys. Perhaps, like so many other scourges, yellow fever did indeed originate in the Old World and not the New.

# 11 POX AND CLAP: THE GREAT UNMENTIONABLES

*Syphilis is an infectious disease, caused by a spirochaete, a cork-screwed shaped microscopic organism, called* Treponema pallidum, *usually spread from person to person by sexual contact, though transmission by kissing and biting is not unknown. It is also spread in infected blood transfusions. Congenital syphilis is the result of infection of the foetus in utero. Transmission by inanimate objects such as lavatory seats is extremely rare, since the organism dies very quickly when dried.*

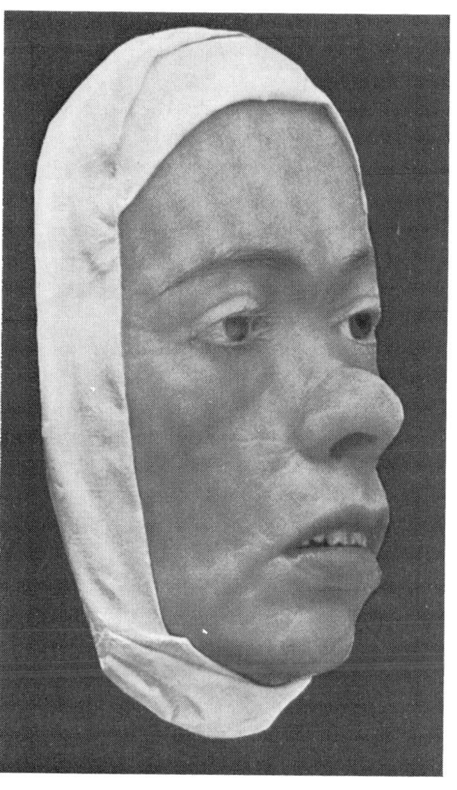

Saddle nose: absence of the bridge of the nose in congenital syphilis

*From the site of entry into the body, e.g., the tip of the penis or the tonsil, the spirochaetes spread to the local lymph glands in the groin or neck, and then pass rapidly throughout the body via the blood stream. About three to six weeks later, a primary lesion, the* chancre, *develops at the site of entry. It resembles a shallow ulcer and heals spontaneously. Six weeks later still, a rash heralds the secondary stage of the infection which also disappears without treatment. Syphilis is most infectious in its primary and secondary stages. A lengthy period with no outward symp-*

*toms then ensues – latent syphilis – though profound destructive changes may be occurring in vital internal organs, especially the heart and brain.*

*After a period of ten to twenty years, the signs of tertiary syphilis may manifest themselves:* gummata, *large areas of tissue destruction affecting any part of the body, but conspicuously the nose; gross deformity of bones and joints; and severe cardiac problems. Most distressing of all are the symptoms referrable to the nervous system: blindness; deafness;* tabes dorsalis, *syphilis of the spinal cord, with difficulties in walking and excruciating 'lightning' pains; and* General Paralysis of the Insane *(GPI), syphilis of the brain, which produces paralysis and dementia, with patients bedridden, doubly incontinent, and unable to feed themselves.*

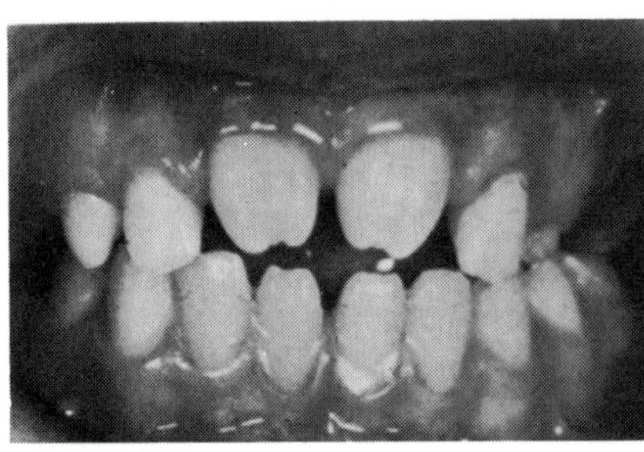

Hutchinson's teeth: notching characteristic in congenital syphilis

*Congenital syphilis frequently results in miscarriages and stillbirths. Infants born with syphilis often present characteristic facial features, including saddle noses, and notched teeth (Hutchinson's teeth).*

*Syphilis can be detected by blood tests and is treated with antibiotics.*

Question: If such a repellant disease as *small*pox has a diminutive prefix, what, in the name of all that's malignant, can be *great*pox?

Answer: Syphilis.[1]

*The antiquity and provenance of syphilis*

The serious student of the history of syphilis has three dates etched upon his brain.

1493: Columbus's return from America
1495: The Siege of Naples
1497: Syphilis reaches the British Isles

Opinion among academics is still deeply divided on who gave syphilis to whom, and scientific objectivity sometimes loses out to nationalism, American authors being as determined to place the blame on Europe as much as Europeans would wish to believe that syphilis originated in the New World and was brought back in 1493 by Columbus's fornicating sailors.

Essentially, the arguments of those who would wish the disease to have originated in the Americas are these: firstly, before Columbus's journey to the New World, no clear-cut description of any disease resembling syphilis was recorded by Egyptians, Greeks or Romans; secondly, the first reference to this 'new' scourge was its appearance at the Siege of Naples in 1495, barely two years after Columbus's return; and finally, minute examination of the bones of ancient Europeans has shown no incontrovertible evidence for the existence of syphilis. Strong arguments in favour of placing the blame squarely upon the shoulders of the American Indians (Amerindians).

The counter-arguments vigorously attack the sanctimonious stance taken by the Old World. These contend, and no one can deny, that just because a disease is not described in pre-Columbian literature, this is no proof that it did not exist. Advocates claim that there is no reference to scabies in ancient times, but that, in all likelihood, such a disease did exist. Nevertheless, an argument which contends that syphilis *did* exist in ancient Europe, but that no one bothered to record the fact, is inherently weak. Another related argument, contends that syphilis did exist before the fifteenth century, but that it was a much more benign disease, and that it was *not* transmitted by sexual intercourse. There is some weight to this hypothesis since it is well-known that diseases do change over time: indeed, syphilis in later centuries has shown little of the virulence and killing potential with which it felled the Italian and French armies in 1495.

And is it mere coincidence that mercury, so effective in the treatment of syphilis, was so widely prescribed in the centuries before Columbus, to treat a wide variety of ailments? Could not one of these ailments have been syphilis in a modified form?

Biblical references to syphilis are not convincing. In Deuteronomy references are made to emerods and sore blotches which some have connoted as buboes and boils. The equating of Biblical references of baldness to syphilitic alopecia is equally shaky. 'For my loins are filled with a loathsome disease' (Psalm 38) cannot with confidence be taken to mean syphilis. And it is medically unwarranted to assume that the visitation of the sins of the fathers 'upon the children unto the third and fourth generation' is a reference to congenital syphilis. More irresponsible still is the assumption that 'he that hath a flat nose' (Leviticus 21:18) is a congenital syphilitic! Again, in Numbers

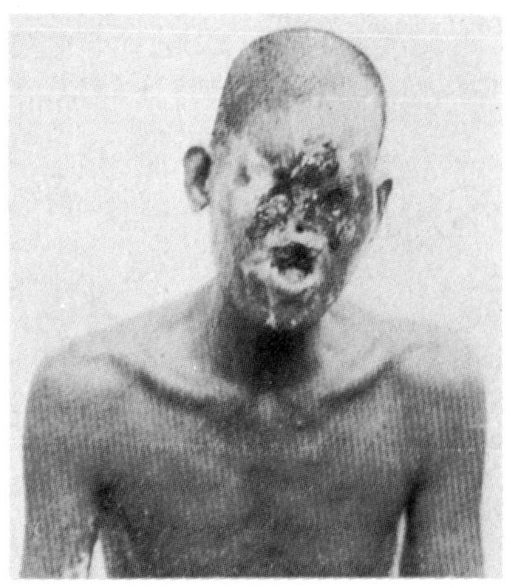

Gangosa: facial destruction in yaws, a disease caused by *Treponema pertenue*, an organism morphologically indistinguishable from *Treponema pallidum*, the causative organism of syphilis

12:12, to interpret 'one dead, of whom the flesh is half consumed when he cometh out of his mother's womb' as anything more than a stillborn child is unjustified, as is the interpretation of 'The fathers have eaten a sour grape, and the children's teeth are set on edge' (Jeremiah 31:29) as an example of the notched Hutchinson's teeth of congenital syphilis. Advice to wash the genitals after copulation, especially in men with urethral discharges, is an obvious reference to gonorrhoea ('clap') and not syphilis.[2]

To the anti-Europeans, the absence of syphilitic bone lesions in Old World skeletons cuts both ways. Anthropologists championing the innocence of the Amerindian have claimed that 'from the evidence of thousands of Indian skulls and skeletons pre-dating the arrival of Columbus, there is, as yet, not a single instance of thoroughly authenticated pre-Columbian syphilis.'

A compromise solution to the origin of syphilis, one which apportions blame equitably to both sides of the Atlantic, is the proposition that the spirochaete existed in both the Old and New Worlds contemporaneously, and that Columbus's sailors merely brought back a new, more virulent, variety.[3]

Syphilis is caused by the organism, *Treponema pallidum*. There are three, closely related treponemes which produce diseases in humans. One is responsible for syphilis, one for the skin disease called pinta and one for the tropical disease called yaws. There is a growing consensus that these diseases go far back into human history, and that the organisms responsible for syphilis and yaws evolved from the causative organism for pinta, a widespread disease of antiquity. In this context, the arguments as to which nation gave syphilis to which, becomes academic, if not irrelevant. Intriguingly, yaws and pinta patients give 'false positive' blood tests for syphilis, showing that the causative organisms are closely related.

### *The siege of Naples*

Medical historians have more reason than most to remember the tawdry imperialistic ambition of Charles VIII, King of France, and his attempt to subjugate Ferdinand II, King of Naples. Spanish mercenaries were not the only soldiers who joined the French and Italian combatants. Each side was joined by a secret adversary bent on the destruction of both sieged and besieging: *Treponema pallidum*, an adversary with a destructive power out of all proportion to its microscopic size. From wherever it came, the Old World or the New, its effect was grotesque and devastating. The new disease began with a sore, usually near the tip of the penis, beneath the foreskin.

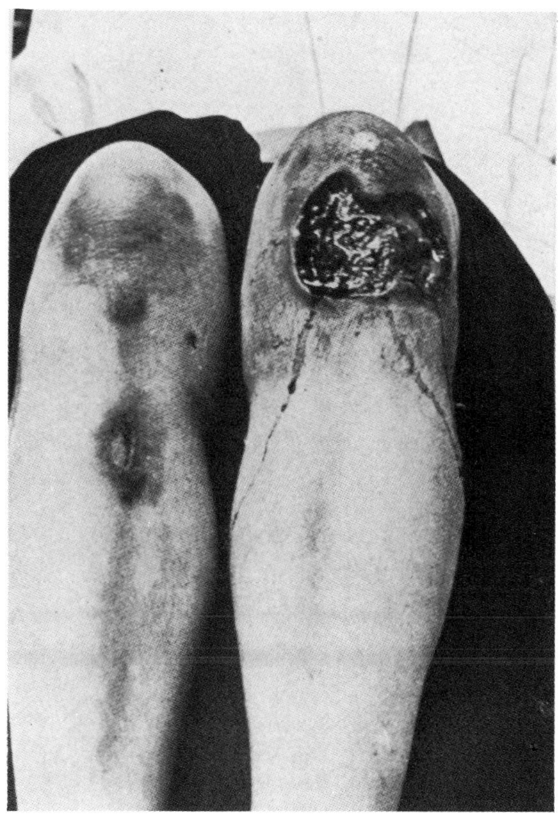

Gumma: gross destruction of the knee in tertiary syphilis

Over the next twelve months pustules spread to cover the whole body, later breaking down to form suppurating ulcers. Characteristic of this early stage were the acute pains which afflicted all parts of the victim's body, especially intolerable at night. With the pains and ulcers came hideous destruction of the eyes, face and limbs. The sufferers were left with their bodies covered with large black scabs exuding foul-smelling pus.

A flavour of the disease can be gleaned from contemporary descriptions:

> Several foot soldiers had 'pustules' on their faces and all over their bodies. Scratching provoked by pruritus [severe itching] produced a gnawing ulceration. Some days later, the sufferers were driven to distraction by the pains they experienced in their arms, legs and feet, and by an eruption of large pustules which lasted for a year or more, if left untreated.
> Cumano

> The entire body is so repulsive to look at and the suffering so great, especially at night, that this sickness is even more horrifying than incurable leprosy or elephantiasis.
> Benedetto

> These pains are more violent towards evening; sufferers feel as if their bones are broken and distended.

> The disease loosed its first arrow into my Priapic glans [penis], which, on account of the wound, became so swollen that both hands could scarcely encircle it.
> Joseph Grunpeck, contracting syphilis after a banquet 'attended by Venus as well as Bacchus and Ceres'. He lived on to the age of eighty-one

> Some are covered from head to knee with a rough scabies dotted with black and hideous lumps. They had become so filthy and repugnant that, left on the battlefield, they hoped to die. Some moaned and wept and uttered heart-rending cries because of the ulceration of their male organ.
> Grunpeck

> The ailment, say they, is a just and proper sentence;
> According to the sin so is the repentance,
> And the part that suffers most is the part most to blame.
> Villalobos

Since the initial pustule usually appeared on the genitalia, attention was drawn to the association between syphilis and sexual intercourse. Pedro Pintor, physician to Pope Alexander VI, identified women as the principal reservoir of infection, adding that priests and nuns were safeguarded from the disease. To spare the sensibilities of syphilitic

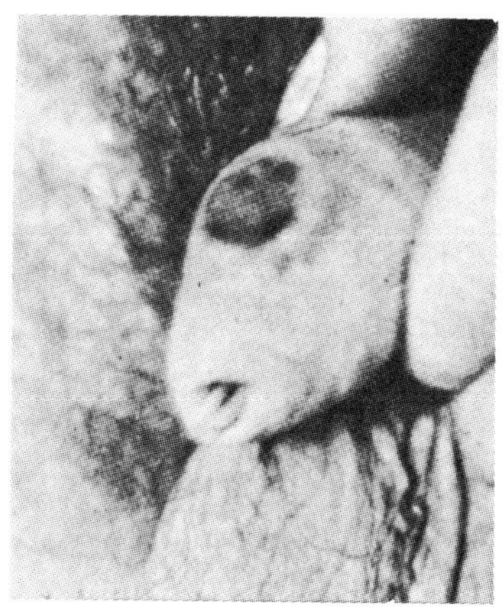

The primary lesion of syphilis on the penis

clergy it was conceded that intercourse was not the *only* method of spread: afflicted priests had obviously been unfortunate enough to use contaminated towels belonging to prostitutes or to breathe corrupt air. One Italian doctor maintained that syphilis could not always be venereal in origin, lest how could virgins and old men possibly contract the disease?

Over the succeeding five years, syphilis spread rapidly across Europe: it reached Nuremburg in the same year (1495), Paris the year after, Bristol the year after that. Hand in hand with the spread of syphilis went repugnance and panic. As the disease became widespread, other manifestations were described: pustules which exuded foul-smelling pus and later became transformed into hard callosities, destroying bones and inducing terrible pain; and ulcers which progressively destroyed the face producing hideous grotesques, impelling others to flee as from lepers. Ironically, many lepers complained about being billeted with syphilitics!

So repellent were those with syphilis that they were first avoided, then excluded and later persecuted. No nation wished to be associated with the new terror, and attribution was usually given to long-standing enemies. By this criterion, it would appear that the French were the most universally unpopular nation, since syphilis, in those early days, was commonly known as *Morbus Gallicus* or the 'French Pox'. The French retaliated by calling it 'Italian' or 'Neapolitan'. Poles knew it as the 'German' disease, Russians as 'Polish', Persians as 'Turkish', Turks as 'Christian', and Tahitians as 'English' – which, nationalism apart, is patently preposterous since the disease entered Britain a full two years after its appearance in Naples! Much of the opprobrium heaped upon the French was self-inflicted since St Denis, patron saint of France and Paris, was

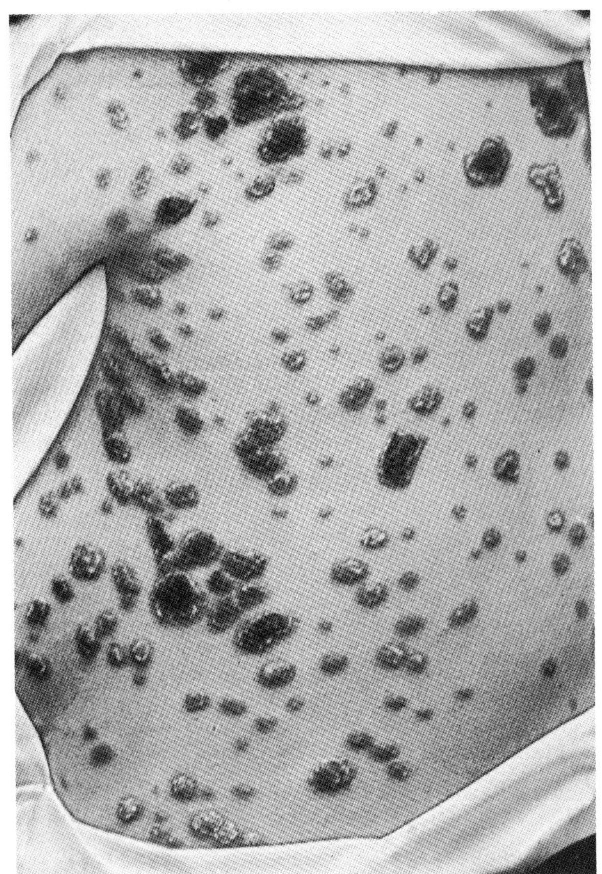

A skin rash caused by syphilis

adopted in 1497 as the patron saint of syphilitics.

The term *venereal disease* to represent 'spread by the agency of Venus' was coined by Jacques de Bethercourt in 1527. *Syphilis* was first used in 1530. In that year Girolamo Fracastoro published his Latin poem *Syphilis, sive Morbus Gallicus*. The poem tells of a disease inflicted by a vindictive deity upon a shepherd called Syphilis who had had the temerity to complain that a drought was killing off his sheep. The excessiveness of the punishment can be judged by Fracastoro's references to rotting pustules the size of acorns, sloughing skin exposing the muscles and joints beneath and the fearful nocturnal agonies of the shepherd. Implicit in the poem was the notion that this most loathsome of diseases was a retribution from on high, the just reward for a dissolute life.

Medical terminology is somewhat academic since both physician and patient alike have called the disease, up to recent times, simply, the 'pox'.

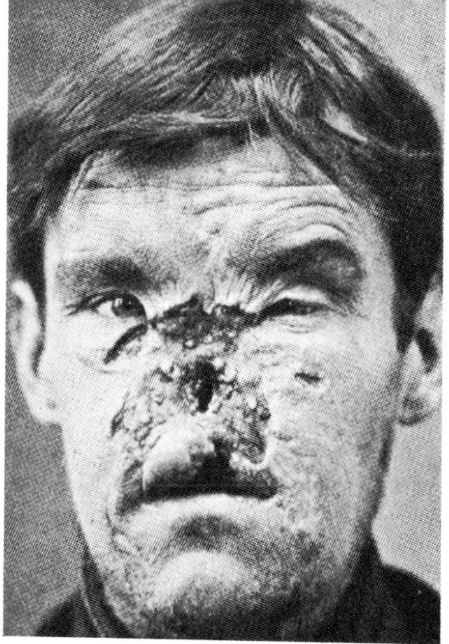

Facial destruction in syphilis

### *Causes and remedies*

The wrath of God was the most widely invoked reason for the appearance of the new disease, and this explanation continued to hold sway until it became uncomfortably obvious that many of the victims of this retributive scourge were innocent babies who were afflicted from birth. Did God, if He was indeed responsible, really intend that the sins of the father be visited on succeeding generations?

Astrologers came up with an alternative explanation, which could account for the affliction of the innocent as well as the guilty. Coradin Gilini, writing in 1497, gave the cause as 'the conjunction of Saturn and Mars which took place on the 16th January, 1496, about noon'. He hedged his bets by adding, 'Or it may have been the conjunction of Jupiter and Mars which occurred on the 17th November 1494.' Either event put syphilis well beyond the control of Man.

Deliberate poisoning was always a popular explanation for medieval death on the grand scale. In Charles VIII's Italian campaign it was rumoured that his troops had been served wine which had been infected with leper blood.

If syphilis came to your town, one option was to get as far away as quickly as possible. If you tarried and came down with the disease, your journey might be an enforced one. In 1497 an epidemic broke out in Scotland. King James decreed that all victims should quit Edinburgh and travel to the island of Inch Keith for treatment. Anyone failing to leave by dusk on the following Monday 'shall be burnt on the cheek with the marking iron'.

Cardinal Wolsey was accused of infecting King Henry VIII with syphilis by blowing in his ear.

Whilst the exact cause of syphilis was unknown to its early victims, it was widely appreciated to be a venereal disease, spread by sexual intercourse. If the greater the number of consorts increased the likelihood of contracting syphilis, then sexual abstinence was the surest way of guarding against the disease. But even when one caught syphilis, and the tell-tale genital ulcer and inguinal buboes appeared, all was not lost. In 1497 Bishop Gaspare Torrella, physician to the Borgias, advised that the genital pustule be sucked 'by some person of low condition'. When the poison was drawn, the penis was washed and wrapped around with a live flayed chicken, pigeon or frog. (This class differential between victim and therapist did not obscure the fact that syphilis was no respecter of social position: 'When it emerged from its hiding place in the body, pox often betrayed the difference between appearance and reality, between bravado and pretended distinction and the common rottenness inside.' Others pointed to the fallacy of rank obscuring the diagnosis: after all an admiral was once a tar, and a bishop an undergraduate!)

In such an atmosphere of fear and ignorance, charlatans were bound to flourish. Foul-tasting and dangerous 'panaceas' were marketed, usually containing mercury. The side-effects of mercury treatment were such as to prompt one sufferer to observe that a night with Venus had resulted in a lifetime with mercury! Patients would

Hogarth's *Marriage à la Mode*, depicting Viscount Squanderfield consulting a venereologist

submit to mercury ointments ladled on to the skin. As a consequence, gums would swell, teeth would loosen and fall out, and vast volumes of fetid saliva would flow from the gaping ulcerated mouth. Some attempted to make mercury treatment more acceptable by connoting the saliva as carrying away the syphilitic poisons from the body. Rabelais paints a vivid picture of a patient having to endure mercury therapy: 'Their teeth quivered like the keys on an organ or spinet when they are played, and they foamed at the mouth like a wild boar driven into the toils by hounds'. Mercury also induced shaking and paralysis, though these were not generally regarded as side-effects, but further manifestations of syphilis. A spurious efficacy was claimed for mercury when treatment coincided with spontaneous recovery in the primary or secondary stages of the disease, or when the patient entered the latency period. The pain of mercury treatment was regarded by the pious as appropriately punitive for sinners. A famous quack, Joseph Cam, attempted to restore faith in mercury: 'How many Fathers have entailed Misery on their Progeny from ill-cured Poxes?'

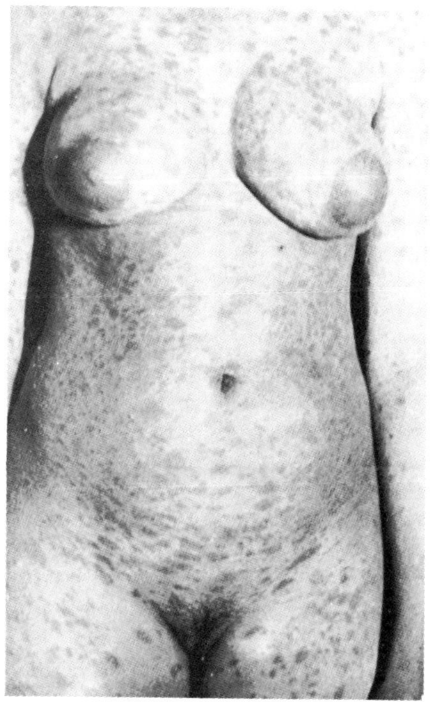

The rash of secondary syphilis

Mercury was used in many different ways. The most usual form was as an ointment: anti-venereal underpants, coated with mercury, became available in seventeenth-century Italy. Increasing doses of mercury were prescribed, until salivation or diarrhoea supervened. Mercury was also given as an enema, or by mouth in the form of pills or medicines. The great advantage of oral administration was that treatment could be carried out in secret: erring husbands and sons could self administer mercurial therapy without the necessity of informing wives or parents. Indeed, an unfaithful husband could ease his conscience by clandestinely treating his spouse by putting mercury chloride into her food or drink. 'By this means concord can be maintained in the household.' Paul Chamberlen (1635–1717) advertised that his lotions would be 'privately sent', doubtless in a former day version of the plain brown envelope!

The 'supremacy' of mercury was intermittently challenged by preparations made from powdered bark of the gaiac tree. Such remedies were drunk in large doses at the same time as the patient was wrapped in blankets to encourage sweating. It was reckoned that as the gaiac tree grew in Hispaniola, and since this was also the source of the deadly new disease, what could be more natural that Nature should have provided the cure close to hand?

What the active ingredient was in guaiac – if indeed there was one at all – was a matter of speculation. It is interesting that the patient was induced to sweat, as if in a fever. Such 'fever therapy' may explain the beneficial effects sometimes found when syphilitic patients are deliberately given malaria! A Viennese scientist, Wagner von Jauregg, gained remarkable success by injecting his patients with malaria parasites. The treatment undeniably worked in some cases, though no one was able to say why. Von Jauregg was awarded the Nobel Prize in 1927, though his discovery may have been made earlier, and serendipitously, by Cellini, some four centuries before (see below).

### *Rakes and whores*

The surest way of keeping out of the clutches of the charlatan was to ensure health through abstinence. Jean Drouyn, a sixteenth-century poet, observed,

> For to keep a man's lance out of any old hole
> The Great Pox was created

Chastity or fidelity was widely expounded, but the message was lost on many. For those unable to resist the temptations of the flesh, there were a number of prophylactic methods to reduce the risk of contracting syphilis. Some semblance of hygiene could be practised by washing the male and female genitalia with wine or vinegar before indulging in the sexual act. Wiser counsel advocated ablutions *after* as well as *before* coitus. One doctor advised a variant of the maxim that 'if it t'were to be done it were best it t'were done quickly', arguing, no doubt, that speed reduced the opportunities for the venereal poison to take root.

In the seventeenth century those not afflicted by syphilis took the moral high ground and roundly condemned those that were. The only exceptions to such censure were babies infected by wet-nurses and wives innocently infected by philandering husbands. Although syphilis was sometimes known as 'cavalier's disease' or the 'gentleman's disease', in general, societies have sought to regard it as shameful and to deliberately underestimate its incidence. Bills of Mortality (the former death certificates) rarely mentioned syphilis. This omission was primarily to protect the memory of the deceased and the feelings of his family, but also served to show that England, say, was a less debauched country than France or Italy or Spain or anywhere else.

Even the unfaithful husband was often regarded (by men, of course) as the innocent dupe of immoral and calculating women who had set out to enslave him and to revel in the consequences of his infidelity:

Those who are full of lust
Carry their wealth and their health
Into my stinking crevasse.

The eighteenth century saw a transitory shift in outlook, to a less condemnatory attitude towards venereal victims. Pangloss, in Voltaire's *Candide*, had ended up as a pustular beggar, nose eaten away and spitting teeth. He had caught his pox from Paquette, a maid, who had been infected by a Franciscan who 'had caught it from an old countess who had got it from a cavalry captain, who had it from a marquess, who had it from a page, who had got it from a Jesuit, who, as a novice, had got it in a direct line from one of the companions of Christopher Columbus'.

But such tolerance was rare. More often the victim had to labour under a profound social stigma. To be a syphilitic was to suffer a terrible affliction. But added to the physical pain was the mental anguish of knowing that friend and foe alike knew exactly how you came to fall the victim of such a dreadful disease. The censorious deemed the syphilitic debauched, a slave to primitive and carnal lusts, a profligate bee savouring the corrupted goods harboured in the honey pots of whores. Such was the abhorrence that virtuous women were known to wear gloves when reading *Bubu de Montparnasse* because it was a book about syphilis.

Men looked for scapegoats – and found them in women. Paracelsus (1493–1541) believed syphilis to have originated 'between a French leper and a Neapolitan whore' whilst she was menstruating.[4] Although the leper was presumably a male, females – especially prostitutes – have long been singled out for especial approbation. Women who enjoyed sex or sought orgasm were particularly dangerous. For the male, the sooner the business was done, the less the risk: all pretence of satisfying the woman was abandoned, and premature ejaculation became a prophylactic against venereal disease.

I send for my whore, when for fear of a clap
I dally about her, and spew in her lap.[5]

Since the early signs of syphilis in the female often involved the cervix, deep within the vagina, the potential male customer was encouraged to carry out an internal examination before introducing his privy part into such a potentially infected cavity. Jean Drouyn again:

But make sure you don't start the job
Without a candle; don't be afraid to
Take a look, both high and low,
And then you may frolic to your heart's content.

In our own century men were made aware of the subtler signs of the pox: they should surreptitiously stroke the woman's neck to check for swellings; give special attention to her mouth, lips, gums and teeth; and look for blotches on the breasts.

The drawback to such advice was two-fold: it made the assumption that the male partner knew what he was looking for; it also overlooked the likelihood that the examination might take place before an infected woman showed any outward physical signs of the disease (some three to five days), or after the primary lesion or secondary rash had disappeared. Consider the difficulties of accurate diagnosis experienced by a lay fornicator operating in a dimly lit bedroom, when even doctors, working in optimal conditions, were prone to misdiagnosis. Medical students have long been taught to regard syphilis as the 'Great Imitator', the 'Proteus of sicknesses'. (Sir William Osler wisely observed, 'He who knows syphilis knows medicine.') Once the grosser manifestations of primary syphilis have passed, the more subtle signs of secondary and tertiary forms often needed a keen medical eye and years of clinical experience in order to detect lumps on the forehead, roseola, Venus' diadem (copper-coloured spots along the hair line), Venus' necklace (a dirty looking neck covered in white blotches), hoarseness due to involvement of the voice box, and a nasal twang caused by perforation of the palate.

I shall return later in the chapter to consider how male hypocrisy and misogyny have always contrived to put the onus for the spread of syphilis on to females.

Inveterate rakes who could not embrace fidelity could always don *armour*, or condoms. Made of the intestines of animals, condoms (named after a mythical Colonel Cundum or Condom) were used initially to protect against the pox and not against conception. The sheath was first described in 1564 by Gabriello Fallopio. In 1704, John Marten gives the first English description of impregnating lint or linen in his secret anti-venereal remedy, allowing to dry, and

Mid-nineteenth-century condoms adorned with erotic illustrations
(Christie's South Kensington Ltd)

applying to the 'Glans or Nut of the Man's Yard, or to cover the inner parts of the Privity of the Woman'.

In the eighteenth and nineteenth centuries, condoms were very expensive and often not very popular even with those that could afford them. 'The *Condom* being the best, if not the only Preservative our Libertines have found at present, yet, by reason of its blunting the Sensation, I have heard some of them acknowledge that they had often to choose to risk a *Clap*, rather than engage with spears thus sheathed.' Certainly James Boswell often chose sensation over protection (see below).

### *The subsequent history of syphilis*

Syphilis today is not the disease it once was. In terms of mortality, very few people now die of it. This decline in the death rate is not attributable to the discovery of penicillin: syphilis began to diminish in virulence within a short time (some twenty to thirty years) of its appearance at Naples. Within decades the acute and fatal form was replaced by a far more insidious manifestation: no longer a swift death but rather a chronic incapacity. In its virulent form the disease was 'exported' to kill tens of thousands of vulnerable people in India and Asia. It reached Japan in 1512, where, following well-established xenophobic tradition, it was dubbed 'Chinese ulcer'.

We now recognize several diseases spread by sexual intercourse. Two such – gonorrhoea and syphilis – were thought by many physicians in the eighteenth century to be different manifestations of a single disease. According to this theory, syphilis was the consequence of untreated or worsening gonorrhoea. This unitary theory, widely championed in France, was held despite convincing evidence to the contrary. Medical students, perhaps wishing to further their careers (or permanently end them!), had deliberately introduced into their penises material from syphilitic lesions – and had developed syphilis, not gonorrhoea.

### *Did John Hunter inoculate himself with venereal disease?*

Much of the medical thinking of the eighteenth century was steeped in an admixture of superstition and the unchallenged authority of Hippocrates and Galen. John Hunter (1728–93) had a different style altogether. His was a very practical approach, which included experimenting on his live patients and minutely dissecting those that had died. He had no qualms about extracting the sound teeth of healthy, but poor, young women for 'transplantation' into the mouths of his own, richer, patients. He would explore the abdomen of an ass while the animal was still alive, its limbs tethered to stakes in the ground: 'In doing this the animal struggled'.

One of Hunter's most fundamental errors was his belief that an individual could not suffer from two diseases of the same part of the body at the same time. This lead him to deduce that gonorrhoea, chancre and syphilis were all manifestations of a single venereal disease. To prove the truth of his theory, Hunter deliberately and repeatedly inoculated the patients at St George's Hospital, London, with pus taken from venereal sores and ulcers. The assumption has usually been made that Hunter chose 'one of the many destitute outcasts of subnormal mentality who roamed the streets of London at that time'. Another view, put forward by Sir D'Arcy Power, was that Hunter also experimented upon himself.

'On a Friday in May 1767, Hunter inoculated himself with pus from a patient with gonorrhoea to determine whether the poison of gonorrhoea was identical with that producing syphilis.' Four days later the tip of the penis became inflamed and ulcerated [symptoms Hunter took to signify gonorrhoea]. Three weeks later he noticed enlarged glands in his groin, and after another month the right tonsil became ulcerated [signs of syphilis].' It is now thought that Hunter inadvertently inoculated himself with pus which contained the organisms of both gonorrhoea *and* syphilis and thus erroneously deduced the two diseases to be identical. In the late nineteenth century, Hunter's word was law, and as a consequence of his error, the unitary theory was deemed proven. Hunter made a second gaff when he stated that he had not seen any evidence to suggest that syphilis affected the internal organs of the body. Perhaps it was fate at its most capricious that had Hunter die of angina pectoris, which many regard as a late complication of his experimentally induced syphilis.[6]

It was Philippe Ricord, physician to Napoleon III in nineteenth-century France, who distinguished between syphilis and gonorrhoea, and showed them to be two quite distinct diseases: henceforth 'syphilitic gonorrhoea' became a redundant diagnosis.

### *A fitting revenge*

Throughout the centuries, syphilis had been used as an instrument of revenge. Men would conspire with infected whores to give syphilis to rivals, and cuckolded husbands would deliberately infect their unfaithful wives. A prostitute in Maupassant's *Le Lit 29*, who was raped by an infected Prussian, chose not to seek treatment, but to revenge herself by spreading syphilis to as many soldiers as possible. Fiction turned into fact in 1871 when the infected prostitutes of Paris were deliberately let loose on the occupying Prussian troops.

In *Les Diaboliques* by Barbey d'Aurevilly, a duchess whose lover was murdered by her husband, conceived a revenge which would dishonour his name. She became a prostitute. 'In only a few months she was rotten to the bones. One of her eyes had suddenly jumped from its socket one day, and had fallen at her feet like a large coin. The other had liquefied and melted. She had died – but stoically – suffering intolerable tortures.'

A lawyer, whose wife had been seduced by the French King Francis I, haunted the stews of Paris until he found himself an infected whore. He deliberately passed the infection on to his spouse, happy in the knowledge that his monarch would soon be in receipt of something more than pleasure.

## *Truly, Morbus Gallicus*

Some have argued that *Morbus Gallicus* is not such a misnomer. Apart from the fact that the patron saint of France and Paris, St Denis, is also the patron saint of syphilis, it would seem that, over the centuries the spirochaete has shown an undue partiality for French victims, including Voltaire, Louis XV and maybe even Napoleon Bonaparte.[7]

Both Flaubert (1821–80) and Maupassant (1850–93) contracted syphilis. It was said that Maupassant was prouder of his amorous exploits than of his stories. 'He could have an erection at will and once coupled with six prostitutes in an hour; one day he painted a false chancre on his penis and paraded thus in front of his mistress, whom he then raped to make her think he had given her a dose of the pox.' In 1877 he proudly writes to his friend about a real dose of the pox:

> For five weeks I have been taking mercury and potassium iodide, and I feel very well on it. My hair is beginning to grow again and the hair on my arse is sprouting. I've got the pox! At last! Not the contemptible clap, nor the ecclesiastical crystalline, nor the bourgeois coxcombs or the leguminous cauliflowers – no – no, the great pox, the one Francis I died of. The majestic pox, pure and simple; the elegant syphilis. I've got the pox … and I'm proud of it, by thunder. I don't have to worry about catching it any more, and I screw the street whores and trollops, and afterwards I say to them 'I've got the pox.' They are afraid and I just laugh.

Pity poor Maupassant, believing that a single dose of the pox ensured lifelong immunity.

Charles Baudelaire (1821–67) was another great French writer to contract syphilis in the nineteenth century. Baudelaire's mother lavished love and attention on her son, the more so when her husband, thirty years older than she, died. Expelled from school, Baudelaire, an outward mixture of egocentricity and eccentricity, plunged into the hedonistic life of the Parisian Latin Quarter, absorbing into his body opium, hashish and the spirochaete. His father's fortune was spent in self-indulgence and self-delusion. He saw himself as setting the standard of fashion, a French Beau Brummel, strolling conspicuously in the Paris parks, a live lobster on the end of a pale blue cord! Few detected the uncertainty and pathological sensitivity which lay behind this public persona.

Baudelaire's inspiration for his erotic love poems was Jeanne Duval, a mulatto actress. In the early 1840s, Baudelaire's creditors became more insistent and, despite occasional work as a book reviewer, he began to lose his friends, his looks and his joy of life. He could find neither romantic love nor literary fame – though he gained literary notoriety when six of his poems were banned as pornographic. Dispirited, he resorted to opium, as syphilis took further hold of his ailing carcass. Syphilitic dementia, long foreseen and much feared by Baudelaire for many years, became horrible reality. It is said that Baudelaire deliberately infected himself with syphilis so as to ensure that his poetry was rooted firmly in the real and experiential world. Always fastidious, he ended up unable to stop himself urinating and defecating, dying at the age of forty-six in his mother's arms.

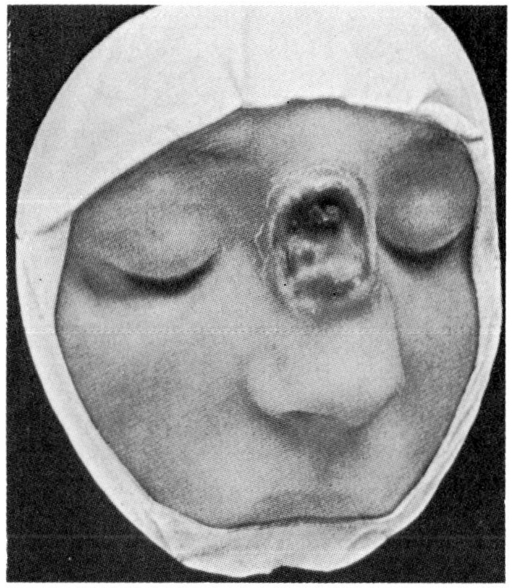

Nasal destruction in syphilis

Théophile Gautier (1811–72), French poet and novelist, describes the pox on a visit to Rome.

> 'The entire French army has been laid up with it; boils are exploding in groins like shells, and purulent jets of clap vie with the fountains in the Piazza Navona; rhagades and papillomata like coxcombs hang in crimson festoons from the seats of sappers, sapped in their own foundations; tibias are exfoliating in extoses like ancient columns of greenery in a Roman ruin; the deltoids of the staff officers are spangled with constellations of pustules; lieutenants walking in the streets look like leopards, they are so dotted and speckled with roseola, freckles, coffee-coloured marks, warty excrescences, horny and cryptogamic verrucae and other secondary and tertiary manifestations.

In more recent times, eminent French victims of the pox have included Paul Gauguin (1848–1903) and Edouard Manet (1832–83).

### *Famous syphilitics who were not French*

It is not surprising that syphilis is so rarely cited as the cause of death of great men, but this fact has done nothing to dampen down the speculation of biographers. Pre-Columbian cases of dubious authenticity include Herod, whose private parts were 'putrefied and eaten up with worms'; Julius Caesar; Tiberius; and Charlemagne. Pope Ubertinus VIII is said to have died in 1345 of 'a malady of the genitals consequent upon libertinage with women'. On no good evidence the disease is said to have afflicted three popes in a row: Alexander VI (who reigned during the Siege of Naples), Julius II and Leo X. Even Columbus himself is said by some to have contracted syphilis!

Medical historians cannot agree whether King Henry VIII (1491–1547) suffered from syphilis. Proponents cite the many stillbirths of Katherine of Aragon before she finally gave birth to Mary, later to reign as 'Bloody Mary'. Mary showed a number of features suggestive of congenital syphilis: misshapen head, premature aging and poor eyesight. The cruelty which characterized Henry's later years as king may have been the result of syphilitic insanity. Others cite the intractable pain of his syphilitic leg ulcer as responsible for the deaths of hundreds – more even, it was said, than the ingrowing toe-nail of Richard the Bold of Burgundy. Cardinal Wolsey, fancifully held responsible for infecting the king by whispering in his ear, was fortunate to expire on his journey back to London to be executed.

Benvenuto Cellini (1500–71), sculptor and goldsmith, describes in his autobiography contracting syphilis at the age of twenty-nine from a 'fine young servant girl' who doubled as his model. He thought he had cured himself by taking guaiac, but there is a strong suggestion that the cure was brought about by contracting malaria on a trip to Rome. But it is unlikely that the cure was complete, for Cellini later developed tertiary mental signs which made him the prey of some clever salesmen who sold him a farm which would revert back to them on his death: all these con men had to do to 're-inherit' the farm was kill the sculptor. They invited him to dinner and attempted to poison him: happily for Cellini, the ensuing fever resulted, once again, in a great improvement in his health and mental state.[8]

Ivan the Terrible (1530–84) changed from an exemplary king into a sex-crazed, paranoid monarch, probably as a result of syphilis. His excesses are recounted elsewhere in this book. Peter the Great (1672–1725), Tsar of Russia, was an epileptic, an alcoholic and a syphilitic debauchee – the disease probably being contracted in Amsterdam whilst on a European tour. It is remarkable that he survived fifty-three years. The appellation 'Great' is even more remarkable an adjective to be applied to such as Peter, for despite his intellect, culture and military successes, he was an inveterate coward, sadist, a father who almost certainly ordered the murder of his son, and a husband who was intent on executing his second wife when he died of urinary obstruction and kidney failure.

The lengths to which Catharine the Great (1729–96) went to guard against contracting syphilis seem to have been wasted. The Russian Empress used six females, *les Epreuveuses* (the testers), to vet her lovers for overall sexual prowess and genital hygiene. Despite these measures, it seems likely that her son, Paul I, was a congenital syphilitic. Certainly Catharine was moved to found the world's first hospital for the treatment of venereal diseases.

King Christian VII of Denmark contracted syphilis and died an imbecile at the age of fifty-nine.[9]

Syphilis as an explanation of Beethoven's (1770–1827) deafness remains contentious and is considered in detail in chapter 5 on creativity. On firmer ground is the diagnosis of syphilis given to the composer Franz Schubert (1797–1828). Gaetano Donizetti (1797–1848) spent the last seven years of his life with tertiary syphilis (General Paralysis of the Insane): 'He sat all day long with his sunken head bent over to the left of his chest. His eyes were seldom opened, but he was dressed in court dress and wearing all his medals, with his helpless hands dangling in white gloves, while his urine dripped uncontrolled into his clothes.' Epileptic convulsions finally carried him off. The composer Hugo Wolf (1860–1903) caught syphilis at seventeen and died, after terrible mental and physical pain, twenty-six years later.

Syphilis, contracted as a student in Göttingen, more than explains the misogyny of the philosopher Arthur Schopenhauer (1788–1860). Heinrich Heine (1797–1856), German poet and essayist, suffered from tertiary syphilis as did his more famous countryman, Friedrich Nietzsche (1844–1900). Nietzsche contracted syphilis in a brothel when he was twenty-one. One of the most influential of philosophers, author of *Thus Spake Zarathustra* in which he developed his ideas about a superman who extolled rejection of weakness and illness (a concept taken up with alacrity by the Nazis), Nietzsche died an imbecile after ten years of syphilitic insanity. 'He who considered pity a vice became himself pitiable.'[10]

Oscar Wilde (1854–1900) caught syphilis from 'Old Jess' when he was an undergraduate at Oxford, and later dedicated a poem to her.[11]

### *Tertiary syphilis: death, the happy release*

During the latency period, which might last for decades, the outward symptoms of syphilis disappear. But, all too often, the spirochaete is merely biding its time, and saving the worst until last. Vidus Vidius commented, 'The pox may well agree a truce with the patient but it never signs a peace treaty.'

Given enough time, especially if treatment is inadequate, the spirochaete appears to wake from its long slumber and wreak internal havoc in the heart, liver, kidneys, muscles, bone and brain. Huge fungating ulcers (gummata) destroy internal organs and external structures (especially the nose); aneurysms, large balloon-like swellings, grow in the walls of major blood vessels, burst and produce fatal haemorrhages; and the involvement of the spinal cord and brain causes paralysis and madness.

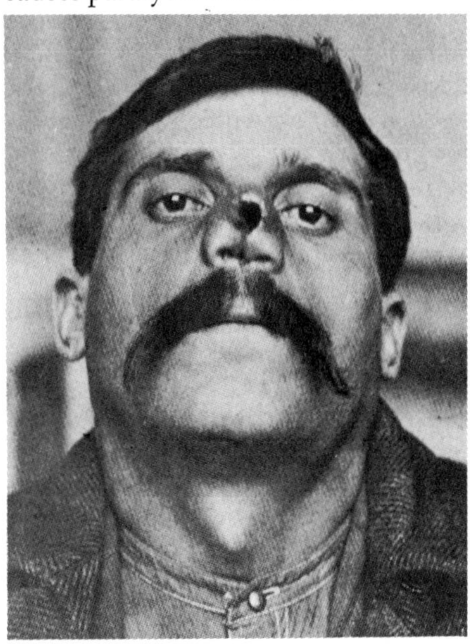

Destruction of the nose in tertiary syphilis

In a mixture of misogyny and commonsense, Addison and Steele wrote about syphilitic destruction of the nose, in *The Tatler* in 1710:

> Whatever young men may think, the nose is a very becoming part of the face; and a man makes a silly figure without it. But it is the nature of youth not to know the value of anything until they have lost it. The general precept, therefore, I would leave with them is to regard every town-woman as a particular kind of Syren that has a design upon their noses, and that amidst her flatteries and allurements they will fancy she speaks to them in that humorous phrase of Old Plautus, *Ego tibi faciem denasabo mordicus*, 'Keep your face out of my way, or I will bite off your nose'.

John Hunter, after his first gaff about the unitary concept of venereal disease, uttered his second when he contended that the brain was one part of the body which was *not* susceptible to the ravages of syphilis. Quite the reverse is the case: according to Fournier 'the nervous system is the victim *par excellence* of tertiary syphilis'. Another called the brain 'syphilis' choice morsel, its treat'. It was not until 1913 that the spirochaete was identified, microscopically hiding in the brains of patients with General Paralysis of the Insane (GPI), thereby providing an organic cause for many cases of previously unexplained madness. Indeed, it is with great sadness and pity that we read of Maupassant's pride in contracting 'elegant syphilis', for sixteen years later, at the age of forty-three, he died incarcerated in a lunatic asylum.

One of the most distressing symptoms of tertiary syphilis is pain – chronic, intractable pain. Pain is a difficult sensation to convey to someone who has not suffered it. And often, when the pain has passed, it is difficult to evoke its quality. Alphonse Daudet, the French poet and novelist, (1840–97) has left us a harrowing account of the agonies – both physical and emotional – of tertiary syphilis. Daudet caught syphilis from a lady of high rank; he then passed it on to his mistress. At the age of forty-four he began to suffer difficulties in walking, an early sign of tabes dorsalis. For the next thirteen years he suffered from the vagaries of the pox. His diary, *La Doulou* ('Pain' or 'Suffering') contains vivid descriptions of his tabetic agonies. Daudet opines 'What use are words for all actually felt in pain? Words come when it [pain] is over and appeased. They describe only the recollections, impotently and falsely. Pain is always fresh for him who suffers it, and banal for the onlookers.'

Daudet wrote: 'Curious pains; great tracks of flame slashing and lighting up my carcass ... Like a ship's keel, so sharp and powerful ... Sometimes under the foot, a fine, fine cut or hair. Or else knife-thrusts under the toe nails. Rats with sharpened teeth, gnawing my toes. Sword-thrusts in the side ... Muscles crushed under a wheel.'

Daudet describes his progressive paralysis, his difficulty in walking, his intolerance of noise and his double vision. His contracted, emaciated state is evoked in poignant prose: 'In my now excavated carcass, made empty by anaemia, pain reverberates like a voice in an empty room. Days, long days, when there is nothing alive within me, except pain.' He ultimately consents to have treatment at a health resort, where he comes across fellow-sufferers. 'Stupor and joy in finding beings who suffer like oneself.' An Italian painter, an appeal judge and the professor of mathematics at Clemont kept him company, to the sound of tabetics falling over their crutches or out of their wheel chairs.

And finally the indignity of the human state brought low by syphilis: 'To watch my neighbours eat was odious; their toothless mouths, their diseased gums, toothpicks in their crumbling molars ... Human bestiality! All their jaws in action, their gluttonous, haggard eyes never raised from their plates ... And the painful digestions, the two WCs at the end of the passage, side by side, lit by the same gas-jet, so that one could hear all the groans of constipation, the splash of excess, and the rustling of paper. The horrors of life!'

## *Randolph Churchill: 'Dying by inches, in public'*

Lord Randolph Churchill (1849–95), father of Winston, born at Blenheim Palace, educated at Eton and Oxford University, married in 1874 the beautiful daughter of an American businessman and entered parliament. His positions under Lord Salisbury, as Secretary for India, Chancellor of the Exchequer and Leader of the House, convinced many that he would eventually lead the Tory party and become Prime Minister. In December 1886, Churchill resigned from high office. Why?

During March to October 1882 Churchill suffered a mysterious and serious illness, which initially changed his life and finally ended it. It was not, as one observer recorded, 'internal piles'. It was syphilis which had taken hold, and General Paralysis of the Insane was destined to foreshorten a brilliant career. His mood swings, always characteristic of the man, became more marked still, often resulting in explosive bouts of temper. He also suffered grievously the side-effects of mercury treatment, whose manifestations, including dizziness, deafness and hoarseness, were becoming noticeable to his friends by the mid-1880s. Although the cause of Churchill's illness was not mentioned openly in his lifetime, the inexorable progression of the disease became a very public matter. His speeches in Parliament became an embarrassment to political friend and foe alike, and Arthur Balfour, an early political ally and later to become Prime Minister, was seen to sit with his face buried in his hands, trying to shut out the painful sight and sound of the inarticulate ramblings of a man losing his reason. *The Times* correspondent recorded that 'nothing more tragical has been seen in the House of Commons in our generation.' Soon the newspapers simply stopped reporting what he said. He died in January 1895 and a vast crowd of mourners were left to ponder on a life prematurely and tragically ended by the spirochaete.

In Frank Harris's *My Life and Loves*, the author records what is purported to be Lord Randolph's own account of how he came to contract syphilis (as told to Louis Jennings). When an undergraduate at Oxford, Churchill, a member of the fashionable Bullingdon Club, had got drunk on brandy and champagne, and had passed out.

> Next morning I woke up with a dreadful taste in my mouth. The paper on the walls was hideous – dirty – and, as I turned in bed, I started up gasping: there was an old woman lying beside me … I slid out of bed and put on shirt and trousers as quietly as I could, but suddenly the old woman in the bed awoke and said, 'Oh, Lovie, you're not going to leave me like that?' She had one long yellow tooth in her top jaw that

> waggled as she spoke ... Downstairs I fled in livid terror. In the street I found a hansom and gave the jarvy the address of a doctor I had heard about ... [the doctor] went to work and said he could find no sign of any abrasion, but he made me up a strong disinfectant and I washed the parts with it. My next week was a nightmare. I made up my mind at once that I deserved gonorrhoea for my stupidity. But no more, no worse: not a chancre, not syphilis! There was nothing, not a sign, for a week. I breathed again. Yet I'd have to wait till the twenty-first day before I could be sure that I had escaped syphilis. Syphilis! Think of it, at my age, I, who was so proud of my wisdom. On the fateful day nothing, not a sign. On the next the doctor examined me again: 'Nothing, Lord Randolph, nothing! I congratulate you. You've got off, to all appearance, scot-free.'[12]

It was a Frenchman, Alfred Fournier, who, in the late nineteenth century, proved that tabes dorsalis and General Paralysis of the Insane (GPI) were late manifestations of syphilis in the spinal cord and brain.

## *Man's scapegoat: woman*

In a civilization, steeped since its inception in ideas of male dominance, it comes as no surprise that the onus of blame for the spread of syphilis should have always fallen on women. The loathing felt for the disease-carrying prostitute is vividly evoked by Zola's *Nana*:

> What lay on the pillow was a charnel-house, a heap of pus and blood, a shovelful of putrid flesh. The pustules had invaded her whole face, so that one pock touched the next ... One eye, the left eye, had completely foundered in the bubbling purulence, and the other, which remained half open, looked like a dark, decaying hole. The nose was still suppurating. A large reddish crust starting on one side of the cheeks was invading the mouth, twisting it into a horrible grin. And around this grotesque and horrible mask of death, the hair, the beautiful hair, still blazed like sunlight and flowed in a stream of gold. Venus was decomposing.

It was inevitable that male-inspired legislation, in the shape of the Contagious Diseases Acts of the late nineteenth century, should target the prostitute, the 'emissary of death', enforcing compulsory medical examinations. (Such examinations of soldiers had been abandoned in 1859 because they were regarded as 'repugnant to the feelings of men'.) The Act of 1866 provided for three-monthly examinations of prostitutes, on the evidence of a single policeman,

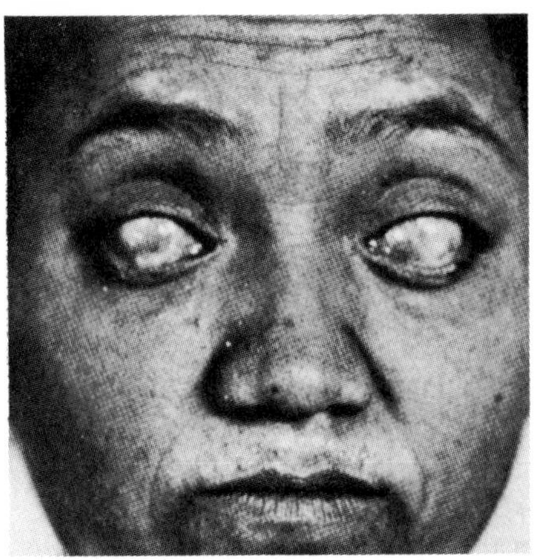

Blindness caused by syphilis

and heard in closed court, and applied especially to those women operating near military bases. Compulsory detention for five days was designed to outwit women who claimed that they could not be examined because they were menstruating. Not surprisingly, women who refused free sexual favours to policemen were more likely to have to submit to these degrading examinations. It was easy for the pious to convince themselves that prostitutes were redeemed by the enforcement of the Acts, and that God's will was being done. But slowly, very slowly, opposition against such barbarism began to be heard, and in 1883 a motion against compulsory examinations was carried in the House of Commons.[13] (Naturally, the virtuous had nothing to worry about. In More's *Utopia*, affianced couples displayed themselves naked to one another so as to prevent deception about their venereal health.)

In 1879, Neisser discovered the gonococcus bacterium, the causative organism of gonorrhoea, but the agent responsible for syphilis proved much more elusive. It was not until 1905 that Schaudinn and Hoffman, working in Berlin, identified the spirochaete, which they christened *Treponema* (because of its resemblance to twisted thread) *pallidum* (because of its pale colour). Soon after, Wassermann reported on a blood test which would detect syphilis.

The search was now on for a substance which would kill the spirochaete, without killing the patient. Paul Ehrlich (1854–1915) was to discover such a 'magic bullet' in May 1909. His discovery was dramatized by Hollywood in 1940 in *Dr Ehrlich's Magic Bullet*, with Edward G. Robinson playing the scientist. Ehrlich, and his Japanese colleague Hata, struck gold on their 606th attempt, an arsenical compound which they called Salvarsan. Their 914th attempt produced a more refined version, Neosalvarsan. With the help of the 'magic bullet', man's defeat of the spirochaete was confidently predicted. Such optimism was to prove premature.

Far from being a spent force, yesterday's scourge, the spirochaete mounted a counter-attack in the chaos that attended the outbreak of the First World War. The numbers of new cases of syphilis soared. As had happened so often in the past, calls went up for the compulsory examination and registration of prostitutes. Patently, the lessons of history had not been learnt and such examinations were to prove mere palliatives to social reformers and quite useless in checking the spread of the disease. Even monthly examinations would miss tell-tale signs if these were carried out during the incubation period of the disease. And besides, a woman given a clean bill of health may contract syphilis on the very same day from her very next client!

In the nineteenth century Ricord had pointed out potential pitfalls in the use of the gynaecological speculum (known by the prostitutes as the government's penis): to conduct a thorough examination it was necessary for the woman to lay on her back, thereby allowing the doctor an unimpeded view of the external and internal genitalia. Since such a position would be awkward to a prostitute wearing a hat, a dangerous 'compromise' was arrived at: the woman would sit back in a reclining chair – but since the doctor's view was thereby severely restricted, the value of the examination was greatly reduced.

When medical examinations were carried out in brothels, madams would spirit away the sick whores and substitute healthier specimens. And even if the prostitute did have the pox, it was still possible to conceal the fact. Animal blood would be daubed on vaginal ulcers as camouflage and make it appear that the woman was having a heavy period: scraps of sheep intestine would be stuck on to hide a chancre; and madam would wipe away any tell-tale mucus when she carried out her own preliminary internal examination. Further, official examinations would have no impact on the armies of casual and unregistered prostitutes (especially teenagers, heavily infected, but considered too young to register), or on high-class prostitutes, the 'ladies of fashion'.

All the regulatory procedures had one fatal flaw: it ignored the client and *his* ability to spread the disease unchecked. Even when attempts were made to keep males under scrutiny – short of actual medical examination, of course – the result was total failure. When Germany occupied France in the Second World War, it allowed its troops to visit brothels, *provided that the prostitutes were for exclusive German use.* (In Germany itself, brothels were forbidden and syphilitics were not to marry on pain of sterilization.) A German doctor was present at the medical examination of the French prostitutes, and a male 'nurse' was posted on the stairs of the brothel to take the names of clients. In every room, 'legible at six metres', a notice required the use of potassium permanganate and a calomel ointment before and after coitus, plus the use of a condom. Any prostitute who flouted the rules was sent to a labour camp, and chemists were forbidden to sell any preparation to German soldiers which could mask venereal disease. And yet, still syphilis raged, and the number of cases increased dramatically, almost all of them referrable to prostitutes who had managed to evade examination.

The amelioration of the symptoms of syphilis over the centuries has been viewed as the monster 'settling in' rather than 'settling down'. Since the Christian Church condemned sexual intercourse other than for procreation, no one was prepared to admit to fornication, with its overtones of indulgent pleasure. Thomas Parran, Surgeon General of the United States Public Health Service in the last century, said, 'Nice people don't talk about syphilis, nice people don't have syphilis, and nice people shouldn't do anything about those who do have it.' Even sworn enemies hesitated from calling each other syphilitic. In Victorian England the disease was almost never referred to by name, and open discussion in polite circles was unthinkable. Consequently, few knew anything about the disease, least of all how to protect themselves from contracting it. It became a commonplace to regard the total abolition of prostitution as the only sure method of eradicating syphilis, on the assumption that the spread of the disease was the sole responsibility of the prostitute. Many who regarded the abolition of prostitution as unrealistic, nevertheless advocated regulation of prostitutes (by regular medical examinations) and notification of those at risk.

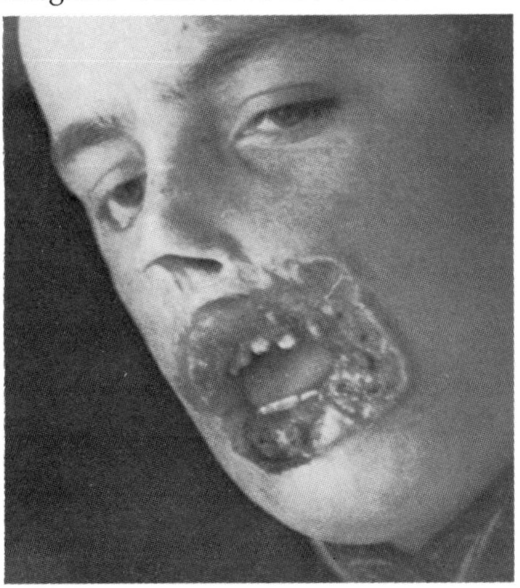

Naso-oral destruction in congenital syphilis

Notification of third parties of their risk of contracting syphilis could only be done with the patient's consent – unless the doctor was willing to break medical confidentiality. What was the doctor to do if, after diagnosing syphilis, his patient refused to inform other people whom he may have infected? In many cases doctors chose to reject Hippocrates in favour of the continuing health of their patients' sexual partners. The doctor in *Les Avariés* chose to keep his patient's secret.

*Les Avariés*, known in England as *Damaged Goods*, was written by Eugène Brieux at the turn of the present century, and sought to address the issue of syphilis in marriage. A man, about to marry, is told by his doctor that he has syphilis, and is advised to postpone his marriage until treatment has been shown to be effective. The patient knows that the doctor must adhere strictly to the code of medical confidentiality, and, despite lurid descriptions of the fate which will befall his wife and any children the couple may have, decides to go ahead with his marriage. Not unexpectedly, the child is born with congenital syphilis. The Avarié's father-in-law visits the doctor to obtain a certificate which will enable his daughter to get a divorce. The doctor refuses on the grounds of medical confidentiality. The doctor also points out to the father-in-law that, unless he can *honestly* say that he has *never* strayed from the straight and narrow, then the fact that he does not suffer from this 'shameful disease' is pure good fortune and nothing else. The doctor goes on to show that the only chance of combatting syphilis is for society to address the issues openly and compassionately.

*Les Avariés* was banned in Paris and it took until the next year, 1902, for it to be staged in Liège and Brussels. In 1913 it went to Broadway and was given a special performance in Washington before President Wilson. Its publication in Great Britain, despite a preface written by George Bernard Shaw, was held up for a decade: publishers turned the play down, saying that their other authors had threatened to leave if a work about syphilis was published. (The subject of congenital syphilis was tackled, head on, by Henrik Ibsen in *Ghosts*, where the sexual excesses of a father are visited upon his son, and a mother has to look on helplessly as he sinks further and further into imbecility.[14])

In Britain, there had been attempts to include syphilis in the Notification of Diseases Act of 1889 which had succeeded in reducing the numbers of some contagious diseases. It was believed by some that notification, followed by compulsory isolation, would effectively stop the spread of syphilis. The Vigilance Association for the Defence of Personal Rights was formed to counter what was seen as legalized intimidation and persecution of transgressors. It invoked the Hippocratic Oath, which upheld the concept of medical confidentiality above all else. Besides, the Association argued, notification was self-defeating: anyone who suspected that he might suffer from syphilis would not seek treatment and would do his very best to conceal the fact for fear of confinement. Or he would seek the help of charlatans. In the face of such cogent arguments against compulsory notification, the issue was quickly dropped – only to be resurrected in the 1980s in connection with AIDS.

### *Clap: the other venereal disease*

Venereal disease is not synonymous with syphilis. It is a medical umbrella term which subsumes a variety of other conditions spread by sexual intercourse, most notably gonorrhoea, commonly known as 'clap'. Gonorrhoea was known as 'chaudepisse' in France and 'brenning' (burning) in England. John Ardene advised in 1370: 'The yard of a man or the wicket of a woman should be treated if they be brent with heat and great swelling.' *Clap*, replaced chaudepisse in the sixteenth century, after which 'pox' and 'clap' became hopelessly confused in public usage.

One of the most inveterate philanderers who suffered from clap was James Boswell (1740–95), famous for his biography of Dr Johnson. The details of his compulsive sexual exploits, and their painful and ultimately fatal medical consequences, were meticulously recorded in his journal. Here, Boswell chronicles his encounters with women, from the time of his sexual initiation in London in 1760 with Miss Sally Forrester at the Blue Periwig.

In that year Boswell had fled Scotland and his father's influence for the high life of London. He began a lifelong dalliance with prostitutes and soon contracted his first attack of gonorrhoea. He is reckoned to have had nineteen attacks in all, between 1760 and 1790. After an attack he would often resolve to mend his ways: 'This season, I have never been, nor do I intend again to be a guest in the mansions of gross sensuality.'

But his resolve was invariably short-lived, as an entry for 1761 testifies. 'I had now been some time in town without female sport, I determined to have nothing to do with whores, as my health was of great consequence to me.' In his quest for safe sex from clean women he attempted unsuccessfully to bed an old flame. He resorted again to prostitutes.

> I picked up a girl in the Strand; went into a court with the intention to enjoy her in armour [i.e., to use a condom]. But she had none. I toyed with her. She wondered at my size, and said if I ever took a girl's maidenhead, I would make her squeak. I gave her a shilling and had enough command of myself to go without touching her. I afterwards trembled at the danger I had escaped. I resolved to wait cheerfully till I got some safe girl or was liked by some woman of fashion.

The 'safe girl' he *thought* he had found was an actress named Anne Lewis (Louisa in his journal). Boswell 'toyed with her' but was horrified to find that he could not get an erection. 'I sweated with anxiety which made me worse.' Fortunately for his delicate ego, at the moment of what should have been his 'triumphal entry', the couple were disturbed by the landlady. Consummation came ten days later in a tavern. 'A more voluptuous night I never enjoyed. Five times was I fairly lost in the supreme rapture. Louisa was madly fond of me; she declared I was a prodigy, and asked me if this was not extraordinary for human nature. I said twice as much might be, but this was not, although in my own mind I was somewhat proud of my performance.'

What Boswell and the medical profession did not know at that time was that a woman could appear healthy and yet be carrying the organism responsible for gonorrhoea. With our retrospectroscope we can be certain that Louisa was just such a 'healthy carrier', because six days later Boswell developed his third attack of the clap after having been symptom-free for two years. He experienced 'a little heat in the members of my body sacred to Cupid'. Boswell was indignant and, at first, refused to believe that Louisa was the source of his troubles. Later he changed his mind. 'There is scarcely a possibility that she could be innocent of the crime of horrid imposition ... she is in all probability a most consummate dissembling whore.' He immediately demanded repayment of five guineas which he had loaned her and stated that he had 'nothing more to say'.

Unable to accept any responsibility for his condition, Boswell, in the manner of 'rakes', was soon recovered and picking up women in St James's Park. Over the years, Boswell was to know many women in many countries, including an affair with Thérèse Le Vasseur, Rousseau's former mistress. In 1765, in Rome, he fell victim to another venereal condition – crabs. 'Discovered beasts. Shaved; ludicrous distress.' Occasionally Boswell appeared to look upon his recurrent bouts of clap as 'a just retribution for my licentiousness', but, as the years passed, he would frequently get drunk and prowl the streets of London looking for whores. It is likely that from the mid-1760s Boswell was never completely free of gonorrhoea. Perhaps it was his dormant sense of conscience that made him resort to drinking a bottle a day of Kennedy's Lisbon Diet Drink – a concoction of sarsaparilla, sassafras, licorice and guaiac wood, purporting to be a cure for venereal diseases – in the months leading up to his marriage.

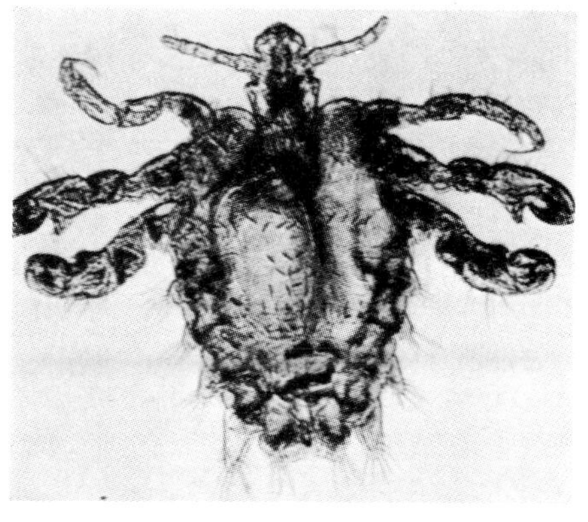

'Crabs': minute creatures which live in pubic hairs

For three years following his marriage Boswell was faithful to his wife, but such fidelity could not possibly last. With fresh whoring came fresh attacks of clap. Boswell had to subject himself to treatment with acidic solutions delivered up into the penis by a hypodermic syringe. His recording of his activities with Betsy Smith, Margaret Rudd and Polly Wilson give these prostitutes' names some form of immortality. Margaret, his long-suffering wife, succumbed to tuberculosis in 1789, leaving him to care for their five adolescent children. But Boswell was on the decline, having developed a urethral stricture (a permanent constriction of the channel through which urine is voided from the bladder) caused by chronic gonorrhoeal infection. Yet still there was a compulsion in his need for sex: 'I had eat and drunk a little at Lord Lonsdale's ... I was heated. I rashly went three times in the course of this day to a stranger.'

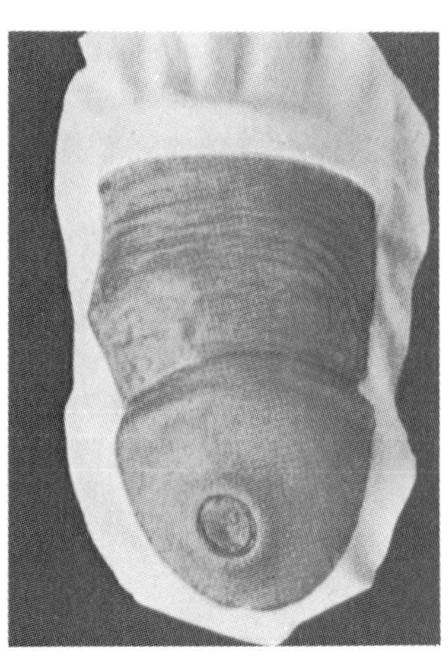

A penile gumma in syphilis

Boswell died on 19 May 1795 from kidney failure, the success of his *Life of Samuel Johnson* in 1791 giving him deserved recognition and establishing his name in English letters. Many authorities have questioned why an intelligent man, so full of potential, indulged in such compulsive self-injurious behaviour, which he must have been aware would cause him chronic ill-health and hasten his death. One theory has been put forward that Boswell's behaviour was a rebellion against the constraints placed upon him by his father, Lord Auchinleck, a distinguished Scottish judge. It is telling that Lord Auchinleck, who did not approve of his son's future wife, refused to attend the wedding. Instead, Boswell's father chose to attend another wedding – his own to his second wife – *on the same day*! As William Ober has observed: 'History records few more striking examples of the use of synchronous sexual competition by a father to perpetuate castration anxiety in his son.'[15]

King Edward VII (1841–1910) gave gonorrhoea to his queen, Alexandra. The gonococcus is held by some to be the cause of the 'Alexandrine limp', a painful condition of the heel caused by Reiter's disease. Frederick the Great developed gonococcal orchitis (inflammation of the testicles) and was castrated.

### *Venereal update: syphilis in the penicillin age*

Penicillin, discovered in the 1940s, was found to be an effective treatment for all forms of syphilis, and prevalence figures plunged dramatically – until the middle of the sixties. The sexual revolution of the 1960s, together with the Gay Liberation movement of the 1970s has seen an upturn in the incidence of syphilis (and all other venereal diseases, including herpes and AIDS). Promiscuous, unprotected sex exacts a fearful price – a lesson that the present younger generation is as unlikely to heed as its predecessors, including the foot soldier laying siege to Naples 500 years ago.

# 12 AIDS

## *The story so far ...*

On 1 December 1992, World AIDS Day, the media trumpeted news of an impending apocalypse: despite the best efforts of governments, someone, somewhere, was becoming infected every eighteen seconds, and by the year 2,000 there would be forty million HIV-positive individuals worldwide. It is likely that the news failed to reach the majority of people in the Third World, and that those in developed countries who did hear it, probably paused over their cornflakes only long enough to utter a loud 'Tut!', and bemoan the fact that gays, blacks and drug addicts never learn.

What is this disease which appears to have governments on the run, and induces such hostility towards minority groups? Acquired Immune Deficiency Syndrome, mercifully abbreviated to AIDS, is a cumbersome but descriptive name for a disease which made its first appearance in America in the summer of 1981. By 1987 it was recognized worldwide: 'AIDS has become a global epidemic threatening the health of mankind throughout the world. With an estimated 80% mortality two years from diagnosis, and with the present lack of any effective preventative or curative therapies, the disease is the most serious epidemic of the twentieth century.'

Essentially, AIDS patients lose the ability to fight infections, and thereby become prey to a multitude of 'opportunistic' micro-organisms which, in the normal course of events, they would have no problem keeping at bay. Because of the sheer number of potential pathogens able to cause disease in man, AIDS can present with a bewildering variety of symptoms. Bacteria, viruses and fungi – many of which are usually fairly innocuous – take on virulent and life-threatening characteristics. The protean manifestations suffered by AIDS victims include pneumonia, liver disease, dementia and skin cancer.

## *AIDS: a worldwide pandemic*[1]

Although retrospective testing of blood samples stored over decades has shown that AIDS predates the 1970s, it was only in the middle of that decade that the current pandemic began. (According to retrospective testing, the first American to die of AIDS was a 28-year-old male from Tennessee who succumbed to pneumocystic pneumonia in 1952.) By 1980, AIDS had spread to most countries in the world, *but still went unrecognized as a discrete disease entity.* It was only in the next year, 1981, when five cases of *Pneumocystis carinii* pneumonia were reported in previously young and healthy men in Los Angeles, that doctors realized a new and sinister disease was abroad. A virus, the putative cause of the new disease, was discovered in 1983, and blood tests soon showed that a person may harbour the virus in the body *without* experiencing any symptoms of AIDS. These carriers were categorised as Human Immunodeficiency Virus-positive (HIV-positive). In time it became clear that people who tested HIV-positive could later go on to develop full-blown AIDS, though this may take many years.

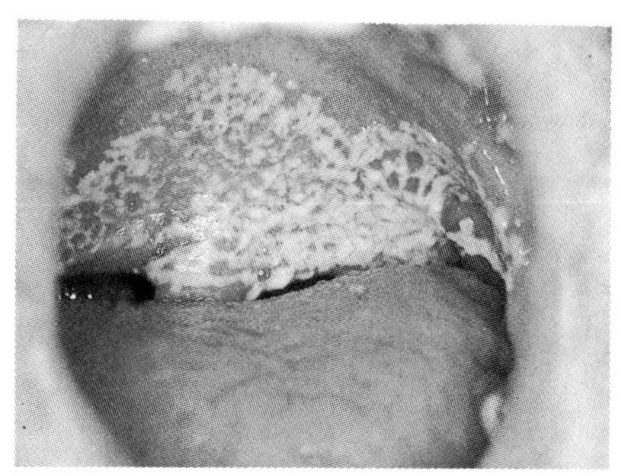

Thrush: caused by a fungus which is allowed to flourish in AIDS because of an impaired immune system

The human immunodeficiency virus (HIV) has been found in semen, cervical secretions, plasma (blood with the cells removed), cerebrospinal fluid (the fluid which bathes the brain and spinal cord), tears, saliva, urine and breast milk. *But this should not to be taken to imply that these fluids are equally capable of transmitting the virus, though semen and blood are particularly infectious.* Although widely regarded as a venereal disease, non-sexual spread can occur in intravenous drug abusers who share infected needles, recipients of transfused blood from an infected donor, or persons receiving infected organ transplants. Pregnant mothers can spread the virus to their unborn babies. It is not possible to catch AIDS (or, to be more precise, the virus which causes AIDS) by shaking hands with someone who is already infected. Neither is it possible to catch the disease in swimming-pools, by sharing eating and cooking utensils, or breathing the same air as AIDS victims.

Another theoretical non-sexual method of spread which has caused concern in the media in recent years is the risk posed to patients from doctors suffering from AIDS. In early 1993, in Britain, a great deal of press and television coverage was given to three separate cases where doctors had died of AIDS. Emergency 'hot-lines' were inundated by former patients seeking reassurance about the minimal risk they ran of contracting the disease – a risk made virtually infinitesimal if the doctor had not been involved in 'invasive' medical techniques and where, therefore, no possibility existed for his infected body fluids to admix with those of his patient. Worldwide, there is no authenticated instance of AIDS having been transmitted from doctor to patient, though there are a number of cases where a patient has given the disease to his doctor. Following the publicity in Britain, many called for three-monthly HIV testing of all medical personnel, placing a patient's right to know his doctor's HIV status above the doctor's right to privacy. Others regarded such compulsory testing as an expensive and largely futile gesture, which might go some way to allay public anxiety but would be of very limited utility in stopping the spread of the disease. It was thought that the medical profession might feel itself threatened and that a positive test would say less about the patient's risk of AIDS, and more about the doctor's sexual preferences.

### *Someone else's problem: AIDS and homosexuality*

The mode of transmission which has caused the most concern and which is not in debate, is the spread of AIDS from an infected to a non-infected person by sexual intercourse. Since the greater the number of partners, the greater the risk of contracting AIDS, the disease flourishes in those who indulge in promiscuous sex. By sexual intercourse, men can transmit the virus to women, women can transmit the virus to men, *and men can transmit the virus to other men*. In the developed world, AIDS has become inextricably linked in the public consciousness with promiscuous homosexuals – a coupling that was not weakened when separate links between AIDS and haemophiliacs became apparent in 1982. Although lesbians are not spared, the risks to male homosexuals, because of the penetrative and traumatic nature of their sexual acts, are infinitely greater. In the early 1980s the disease was often called GRID: Gay-related Immune Deficiency. The acronym AIDS was given a second meaning which signified the reaction of many Americans to the disease and homosexuals who suffered from it: America's Ideal Death Sentence.

Sociologists have identified three possible trends in the 1970s which may have contributed to homosexuals' increased risk of contracting AIDS: the Gay Liberation Movement and the profusion of homosexual bath-houses and sex clubs which sprang up, where a man might have fifteen to twenty anonymous partners in a single night; the emergence of a wide variety of sexually transmitted micro-organisms; and the widespread use of recreational drugs, such as nitrites, used to promote relaxation of anal muscles, and associated with 'fast lane sex'.

In America, homophobic prejudice was widespread and not confined to right-wing politicians or members of the Moral Majority. A man refused to serve on a jury because the defendant was a homosexual; Delta airline staff attempted to stop gays flying; victims were abandoned by relatives or dismissed by their bosses. One employer demanded that a gay member of his staff, who had been absent for one day, bring a medical certificate as proof that he did not have AIDS. More reprehensible was the prejudice of medical, nursing and dental staff: some doctors would refuse to operate on anyone thought to have AIDS, except in the direst of life-threatening emergencies. Apart from pitiable haemophiliacs and those congenitally infected, it was customary to regard all other AIDS victims as having brought about their own demise, as if they had deliberately chosen to reject health, happiness and life in favour of disease, misery and death.

Some believed that harsh penalties must be meted out to those homosexuals who knowingly and deliberately spread the virus to others. A lesbian protester who spat at a policeman was threatened with a charge of attempted murder. In America, a court found a man with AIDS guilty of 'assault with a deadly or dangerous weapon' when he bit two prison officers. Another was convicted for attempted murder for splattering his blood at a policeman.

Conspiracy theories abounded. Gay men were accused of deliberately entering into bisexual relationships in order to spread the disease to the heterosexual population. The deliberate contamination of blood for transfusion into heterosexuals was regarded as another gay plot, reminiscent of Jews accused of poisoning wells at the height of the Black Death. One thug, a member of a gang which had just beaten up a homosexual, telephoned the San Francisco AIDS Foundation wondering about his chances of having contracted the disease.

Even though AIDS has never been regarded as the *exclusive* province of homosexuals – witness *The Sun*'s headline, 'Gay Bug Kills Gran' – the threat to heterosexuals has been judged to be mainly from infected bisexuals and prostitutes. Press coverage of AIDS, especially on the annual World AIDS Days, served to focus the public's attention on the risks of heterosexual spread. Such publicity would induce transitory panic and resolution, followed by apathy and ennui. Rationalization would soon revert to conceptualizing AIDS as the 'Gay Plague'. People persuaded themselves that the risk to heterosexual, non-drug abusing individuals was extremely remote: all one had to do was avoid the company of gays – if possible, avoid breathing the same air, just to be on the safe side. To rid society of this scourge it was necessary to wage war on homosexuals (and drug addicts), nice ones like Rock Hudson notwithstanding. Sexual deviancy must not go unpunished: decency must prevail, the innocent must be protected at all costs. In 1986, a county councillor in Britain came up with his final solution – 'gas 90 per cent of queers'. What criteria did the other 10 per cent fulfil in order to escape this Nazi solution?

## *Out of Africa?*

The student of AIDS can draw many parallels with the scourges of the past. Two prominent themes in the history of syphilis were the propensity to deny its very existence in a country, and the reluctance to even consider that it may have actually originated in that country. Thus has it been with AIDS. The First International Conference on AIDS, held in Atlanta in 1985, sought to focus on AIDS as a disease which threatened the health of the whole world, but such was the stigma attaching to AIDS that many countries denied its existence on their soil. These countries, aping the reactions of individuals, contrived to show that AIDS was someone else's problem: to the East it was a disease of the West; to the communists it was a capitalist affliction; Americans have pointed the finger at Africa and Haiti; the French right has blamed Arabs; and Japan has blamed 'foreigners' indiscriminately. National governments are increasingly demanding proof of freedom from AIDS when a traveller returns from what is considered a high-risk area.

One popular theory to account for the emergence of AIDS was that the virus originated in animals, particularly monkeys, in Central Africa, spread to man, then travelled on to Haiti, America and Europe. Whatever its scientific merits, this theory fits neatly into the white man's commonly held conception of AIDS as a disease of black people and Africa, affecting the whole of the continent to an equal extent – ignoring wide racial, ethnic and cultural variations. An example of this cavalier approach to Africa is the television journalist who said in a news bulletin, 'A million people may die, or maybe two million, we just don't know.' It has been pointed out that such a statement would not be tolerated if applied to estimates of European mortality. Edinburgh Scots who vehemently objected to AIDS being attributed to their city had no such reservations about its attribution to African blacks.

Further, there is often a covert racist agenda whereby 'primitive' black sexual mores are assumed to include homosexuality and bestiality – some have even explained the origin of AIDS in humans by envisaging sexual intercourse between man and monkey. The term 'New Black Death' emphasizes in the minds of many the racial dimension to this modern scourge.

AIDS in tropical countries has little to do with homosexuality or drug abuse: it is a disease found more commonly in promiscuous heterosexuals, affecting as many women as men, especially prostitutes, and frequently associated with other sexually transmitted diseases such as gonorrhoea and syphilis. Unborn babies are at high risk from their infected mothers. In Africa, men tend to marry late and often have to leave their wives in rural areas while they seek work in the towns. In many African cultures there are strong taboos forbidding sexual intercourse during pregnancy and menstruation. Consequently, many African men have a large number of sexual partners, often prostitutes, and this situation encourages the spread of sexually transmitted diseases, including AIDS – especially given the low rate of condom use.

The opportunistic infections afflicting African AIDS patients include cryptococcosis, oro-oesophageal candidiasis, toxoplasmosis, cryptoporidiosis, herpes, cytomegalovirus infection and tuberculosis. Only 14 per cent of Africans present with *Pneumocystis carinii* pneumonia, compared to 60 per cent Americans or Europeans. Clearly, opportunistic infection reflects those micro-organisms which are most common locally, and it can be anticipated that African AIDS will be found in association with such diseases as malaria, tuberculosis and leprosy. The clinical presentation with diarrhoea and gross weight loss has been popularly referred to as 'slim disease'. Aggressive Kaposi's sarcoma, a form of skin cancer, is also found in African AIDS.

Grave misgivings have recently been voiced about the supposed prevalence of AIDS in Africa. Doctors and researchers working in Africa openly doubt the accuracy of findings reported in the Western medical journals. The vast majority of people in Africa who have been labelled HIV-positive *have never had a blood test*. The diagnosis has been made solely on clinical findings. Unfortunately, the three major clinical symptoms of AIDS – weight loss, diarrhoea and chronic cough – are the very same clinical symptoms as tuberculosis. Without laboratory tests these two diseases are indistinguishable! Even when blood tests are carried out, it is claimed that the majority are completely unreliable, giving 'false-positive' reactions in a high percentage of cases – i.e., the test shows positive despite the absence of HIV. Further, when blood tests are carried out which are accurate and reliable, only one in ten test positive, which, although it is a higher proportion than is found in the West, *is barely 20 per cent of the previously reported prevalence!*

How can such inconsistencies be explained? Does it suit the West to attribute AIDS to Africa uncritically, even when blood tests are not carried out, and when the symptoms can equally be referrable to tuberculosis? The developed countries are putting vast amounts of money into combating the spread of AIDS in Africa. Would not this money be better spent on programmes to rid that continent of the true killer diseases – tuberculosis, malaria and malnutrition?

## *Other possible sources*

Besides Africa, other sources have been claimed for AIDS, as is clear from its appellation, 'The Disease of the Four Hs: homosexuals, heroin addicts, Haitians and haemophiliacs'. The attribution of AIDS to Haiti has had a catastrophic effect upon its tourist industry. American visitors dropped from 70,000 in 1982 to 10,000 in 1983. The President, Jean-Claude Duvalier, cracked down on homosexuals, vowing that the island would not become the 'brothel of the Caribbean'.

An alternative theory holds that the virus was deliberately created in the laboratories of mad scientists at the behest of mad governments. As an agent of germ warfare the HIV comes way down, being a germ which takes years to work, does not inevitably cause disease, and depends on the enemy having sex with one another – *unless it was created by the establishment to eradicate homosexuals!* Such theories are fuelled by recent newspaper stories which have reported that Russian scientists continue to manufacture deadly viruses even though the Cold War is long gone. And would it be naïve to assume that mad scientists are the sole prerogative of the former Eastern bloc countries!

## *Combating prejudice and prospects for control*

There is a palpable sense of disenchantment with the medical profession at its painfully slow progress in producing a vaccine to protect against HIV virus. People are casting around for alternative strategies for controlling the disease – some deeply disquieting. If extermination is thought too draconian by the faint-hearted, then maybe it is necessary to make homosexuality, prostitution and intravenous drug use criminal offences, incurring long prison sentences, thereby protecting society from these high-risk individuals.

Deliberate sexual spread of AIDS should be severely dealt with, especially infected prostitutes. The story is told of a client who awoke from a post-coital snooze to find the lady gone. She had left her goodbyes written in lipstick on the mirror: 'Thanks. It was good! By the way – welcome to AIDS!' More subtle issues were raised recently when a *haemophiliac heterosexual* (doubly mitigating!) man, knowing himself to be HIV-positive, wantonly had sex with a number of women without telling them of the danger they were in: should he be pitied, castrated or incarcerated?

The response of the gay community to the AIDS threat has not been uniform. Many homosexuals found it expedient to go back into the closet and distance themselves from the more overt. Some gay men became overwhelmed with guilt and shame: one told his nurse, 'If I pull through I promise I shall find a girl friend.' Others found the prospect of giving up their newly won sexual liberation an anathema: 'Ultimately it may be more important to let people die in the pursuit of their own happiness than to limit personal freedom by regulating risk.'

Public fear, when the risk is close, is largely immune to reason. Haemophiliac children who have contracted AIDS from infected blood transfusions have been ostracized by their peers, parents and teachers, and this has encouraged others to keep their HIV status to themselves. More bizarre still is a report written by an executive of the National Haemophilia Foundation: 'How sad it was the other day when I learnt from one of our chapters that their haemophilia camp enrolment was down 75% this year because parents of haemophiliac children had fear of their children being exposed to other children with haemophilia.'

Many governments have put great store in information and education – especially of the young – about the risks of contracting AIDS. With varying degrees of realism, high-risk groups have been invoked to adopt chastity, celibacy, fidelity, sheath contraception, and abstinence from drugs. The evidence suggests that the retention of sensible advice is short-lived and soon forgotten. The majority revert quickly to former habits, confident that AIDS remains 'someone else's problem'. Publicity campaigns to discourage intravenous drug abuse have not been conspicuously successful, though advice against sharing of needles has been generally heeded.

If medical science does not come up with a vaccine pretty quickly, ignorance and indolence, HIV's greatest allies, will set it on target to infect forty million within six years.

### *But is HIV the true culprit?*

Many scientists have felt for some time that the 'one virus theory' of AIDS is over-simplistic. Because of a number of findings which simply do not fit the virus theory – and to the utter consternation of the orthodox – the notion has been mooted in the medical press that HIV *does not cause* AIDS. The fact that dire predictions, made in the mid-1980s, that AIDS would increase exponentially in the heterosexual population, have not come to pass, has encouraged some to the heresy that any link between the virus and the disease is spurious at worst and unproven at best. Although most sceptics do not deny that the virus *may* be contributory, they maintain that in some cases of AIDS it may be present as a harmless 'passenger', and they cite cases of persons who have been HIV-positive for a decade but who have never developed AIDS. This hypothesis challenges the idea that the HIV-positive person will inevitably have his immune system destroyed.

Others go still further and contend that the virus is *always* harmless, is *not* transmitted by sexual intercourse, and has been around for centuries. These experts say that the presence of the virus is a reflection not of a disease state but of a way of life, especially the widespread abuse and pernicious effects of drugs – including those very drugs given by doctors to treat the disease! These sceptics attribute AIDS in haemophiliacs to *haemophilia*: they believe that when a haemophiliac falls ill and is subsequently found to be HIV-positive, a spurious cause-and-effect is deduced between virus and disease. If the link is so clear-cut, why is it that only 120,000 out of six million HIV-positive Africans have developed AIDS? And may it be that the long-established African killers – malnutrition, malaria and tuberculosis – are being diagnosed as AIDS simply because of the *coincidental* presence of the virus?

The doubters want an urgent reappraisal of the HIV-AIDS link, and claim that they are being blocked at every turn, imputing skulduggery by those whose livelihoods and reputations depend upon the continuance of orthodoxy. They ask for answers to some puzzling inconsistencies in the HIV-AIDS theory:

> Why have so few HIV-positive people developed AIDS, and why does it take so long?

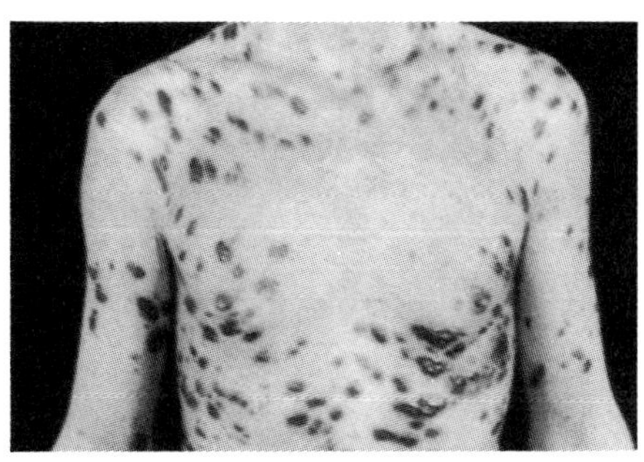

Kaposi's sarcoma: a skin cancer common in advanced AIDS

Why do wild chimpanzees, experimentally infected with HIV and the simian equivalent (SIV), not develop AIDS?

Why are 3 in 100 men *and* women HIV-positive, yet 90 per cent of AIDS patients are men?

It is also pointed out that other agents cause immunosuppression of the body's defenses, including semen, drugs (amphetamines, cocaine, opiates), *repeated blood transfusions* (the possible mechanism in haemophiliacs), anaesthetics, poverty, malnutrition (in the Third World or as a result of drug abuse) and infection by a variety of other viruses and microbes.

Even the isolation of the virus has been a source of bitter controversy. In 1984 it was announced that the virus had been discovered by Dr Robert Gallo at the National Cancer Institute. It has subsequently emerged that the virus was in fact discovered in 1983 by Dr Luc Montagnier at the Pasteur Institute in Paris, who had then sent a sample to Gallo for further testing. By 1984 Gallo had cornered the lucrative market in testing patients for the presence of HIV. Ironically, Montagnier leans to the 'alternative' camp in believing that the virus he discovered may be benign, at best needing other agents to produce AIDS. (Some conjecture that continuing trans-Atlantic rivalries were at the root of the recent French scandal when doctors, working in the transfusion service, continued to issue blood, knowing it to be contaminated. It is claimed by some that the French refused on principle to decontaminate the blood, since this would have involved the use of expensive *and American* apparatus! Penny-pinching America committed the same crime back in 1983.)

If AIDS is not caused by HIV, how is it that the wives of HIV-positive haemophiliacs occasionally die of AIDS? One expert, Peter Duesberg, believes that these women, roughly thirteen a year, have died from other causes and have *not* shown the classic AIDS symptoms: that is, the women – no greater a number of deaths than would be expected statistically anyway – have died from unrelated causes, but that the deaths have been attributed to HIV simply because the virus was searched for and was found. Duesberg contends that HIV was present but did not cause the women's deaths: 'Because they are the wives of haemophiliacs, the pneumonias are called AIDS.'

The change that occurred in the 1970s was not in the incidence of HIV, but in the increased availability and use of drugs which could destroy the body's immune system. And drugs and promiscuity often went hand in hand. Card-carrying gays attested to their sexual potency by the sheer number of their partners, their motto being 'so many men, so little time'. The greater the promiscuity – perhaps fifteen partners in a night – the greater the onslaught on the immune system. Imagine the potential for immunosuppression caused by 'fist fucking' where one man pushes his fist into another's rectum (often the recipient's anus would be artificially relaxed by nitrites [poppers], another immunosuppressant) exposing the traumatized mucosa to blood, faeces, and microbes of all kinds (and semen in anal intercourse). Gonorrhoea, syphilis and hepatitis B soared, but to preach continence and fidelity went against the gay canon.

AIDS appeared in Africa at the same time that smallpox was eradicated. Did the vaccinia virus spark off an AIDS epidemic in a population which was HIV-positive but disease-free?

It is easier to focus on a viral cause and pour vast sums of money into producing a vaccine, than to tackle the problems of poverty, malnutrition, unemployment, urban renewal and drug addiction. Scientists are not enthusiastic about social factors in the causation of disease, in much the same way that doctors prefer physical (and, by implication, treatable) to psychological causes of illness. If HIV is co-contributory or even non-contributory to the development of AIDS, it means that the holy grail of an AIDS vaccine will not be the definitive answer to the problem, and a great deal of time and energy is going into research which might bring about neither eradication or profit.

# AFTERWORD: DEATH, THE ULTIMATE DISEASE

The story goes that Gilgamesh set out to find the herb 'Old Man Becomes Young'. Being told that it grew at the bottom of the sea, he weighted himself down with stones and sank to the depths of the Persian Gulf. Having gathered the herb, he set off for home. *En route* he rested. Whilst relaxing, an enormous serpent devoured the plant. With immortality thus stolen from its grasp, mankind's lot has been to grow old and suffer death, the ultimate disease.

## *In search of the philosopher's stone*

Common sense tells us that longevity and freedom from disease depend upon an interplay of constitutional and environmental factors, nature and nurture. That genetic factors play an important part in ageing and infirmity is demonstrated by progeria, a condition which brings about premature ageing in adolescence, giving to teenagers the appearance of persons in their seventies or eighties.

In ancient and medieval times many adventurers would search for, and many charlatans would claim to have found, the fountain of eternal youth and the panacea against all disease. Alexander the Great believed he had discovered such a fountain. It is recorded that it was 'surrounded by everglades in a refulgent landscape: the magic waters gush from the mouth of an old gelder lion into a basin in a crystal pavilion: Alexander and fifty-six of his men drank deeply and were rejuvenated, their complexions being restored to the age of thirty'. Perhaps the recent renewed interest in the health-giving claims made for spa water is a similar phenomenon – despite the fact that Alexander died after an alcoholic binge, aged thirty-three.

Alchemists, after giving up the search for methods to turn base metals into gold, turned their attention to the quest for 'the philosopher's stone', which would bring eternal youth through perpetual health: 'specifics for curing old age, driving away its

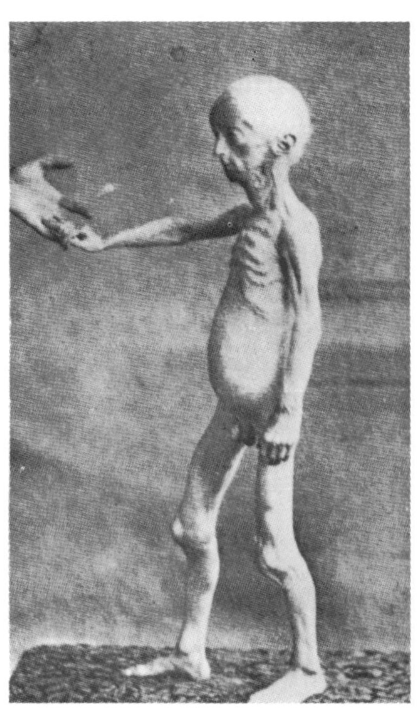

Progeria: premature ageing in teenagers

infirmities, recalling youth and prolonging life indefinitely'. In the thirteenth century, Friar Roger Bacon (1214–92) claimed to have found the secret: he died in 1292, aged seventy-eight. Paracelsus, physician and mystic of the Middle Ages, boasted that he would evade infirmity and death – he did, but only for forty-nine years. Medieval mixtures with names like 'The Red Dragon' and 'The Swan' almost invariably contained traces of gold, usually as *aurum nostrum*, since this element was known to resist corrosion. Other concoctions might contain mercury (magical as the only liquid metal in nature) or brandy, *eau-de-vie*.

The vampire legends depict the undead as living forever, feeding off the blood of virgins. Mere mortals would attempt to emulate Dracula by feeding on human blood from the young and healthy, either sucked straight from a freshly opened vein or else mixed with wine. There is an unconfirmed account of three boys slain in an unsuccessful attempt to rejuvenate Pope Innocent VIII in 1492.

By no means all of the literature dealing with panaceas and longevity has been the work of cranks. Charles Edouard Brown-Séquard had impeccable scientific credentials, becoming Professor of Experimental Medicine at L'École de Médicine in Paris in 1878, and giving his name to a neurological syndrome. But he is better remembered today for giving elderly humans injections of animal sperm. He reported his findings in 1889 to a scientific meeting, shortly after marrying his third wife, a woman much younger than his seventy-two years. He was indiscreet enough to boast to his audience that he had been able to *rendre visite* to the young Madame Brown-Séquard after only three injections. The newspapers were full of the story, but his colleagues ridiculed him and dismissed his experiments as senile aberrations. Very soon his young wife deserted him.

Just after the turn of the present century, Ilya Metchnikoff (1845–1916), a Russian scientist working at the Pasteur Institute in Paris, published his theory that the life span of man and his susceptibility to disease depended on the length of the intestine: the longer the colon, the shorter the life. Metchnikoff postulated that the bacteria which colonized the human colon released toxins which poisoned the host by slow degrees. In order to live longer, Metchnikoff prescribed 'detoxification' through taking large quantities of sour milk and yoghurt. Another application of Metchnikoff's theory of auto-intoxication came briefly into vogue: those wishing to combat disease and prolong life (and who had enough money) would have sections of their large bowel surgically removed.

The work of Brown-Séquard and Metchnikoff was carried on in this century by, among others, Voronoff and Niehans, each bent on finding the key to human health and, by implication, happiness. Serge Voronoff, another Russian who worked in France, gained fame and fortune by stitching slices of a young chimpanzee's testicles on to the testicles of his rich and infirm clients. Paul Niehans earned for himself the right to be called 'Rejuvenator of the Famous'. His method was to inject a variety of animal organs into the human rump, including placenta of sheep, parathyroids of calves and testes of bulls (though not, apparently, eyes of newts or toes of frogs!) Niehans treated Konrad Adenauer, Gloria Swanson and the conductor Wilhelm Furtwängler. It was rumoured that he refused to treat Winston Churchill because of Britain's blanket bombing of Germany during World War II. A suggestion that he might be invited to treat King George VI was vetoed by the British government.

It was Furtwängler who introduced Niehans to his most famous client. Although Niehans did little to rejuvenate Pope Pius XII, then seventy-seven, the pontiff did much to rejuvenate Niehan's declining reputation. Noel Coward, denying being one of Niehan's patients, put things into perspective when he referred to the use of solutions made from unborn ewe injected in enormous syringes. Coward judged the process 'very non-U' and professed his intention to grow old gracefully without any help from the animal kingdom.[1]

People ask, 'Who wants to live for ever anyway?' The answer is 'Most of us, given the chance.' If health and quality of life were guaranteed, the vast majority would opt to remain for as long as possible in this world rather than gamble on the uncertainty of what lies beyond. The reality at the present time is more attuned to the cynicism of Ambrose Bierce (1842–1914) when he defined *longevity* as 'an uncommon extension of the fear of death' (*The Devil's Dictionary*). It is likely that mankind will have to contend with disease, ageing and death for some little while yet. The reputation of medical science has suffered greatly as a result of the (seemingly) inordinate time it has taken to come up with a cure for AIDS, and has been compared by some to the emperor without his clothes. It is unlikely that micro-organisms will all evolve into friendly parasites, or that virulent new mutants will not appear to plague the human race – literally. In time, spare-part surgery will be able to replace diseased organs with mechanical substitutes – after all, the heart is only a pump, the lung a bellows, and the kidneys a filter – and perhaps the only micro-organism which will cause us any problems in the future will be one that causes rust.

# REFERENCES

## *1 Diseases, Ancient and Modern*

1. There is a very real danger of overloading the reader with references to obscure journals or books which are long out of print. I intend, therefore, to be selective rather than comprehensive, and to confine myself to references which are essential or which, in a variety of ways, have appealed to me personally.

The three essential books on palaeopathology are:

Brothwell, Don, and Sandison, A., *Diseases in Antiquity* (Charles C. Thomas, 1967)

Cockburn, Aidan, and Cockburn, Eve, *Mummies, Disease and Ancient Cultures* (Cambridge University Press, 1980)

Ruffer, Sir Marc, *Studies in the Palaeopathology of Egypt* (University of Chicago Press, 1921)

A useful little book is A. Randle Short's *The Bible and Modern Medicine* (Paternoster Press, 1955).

There are numerous books which give an overview of disease over the centuries. One of the most readable is Walter Bett's *The History and Conquest of Common Diseases* (University of Oklahoma Press, 1954). An invaluable source of original descriptions of diseases is Ralph Major's *Classic Descriptions of Disease* (Charles C. Thomas, 1978). Wilfred Bonser's *The Medical Background of Anglo-Saxon England* (Wellcome Historical Medical Library, 1963) is packed with fascinating information about medieval epidemics, magical remedies and medical slants on medieval kings (was Edward the Confessor an albino?). Social and environmental influences on the course of diseases are addressed by G. Melvyn Howe's *Man, Environment and Disease in Britain* (David & Charles, 1972); the same theme, from an American point of view, is tackled by P.M. Ashburn's *The Ranks of Death* (Porcupine Press, 1980). Frederick Cartwright's *Disease and History* (Rupert Hart-Davis, 1972) is prescribed reading.

The role of the doctor is highlighted in Kurt Pollack's *The Healers: The Doctor, Then and Now* (Nelson, 1963). And finally, a brace of books on the history of medicine by Howard Haggard: *The Doctor in History* (Yale University Press, 1934) and *Devils, Drugs and Doctors* (Heinemann, undated but old). Sheer delight!

2. See W.D. Foster's *History of Parasitology*, (E. & S. Livingstone, 1965).

Also F.R. Sandbach's 'The History of Schistosomiasis Research and Policy for its Control', *Medical History* (1976), vol. 20, no. 3, pp. 259–75. Did schistosomiasis do for Jericho? E.V. Hulse believes so: 'Joshua's Curse and the Abandonment of Ancient Jericho: Schistosomiasis as a Possible Medical Explanation', *Medical History* (1971), vol. 15, pp. 376–86. A.T. Sandison's 'The Last Illness of Herod the Great, King of Judea', *Medical History* (1967), vol. 11, pp. 381–7, invites us to consider a literal meaning to 'produced worms', as a contributory ailment suffered by this massacre of the innocents. (The fact that I shall always remember about Herod is that he had a wife called Doris.)
3. Dr John Caius (1510–73) endowed his old college at Cambridge, changing its name from 'Gonville Hall' to 'Gonville and Caius College'. Cambridge graduates are prone to use the pronunciation of Caius's name as a shibboleth of good breeding: your academic credentials are impeccable if you know that it is 'Gonville and Keyes'!
4. See David Meltzer's 'How Columbus Sickened the New World', *New Scientist* (10 October 1992), pp. 38–41.

## 2 *Three Deadly Scourges*

1. The best book about the plague, by far, is Johannes Nohl's *The Black Death: A Chronicle of the Plague* (George Allen & Unwin, 1926). More recently, Philip Ziegler's *The Black Death* (Alan Sutton, 1969) concentrates on the disease in Britain, especially its social consequences. More scholarly are J.F.D. Shrewsbury's *A History of Bubonic Plague in the British Isles* (Cambridge University Press, 1970), and Paul Slack's *The Impact of Plague in Tudor and Stuart England* (Routledge & Kegan Paul, 1985). Fascinating insights on how societies attempted to combat the plague are given by Carlo Cipolla in his *Fighting the Plague in Seventeenth-century Italy* (University of Wisconsin Press, 1981).

For the natural history of scourges, William McNeill's *Plagues and Peoples* (Penguin, 1976) is highly recommended. The Black Death is one of a number of diseases included in Andrew Nikiforuk's *The Fourth Horseman* (Fourth Estate, 1991) – the fourth horseman of the Apocalypse being the bringer of Pestilence and Death.
2. Hecker, J.F.C., *The Epidemics of the Middle Ages* (Sydenham Society, 1846). Besides the Black Death, Hecker writes about Dancing Manias and English Sweating Sickness.
3. Christos Bartsocas, 'The Fourteenth-century Greek Descriptions of the Black Death', *Journal of the History of Medicine* (1966), vol. 21, no. 4, pp. 394–400.
4. The Antonine plague set a precedence for fleeing physicians. Every sovereign has the physician he deserves, and Galen was physician to Marcus Aurelius. At the first onset of the pestilence, Galen made off to Campagnia, and finding no safety there took ship to Pergamus. He absented himself for two years. Marcus Aurelius died of the pestilence in AD 180. Later physicians to desert their posts have included Thomas Sydenham, 'The

'The English Hippocrates' (1624–89) and Giovanni Morgagni (1682–1771).
5. Ambroise Paré (1510–90), a master barber-surgeon, whose faith in the healing powers of nature was encapsulated in his famous remark '*Je le pansay, Dieu le guarist*' (I dress him, God cures him). Those interested in the lives of physicians and surgeons are referred to Henry Sigerist's *Great Doctors* (George Allen & Unwin, 1933), Sir D'Arcy Power's *British Masters of Medicine* (Medical Press and Circular, 1936), and Peter Greta Beighton's *The Man Behind the Syndrome* (Springer-Verlag, 1986)
6. The most intriguing magic word square used to prevent and cure disease was

S A T O R
A R E P O
T E N E T
O P E R A
R O T A S

derived from the Latin for 'a sower', 'I creep', 'he holds', 'works' and 'wheels'. The mystery of its potency as a panacea was believed solved when, in 1926, Felix Grosser, demonstrated that the letters can be arranged in the shape of a crucifix, crossing at the 'N' and spelling PATERNOSTER, the first two words of the Lord's Prayer, horizontally and vertically. The two As and Os left over represent Alpha and Omega, the beginning and the end. For more information consult Thomas Forbes' *The Midwife and the Witch* (Yale University Press, 1966) about all things obstetric in the Middle Ages.
7. See also 'Psychic Epidemics in Europe and the United States' in George Rosen's *Madness in Society* (Routledge & Kegan Paul, 1968). A flavour of medieval suggestibility can be got from study of the Children's Crusades. The first was in 1212, when a shepherd boy named Stephen appeared in France and induced thousands of children to leave their parents, promising that the sea would part and they would walk dry-shod to the Holy Land. In Germany a child called Nicolas from Cologne gathered 20,000 young crusaders and led them to Italy. Stephen's army was kidnapped by slavers and sold into Egypt; Nicolas's expedition 'left nothing behind it but an after echo in the legend of the Pied Piper of Hamelin (1284)'.
8. A Pepysian medical aside: Samuel Pepys only kept his famous diary between 1660–9. It is generally assumed it stopped at his death. Not so, since he did not die until 1703. Pepys gave up his diary under the mistaken notion that he was going blind – an error which robbed posterity of thirty more years of fascinating insights into seventeenth-century English life.
9. It is frequently pointed out that Defoe's was not a first-hand account of the plague in London, since he was only a boy of six at the time. What is less well-known is that Boccaccio's account of the plague in Florence is also hearsay since he was living in Naples at the time!
10. See David Van Zwanenberg's 'The Last Epidemic of Plague in England? Suffolk 1906–1918', *Medical History* (1970), vol. 14, no. 1, pp. 62–74. Also 'The Visitor from a Far Country' in Michael Howell and Peter Ford's *Medical Mysteries* (Viking, 1985).

11. Cholera references consulted in the writing of this chapter include:

Longmate, Norman, *King Cholera* (Hamish Hamilton, 1966)
Morris, R.J., *Cholera 1832: The Social Response to An Epidemic* (Croom Helm, 1976)
Durey, Michael, *The Return of the Plague: British Society and Cholera, 1831–2* (Gill and Macmillan Humanities Press, 1979)
Evans, Richard, *Death in Hamburg* (Penguin, 1990)
More medical than historical is S.N. De's *Cholera, its Pathology and Pathogenesis* (Oliver and Boyd, 1961). More historical than medical is W. Luckin's 'The Final Catastrophe – Cholera in London, 1866' *Medical History* (1977) vol. 21, pp. 32–42.

12. Sir Henry Halford was one of the foremost physicians of his day. He was present when the coffin of King Charles I was opened in 1813. Identification of the corpse was made easier by the fact that the 'fourth cervical (neck) vertebra was sliced clean through', as one might expect in someone who had been beheaded. Sir Henry was accused of palming this bone as a souvenir which he would proudly show to his dinner guests. When, years later, the Prince of Wales (later King Edward VII) heard about the indignity done to one of his predecessors, the bone was returned by the Halford family to its rightful owner, lying in the vault of St George's Chapel, Windsor.

13. Man has always been able to use scourges to serve his own evil ends. In India people with a grudge are known to have taken the opportunity of a cholera epidemic to poison an enemy: the symptoms of cholera and arsenical poisoning are very similar. An epidemic, when large numbers are dying, provides the ideal cover for murder.

14. For a detailed account of events leading up to the introduction of the Anatomy Bill of 1832, see Ruth Richardson's epic *Death, Dissection and the Destitute* (Routledge & Kegan Paul, 1987).

15. For ghouls wanting to read more about premature burial and other death-related anxieties, dip into my own *Fireside Book of Death* (Robert Hale, 1990).

16. Fascinating sidelights on epidemics in general and typhus in particular are given by Hans Zinsser in *Rats, Lice and History* (Blue Ribbon Books, 1927). Truly, a gem, combining wit and scholarship.

## 3 *Smallpox, Conqueror of the New World*

1. Eby, Clifford and Evjen, Harold, 'The Plague of Athens', *Journal of the History of Medicine* (1962), vol. 17, no. 2, pp. 258–63. Although the consensus is that the plague was smallpox, others have mooted a variety of diseases, including typhus: see Keil, H., 'The louse in Greek antiquity', *Bulletin of the History of Medicine* (1951), vol. 25, pp. 304–23. Some experts believe that the matter is far from settled and that the jury is still out.

2. The most agreeable account of the history of smallpox, taking a world perspective, is Donald Hopkins's *Princes and Peasants* (University of

Chicago Press, 1983). A scholarly work, combining history and diagnosis, is Professor C.W. Dixon's *Smallpox* (J. & A. Churchill, 1962). The definitive book on diagnosis is the aptly titled *Diagnosis of Smallpox* (Cassell, 1908) by T.F. Ricketts and J.B. Byles – not for the faint-hearted.

3. See MacNalty, Sir Arthur, 'The Medical History of Queen Elizabeth I of England' *History of Medicine* (1971), vol. 3, no. 1, pp. 9–12.

4. Lady Mary Wortley Montagu (1689–1762) was an enigmatic and colourful figure, daughter of the Earl of Kingston. She was an intimate and later a sworn enemy of Alexander Pope (see chapter 5 on creativity). Some twenty years before her death, she parted, amicably, from her husband and went to live in Italy. In 1740, when she was fifty-one, Horace Walpole, never known for his tact, described her as an 'old, foul, tawdry, painted, plastered personage'.

5. ... and Thompson after him (see Sir Henry Thompson and Leopold I, in chapter 6).

6. Following his discovery of vaccination, people attempted to entice Jenner to leave his beloved Gloucestershire and take up a lucrative private practice in London. He replied, 'Shall I, who even in the mornings of my days, sought the lowly and sequestered paths of life, the valley, and not the mountains; shall I, now my evening is fast approaching, hold myself up as an object for fortune and for fame? My fortune is sufficient to gratify my wishes. And as for fame, what is it? A gilded butt, forever pierced with the arrows of malignancy.' George Eliot has Dr Lydgate in *Middlemarch* eschewing 'London intrigues and jealousies' and wishing to 'win celebrity, however slowly, as Jenner had done, by the independent value of his work'.

## 4 *Deadly First Cousins*

1. The relentless progress of tuberculosis is harrowingly charted in Robert Gittings' *The Letters of John Keats* (Oxford University Press, 1987).

2. See Brothwell, Don, and Sandison, A., *Diseases in Antiquity*, (Charles C. Thomas, 1967).

3. See McHenry, L., and MacKeith, R., 'Samuel Johnson's Childhood Illnesses and the King's Evil', *Medical History* (1966), vol. 10, pp. 21–42. The definitive medico-historical work is Raymond Crawfurd's *The King's Evil* (Clarendon Press, 1911). Johnson suffered ill-health throughout his long life and has been a source of endless speculation and post-mortem diagnoses. Samplers include Peter Chase's 'The ailments and physicians of Dr Johnson' *Yale Journal of Biological Medicine* (1951). vol. 23, pp. 370–9; and 'Dr Samuel Johnson's Aphasia' in Macdonald Critchley's *The Black Hole and Other Essays* (Pitman Medical Publishing, 1964). It is likely that Johnson's poor eyesight was caused by tuberculosis: he would regularly singe his wig through holding a candle too close to his face, and would be quite unable to recognize friends at distances of more than half a yard.

4. The outstanding book about tuberculosis, which has never been equalled, is René and Jean Dubos' *The White Plague: Tuberculosis, Man and Society*

(Rutgers University Press, 1952). Comprehensive, scholarly and, above all, readable. A very useful book to place tuberculosis in historical perspective is Richard Burke's *An Historical Chronology of Tuberculosis* (Charles C. Thomas, 1955).

5. See Edward Wilson's 'Anal Fistula: An Historical review', *Medical Journal of Australia* (April 1963), pp. 630–2.

6. See Edgerley, C. Mabel, 'Causes of Death of the Brontës', *British Medical Journal* (2 April 1932), p. 619.

7. According to Richard Selzer in *Mortal Lessons: Notes on the Art of Surgery* (Chatto & Windus, 1981), doctors the world over should give thanks to Laënnec for 'his gift of space interpersonal'.

8. Elizabeth Siddal's tuberculosis would not have been helped by the long hours she had to spend immersed in a bath of cold water while modelling for John Everett Millais's *Ophelia*. When Siddal died, her husband, Dante Gabriel Rossetti, placed a collection of his unpublished poems next to her cheek. In time he came to regret such a show of romantic excess, and seven years later, in 1869, had his wife exhumed from her coffin at Highgate Cemetery in order to retrieve his verses.

9. Shelley's trip south was as tragic as that of Keats. In Venice his daughter Clara died; in Rome, his son William; and he himself drowned in a yachting accident.

10. See Anthony Alpers' *The Life of Katherine Mansfield* (Oxford University Press, 1982).

11. For a salutary warning about the imminent dangers posed by tuberculosis, see Phyllida Brown's 'The Return of the Big Killer', *New Scientist* (10 October 1992), pp. 30–7; and John Watson's 'Tuberculosis in Britain Today', *British Medical Journal* (23 January 1993) vol. 306, pp. 221–2.

12. The best book about this disease is Peter Richards's *The Medieval Leper* (Brewer, Rowman & Littlefield, 1977).

## 5 *Creativity and Illness*

1. The number of books and scientific papers linking genius (sometimes labelled 'creativity') and disease is vast, and I have tried to be selective. The major works include:

Nisbet, J.F., *The Insanity of Genius and the General Inequality of Human Faculty* (Ward & Downey, 1891)

Lombroso, Cesare, *The Man of Genius* (Walter Scott, 1891)

Galton, Francis, *Hereditary Genius: An Inquiry into its Laws and Consequences* (Macmillan, 1892)

Ellis, Havelock, *A Study of British Genius* (Hurst and Blackett, 1904)

Türck, Hermann, *The Man of Genius* (Wilhelm Borngräber Verlag, 1914)

Kretschmer, Ernst, *The Psychology of Men of Genius* (Kegan Paul, Trench and Trubner, 1931)

Moorman, Lewis, *Tuberculosis and Genius* (University of Chicago Press,

1940)
Bett, W.R., *The Infirmities of Genius* (Christopher Johnson, 1952)
Sandborn, Philip, *Creativity and Disease* (Marion Boyars, 1992)
Dean Keith Simonton has attempted to apply scientific method. His output is prodigious, *Genius, Creativity and Leadership* (Harvard University Press, 1984) being fairly typical of his approach.

If one is tempted into this field of inquiry, one must have to hand sources of medical biographies. Besides annual indices of *The Bibliography of the History of Medicine*, published by the National Library of Medicine, the following are recommended:

Dale, Philip Marshall, *Medical Biographies: The Ailments of Thirty-three Famous Persons* (University of Oklahoma Press, 1952)
Fabricant, Noah, *Thirteen Famous Patients* (Chilton Company, 1960) – includes a number of unexpected celebrities, such as James Joyce, George Gershwin and Enrico Caruso.
Stevenson, R. Scott, *Famous Illnesses in History* (Eyre & Spottiswoode, 1962)

An invaluable source of sources is Johan Schioldann-Nielsen's *Famous and Very Important Persons: Medical, Psychological and Psychiatric Bibliography* (Odense University Press, 1986). My own overview, 'Creativity, Madness and Pathography', was published in *Current Opinion in Psychiatry* (1990), vol. 3, no. 5, pp. 657–60.

The most fruitful field is undoubtedly tuberculosis. Here is a *brief* list of some famous consumptives not mentioned in this book: Milton, Whitman, Goethe, Schiller, Molière, Thoreau, Descartes, Locke, Kant, Spinoza, Goldsmith, Sterne, Leigh Hunt, Jane Austen, Balzac, Rousseau, Southey, O'Neill and Gorky.

2. Anton Chekhov (1860–1904) was a playwright and doctor. 'You advise me not to pursue two hares at a time and to abandon the practice of medicine. I feel more contented and more satisfied when I realize that I have two professions, not one. Medicine is my lawful wife and literature my mistress. When I grow weary of one, I pass the night with the other. Neither of them suffers because of my infidelity.' (Letter, 11 October 1889). It is generally agreed that Chekhov's finest output was when tuberculosis had him firmly in its grip.

3. Two general references to opium are Virginia Berridge and Griffith Edwards's *Opium and the People: Opiate Use in Nineteenth Century England* (Allen Lane, 1981), and Arthur Dickson Wright's 'The History of Opium', *Transactions & Studies of the College of Physicians of Philadelphia* (1961), vol. 29, no. 1, pp. 22–7.

Papers specifically making the link with creativity and genius are: Douglas Hubble's 'Opium Addiction and English Literature', *Medical History* (1957), vol. 1, pp. 323–35; and John Todd's 'Drug Addiction and Artistic Genius', *The Practitioner* (1968), vol. 201, pp. 513–23.

4. My favourite story about Keats and his inspiration:

In the year 1813 there lived in the Borough as students of Guy's and St

Thomas's, three young men, who occupied the same rooms. Their names were John Keats, Henry Stephens and George Wilson Mackereth. One evening, in the twilight, Stephens at his medical studies, Keats at his dreaming, Keats broke out to Stephens that he had composed a new line:

A thing of beauty is a constant joy

'What do you think of that, Stephens?'

'It has a true ring but is wanting in some way.' An interval of silence, and again the poet:

A thing of beauty is a joy for ever

'What do you think of that, Stephens?'

'That will live for ever.'

Benjamin Ward Richardson
*The Asclepiad*, January 1884

5. See reference 1, this chapter.
6. In his book, Galton taps a more sinister vein: 'If we can improve the stock by limiting the unfit or by favouring the endowed – if we give to those who have and take away from those who have not even that which they have – we can greatly accelerate and direct the course of evolution ... We may have still stocks that are immature – the Slavs, the Czechs, and the Scandinavians – and there is a possibility of vitality in the negroes.'
7. See reference 1, this chapter. The title of Kretschmer's book is not accidental: 'Every woman genius is a man at heart. The genius of womanhood is in a male offspring.'
8. See reference 1, this chapter.
9. See reference 1, this chapter.
10. See Kay Redfield Jamison's 'Mood Disorders and Patterns of Creativity in British Writers and Artists', *Psychiatry*, vol. 52, pp. 125–34. Many additional references are given at the end of this paper. Also recommended is Arnold Ludwig's 'Reflections on Creativity and Madness', *The American Journal of Psychotherapy* (1989), vol. 43, no. 1, pp. 4–14.
11. See N.C. Andreasen's 'Creativity and Mental Illness: Prevalence Rates in Writers and Their First-degree Relatives', *American Journal of Psychiatry* (1987), vol. 144, pp. 1288–92.
12. See Milo Keynes's 'Sir Isaac Newton and His Madness of 1692–93', *The Lancet* (8 March 1980), pp. 529–30, and Julian Lieb's 'Isaac Newton: Mercury Poisoning or Manic Depression?' *The Lancet* (24 December 1983), pp. 1479–80.
13. See J. Ernest Bryant's *Genius and Epilepsy* (Ye Old Depot Press, 1953). This slim volume gives very brief accounts of the lives of famous epileptics, including Blaise Pascal, George Fox and Charles Swinburne. Better by light years is O. Temkin's *The Falling Sickness* (The Johns Hopkins Press, 1971).
14. See N. Asherson's 'Beethoven's Deafness and the Saga of the Stapes', *The Presidential Address to the Hunterian Society*, 18 October 1965. Also, Herbert Bower's 'Beethoven's Creative Illness', *Australian and New Zealand Journal of Psychiatry* (1989), vol. 23, pp. 111–16, and Terence Cawthorne's 'The Influence of Deafness on the Creative Instinct', *The*

*Laryngoscope* (1960), vol. 70, no. 8, pp. 1110–18. Smetana and Fauré were two more deaf composers: Fauré used to bewail that he heard 'only horrors'.
15. See Bernard Puech et al., 'Craniofacial Dysmorphism in Mozart's Skull', *Journal of Forensic Sciences* (1989), vol. 34, no. 2, pp. 487–90. Recently a new diagnosis has been given to Mozart to explain his penchant for obscene utterances: Oliver Sacks's 'Tourette's Syndrome and Creativity', *British Medical Journal* (19 December 1992), vol. 305, pp. 1515–16. (The Christmas edition of the *British Medical Journal* is a feast for all who love the sidetracks of medicine.)
16. See Henry Rollin's 'Lord Byron: "The careful pilot of my proper woe" ', *History of Medicine* (1975), vol. 6, no. 1, pp. 2–9. Perhaps the best known malformed king is Richard III, though his skeletal shortcomings are largely conjectural since Shakespeare cannot be considered unbiased in his description of a Tudor adversary. Nevertheless, see Pasquale Accardo's 'Deformity and Character: Dr Little's Diagnosis of Richard III', *Journal of the American Medical Association* (19 December 1980), vol. 244, no. 24, pp. 2746–7.
17. See E.M. Papper's none-too-insightful, 'The Influence of Chronic Illness Upon the Writings of Alexander Pope', *Journal of the Royal Society of Medicine* (1989), pp. 12–15.

## 6 *Bones, Stones and Groans*

1. A very readable book is W.S.C. Copeman's *A Short History of the Gout* (University of California Press, 1964). For accounts of a famous martyr to gout, see W.S.C. Copeman's 'The Gout of William Cecil, First Lord Burghley (1520–98)', *Medical History* (1957), vol. 1, pp. 262–4.
2. As good a place as any to give the best source for anyone looking for a Shakespearean quote on medical matters: R.R. Simpson's *Shakespeare and Medicine* (Livingstone, 1959). The Bard probably picked up a lot of his knowledge from Dr John Hall, his son-in-law.
3. See Harold Ellis's *A History of Bladder Stone* (Blackwell Scientific Publications, 1969) and Sir Eric Riches' 'The History of Lithotomy and Lithotrity', *Annals of the Royal College of Surgeons of England* (1968), vol. 43, pp.185–99. For the agonies of a famous sufferer, see Edmund Spriggs' 'The Illnesses and Death of Robert Walpole', *Medical History* (1982) vol. 26, pp. 421–8. It has been suggested (though not very convincingly) that Judge Jeffreys, who presided over the 'bloody assize' after the collapse of Monmouth's rebellion in 1685, would have been more lenient, but for the agonies he suffered from his bladder stones.
4. See Sir D'Arcy Power's 'The Medical History of Mr and Mrs Samuel Pepys', *British Journal of Medicine* (25 February 1933) pp. 325–6.
5. See also Harold Ellis's *Famous Operations* (Harwal, 1984). Sir Henry Thompson is the subject of Zachary Cope's *The Versatile Victorian* (Harvey Blythe, no date). Thompson was an artist, novelist (*Charley Kingston's Aunt*), social reformer and friend of the famous. He is remembered for his 'Octaves': weekly dinner parties at which eight guests tucked into eight

courses, starting at eight o'clock sharp. It was definitely 'in' to be invited – over the years guests included the Prince of Wales, Robert Browning, Charles Dickens, William Makepeace Thackeray, Sir John Tenniel and Arthur Conan Doyle. No woman ever graced the guest list.

6. The graphic description of an operation before the days of anaesthetics is taken from Joyce Hemlow's *The Journals and Letters of Fanny Burney (Madame D'Arblay)*, vol. 6, (Clarendon Press, 1975). Another historical mastectomy is described in Alan Steinfeld's 'A Historical Report of a Mastectomy for Carcinoma of the Breast', *Surgical Gynaecology and Obstetrics* (1975), vol. 141 (2), pp. 616–17. Because of Fanny Burney's survival long after her operation, doubt has been cast on the diagnosis of cancer – a similar doubt exists about Queen Atossa who is now believed to have suffered from mastitis: see A.T. Sandison's 'The First Recorded Case of Inflammatory Mastitis – Queen Atossa of Persia and the Physician Democedes', *Medical History* (1959), vol. 3, no. 4, pp. 317–22.

## *7 A Therapeutic Interlude*

1. A fascinating book, excellently illustrated, is William Brockbank's *Ancient Therapeutic Arts* (Heinemann, 1954). It concludes with 'The Less Ancient Art of Intravenous Injection of Drugs'.

2. From George Gould and Walter Pyle's *Anomalies and Curiosities of Medicine* (W.B. Saunders, 1900). Not a dull page, but definitely not for the squeamish!

3. See Raymond Crawfurd's *The Last Days of Charles II* (Clarendon Press, 1909).

## *8 Diseases of Those Who Govern*

1. Some have unkindly inferred that the recent problems of the British royal family have been brought about, in part, by marriages to former commoners – now the Princess of Wales and the Duchess of York.

2. See Bernadine Paulshock's 'Tutankhamun and His Brothers: Familial Gynecomastia in the Eighteenth Dynasty', *Journal of the American Medical Association* (11 July 1980), vol. 244, no. 2, pp. 160–4; and the correspondence that followed in the letter columns. Also, Guenter Risse's 'The Presumed Illness of Pharaoh Akhenaton', *Journal of the History of Medicine* (1971), vol. 26, no. 1, pp. 3–17. A classic text is Sir Marc Ruffer's *Studies in the Palaeopathology of Egypt* (University of Chicago Press, 1921).

3. See Hugo Iltis's 'Hemophilia, The Royal Disease', *Journal of Heredity* (1948), vol. 39, no. 4, pp. 113–16; and Victor McKusick's 'The Royal Hemophilia', *Scientific American* (1965), vol. 213, no. 2, pp. 88–95. An insight into the lives (and all-too-premature deaths) of haemophiliacs before the introduction of blood transfusions is vividly depicted by C.B. Kerr's 'The Fortunes of Haemophiliacs in the Nineteenth Century', *Medical History* (1963), vol. 7, no. 4, pp. 359–70.

4. See Frederick Woods's *Mental and Moral Heredity in Royalty* (George Bell, 1906).

5. Jean Etienne Esquirol's *Mental Maladies: A Treatise on Insanity* (Hunt, 1845). Esquirol was the foremost psychiatrist in nineteenth-century France, and was the first man to distinguish between hallucinations, delusions and illusions.

6. Besides the classic texts (Suetonius, Tacitus, Dio), Michael Grant's *The Twelve Caesars* (Weidenfeld and Nicolson, 1975) is a 'jolly good read'. See also A.T. Sandison's 'The Madness of the Emperor Caligula', *Medical History* (1958), vol. 2, no. 3, pp. 202–9. Two overviews of the pernicious effects of madness in royalty are William Ireland's *The Blot Upon the Brain* (Books for Libraries Press, 1886), and Hubert Norman's 'The Relation of Mental Disorder to Events in History', *Bulletin of the Medical Library Association* (1945), vol. 33, pp. 60–79.

7. A delightful book on the excesses of lunatic kings and queens is that by Angelo Rappoport, *Mad Majesties or Raving Rulers and Submissive Subjects* (Greening & Co, 1910). See also Gerald Hodge's 'A Medical History of the Spanish Habsburgs As Traced in Portraits', *Journal of the American Medical Association* (1977), vol. 238, no. 11, pp. 1169–74.

8. George Greville, in a diary entry for 5 December 1788, records this exchange between George III and Willis on their first meeting:

'Sir, Your dress and appearance bespeaks You of the Church. Do you belong to it?'

'Sire, I did formerly, but lately I have attended chiefly to physick.'

The King became agitated: 'I am sorry for it. You have quitted a profession I have always loved, and You have Embraced one I most Heartily detest.'

9. For an account of the ailments of 'the wisest fool in Christendom', see Archibald Goodall's 'The Health of James the Sixth of Scotland and First of England', *Medical History* (1957), vol. 1, pp. 17–27.

10. The case for porphyria-induced madness is put by Ida Macalpine and Richard Hunter (actually mother and son) in *George III and the Mad-Business* (Allen Lane, 1969). Shorter accounts, by the same authors, are 'The Insanity of King George III: A Classic Case of Porphyria', *British Medical Journal* (8 January 1966), pp. 65–71; and 'Porphyria and King George III' in *Scientific American* (1969), vol. 221, no. 1, pp. 38–46. Porphyria has also been mooted as the cause of another's insanity: see, Loretta Loftus and Wilfred Arnold's 'Vincent van Gogh's Illness: Acute Intermittent Porphyria?', *British Medical Journal* (21 December 1991), pp. 1589–91. In another form of porphyria – porphyria cutanea tarda hereditaria – patients become ultra-sensitive to sunlight which causes the skin to blister. Consequently affected persons tend to venture out only at night, giving the condition its alternative name – the vampire disease.

Another English king to come under psychiatric scrutiny is Henry VI: see 'Henry VI, His Person and His Grandfather' in Basil Clarke's *Mental Disorder in Earlier Britain* (University of Wales Press, 1975).

11. A great deal has been written about the Emperor's throat, not least by Sir Morell Mackenzie. See R. Scott Stevenson's *Morell Mackenzie*

(Heinemann, 1946). Also William Ober's 'The Case of the Kaiser's Cancer' in S. Sommers' *Pathology Annual* (Appleton-Century-Crofts, 1970). And finally, see W. David McInnis's et al. 'Did Morell Mackenzie Really Cause World War I?', *American Journal of Surgery* (1975), vol. 132, pp. 515–22.

12. The definitive work in this field is Hugh L'Etang's *The Pathology of Leadership* (Heinemann, 1969). It includes a close scrutiny of the health of leaders in both world wars. See also L'Etang's 'Prime Ministers and Their Physicians', *History of Medicine* (1973), vol. 3, no. 3, pp. 12–15.

13. For a broader sweep of the endocrine glands of the famous, see Ivo Cobb's *The Glands of Destiny* (Heinemann, 1936), which includes, among others, Henry VIII, Charles II, Voltaire and Mussolini. Note the date of publication, and match it with the verdict on Mussolini: 'For success, it is needful for a man to believe in himself, but it is also necessary for him to possess the power of imparting his belief to others. Such a man, or I am very much mistaken, is Signor Mussolini – Il Duce.'

14. Another famous sufferer from cancer of the jaw was the psychoanalyst Sigmund Freud who, in the last sixteen years of his life, had thirty-three operations to better fit his prosthesis, which he called his 'monster'.

15. Type A, coronary-prone individuals display the pathological triad of time-urgency, competitiveness and internalized hostility. A supposed marker to identify Type A time-urgency is whether a man flushes the lavatory before he has finished urinating. I have recently been informed that the same criterion can be used of women!

16. See John Nichols's 'President Kennedy's Adrenals', *Journal of the American Medical Association* (1967), vol. 201, no. 2, pp. 129–30.

17. Moran gives this account of his first meeting with Churchill in 1940:

> After what seemed quite a long time, he put down his papers and said impatiently: 'I don't know why they are making such a fuss. There's nothing wrong with me.' He picked up his papers and resumed his reading. At last he pushed the bed-rest away and, throwing back the bed clothes, said abruptly: 'I suffer from dyspepsia, and this is the treatment.' With that he proceeded to demonstrate to me some breathing exercises. His big white belly was moving up and down when there was a knock on the door, and the PM grabbed at the sheet as Mrs Hill came into the room.

See also Douglas Hubble's 'Lord Moran and James Boswell: Two Diarists Compared and Contrasted', *Medical History* (1969), vol. 13, no. 1, pp. 1–10. It is worth recalling that Churchill was a patient of Stephen Ward, the fashionable London osteopath involved in the Profumo-Keeler spy scandal of the 1960s.

18. A famous Churchill anecdote: A woman complained that he was drunk. He replied that he was, and that she was ugly – but that he would be sober by morning.

## 9 *The Medical Detective*

1. Today ergot is still used in the treatment of migraine and to stimulate

contractions of the womb in childbirth. Great care must be exercised so as not to overdose patients and produce in them all the symptoms, including gangrene, of St Anthony's Fire.
2. See H.A. Waldron's 'The Devonshire Colic', *Journal of the History of Medicine* (1970), vol. 25, no. 4, pp. 383–413.
3. I cannot resist this cautionary tale of doubtful origin and dubious authenticity: 'In a case of suspected diabetes, examination of the urine is of paramount importance', the lecturer told the medical students. 'I want you all to dip your fingers in the samples of urine in front of you and taste the sugar.' The doctor demonstrated and each student followed his example with varying degrees of hesitancy and disgust. 'Medicine is also about the art of appearances', he continued. 'Notice how I dipped with my index finger and sucked of my ring finger.'
4. See Michael Howell and Peter Ford's *Medical Mysteries* (Viking, 1985).
5. See Macdonald Critchley's 'Huntington's Chorea: Historical and Geographical Considerations' in *The Black Hole and Other Essays* (Pitman Medical Publishing, 1964). The black hole referred to in the title is the Calcutta tragedy of 1756.

### *10 The Three Mosquiteers – Manson, Ross and Reed*

1. The definitive book is Charles Wilcocks and P.E. Manson-Bahr's revision of *Manson's Tropical Diseases* (Ballière Tindall, 1972). Originally published in 1898.
2. Other famous victims include Dante, Byron, Garibaldi, King James I and Nelson.
3. The best book about the impact of malaria and the attempts to find cause and cure is Gordon Harrison's *Mosquitoes, Malaria and Man: A History of the Hostilities Since 1880* (John Murray, 1978).
4. King was present at Ford's Theater the night Lincoln was assasinated, and he attempted to save the President's life.
5. The full story about the history of quinine is given in Leon Warshaw's *Malaria: A Biography of a Killer* (Rinehart & Co., 1949).
6. See 'Malaria Threat Uncontainable' a news article in the *British Medical Journal* (5 September 1992), vol. 305, p. 544; and Phyllida Brown's 'Columbia's Malaria Vaccine Approved For Trials', *New Scientist* (26 September 1992), p. 6.
7. For doctors who research on themselves, see note 6, chapter 11.
8. The story of yellow fever is well told by Michael Howell and Peter Ford in *Medical Mysteries* (Viking, 1985).

### *11 Pox and Clap: The Great Unmentionables*

1. There are a multitude of books about syphilis, but the best is Claude Quétel's *History of Syphilis* (Polity Press, 1990). Running Quétel a close second is James Cleugh's *Secret Enemy: The Story of a Disease* (Thames and

Hudson, 1954), and Charles Dennie's *A History of Syphilis* (Charles C. Thomas, 1962). Two others highly recommended are David Barlow's *Sexually Transmitted Diseases: The Facts* (Oxford University Press, 1979) and Allan Brandt's *No Magic Bullet: A Social History of Venereal Disease in the United States Since 1880* (Oxford University Press, 1987). Richard Davenport-Hines' *Sex, Death and Punishment: Attitudes to Sex and Sexuality in Britain Since the Renaissance* (Collins, 1990), is an authoritative and readable text on attitudes to syphilis, homosexuality and AIDS.

2. See Leon Goldman's 'Syphilis in the Bible', *Archives of Dermatology* (1971) vol. 103, pp. 535–6.

3. For a comprehensive treatment of this topic, see Don Brothwell and A. Sandison's *Diseases in Antiquity* (Charles C. Thomas, 1967), 'Syphilis and Neanderthal Man' is addressed by D.J.M. Wright in *Nature* (5 February 1971), vol. 229, p. 409. See also R.C. Holcomb's 'The Antiquity of Congenital Syphilis', *Bulletin of the History of Medicine* (1941), vol. 10, pp. 148–77.

4. Opinion has always been sharply divided about Aureolus Philippus Theophrastus Bombastus von Hohenheim, better known as Paracelsus (1493–1541). This mystic cum alchemist cum physician was, if nothing else, a truly original thinker, who courted the antagonism of the medical establishment by lecturing students in German, rather than Latin, and teaching from his own practical experience, rather than uncritically parroting Galen. He died, it is said by some, from a fractured skull received in a tavern brawl.

5. For more bawdy you are invited to dip into 'The Earl of Rochester and Ejaculatio Praecox' in William Ober's *Boswell's Clap and Other Essays* (Southern Illinois University Press, 1979).

6. Many books have been written about this fascinating genius. Details of the infamous self-experimentation can be found in 'John Hunter, A Martyr to Science', in Sir D'Arcy Power's *Selected Writings, 1877–1930* (Augustus Kelley, 1970). George Qvist doubts that the experiment ever took place and argues his case in *John Hunter, 1728–93* (Heinemann, 1981). Self-experimentation has a long history in medicine: Hugo Glaser's *The Drama of Medicine* (Lutterworth Press, 1962) cites cases where doctors have deliberately given themselves the Black Death, yellow fever, typhus and malaria – many of whom are included in this volume.

7. For a post-mortem diagnosis of syphilis on Frenchmen and others, see A. Dickson Wright's 'Venereal Disease and the Great', *British Journal of Venereal Disease* (1971), vol. 47, pp. 295–306. Some are a lot more convincing than others.

8. See Glenn Geelhoed's 'Cellini and His Syphilis', *Journal of the American Medical Association* (1968), vol. 204, no. 7, pp. 245–6.

9. See Angelo Rappoport's *Mad Majesties, or Raving Rulers & Submissive Subjects* (Greening & Co, 1910). A sheer delight!

10. Thomas Mann was moved to write *Doctor Faustus* with Nietzsche in mind. The theme of *Doctor Faustus* is explored further in chapter 5 on creativity.

11. Those wishing to know more about Wilde's illnesses are referred to

'Oscar Wilde: A Medical Appreciation', in Macdonald Critchley's *The Black Hole and Other Essays* (Pitman Medical Publishing, 1964).

12. For a biography of Churchill, see R.F. Foster's *Lord Randolph Churchill: A Political Life* (Clarendon Press, 1981). The account of how Churchill caught syphilis, doubted by many, is contained in Frank Harris's *My Life and Loves* (W.H. Allen, 1922–7).

13. See Richard Davenport-Hines, *Sex, Death and Punishment: Attitudes to Sex and Sexuality in Britain Since the Renaissance* (Collins, 1990).

14. See H.P. Collins's 'Ibsen's Doctors', *History of Medicine* (Spring 1971), vol. 3, no. 1, pp. 13–17.

15. See the title essay in William Ober's *Boswell's Clap and Other Essays* (Southern Illinois University Press, 1979). The other essays include Swinburne's masochism, Keats's penchant for opium, a trio of mad English poets (Collins, Cowper and Smart), and an attempt to answer the question, 'Did Socrates die of Hemlock Poisoning?' Compulsive reading.

## *12 AIDS*

1. There is a burgeoning literature on AIDS. Here are three of the best: Dennis Altman's *AIDS and the New Puritanism* (Pluto Press, 1986), Randy Shilts' *And the Band Played On* (Penguin, 1988), and Peter Aggleton's et al. *AIDS: Rights, Risk and Reason* (Falmer Press, 1992). A medical approach is taken by Michael Alder's *ABC of AIDS* (British Medical Journal Publications, 1988). For AIDS in context, see Richard Davenport-Hines's *Sex, Death and Punishment: Attitudes to Sex and Sexuality in Britain Since the Renaissance* (Collins, 1990) – compelling and persuasive.

## *Afterword: Death, the Ultimate Disease*

1. A great deal of the literature about prolongation of life is written by cranks and is, frankly, very boring. A more objective approach in the older literature was taken in Maurice Ernest's *The Longer Life* (Adam & Co, no date – but probably late 1930s). There has been a recent printing of Elie [sometimes spelt Ilya] Metchnikoff's *The Prolongation of Life: Optimistic Studies* (Arno Press, 1977). Two overviews are Eric Trimmer's *Rejuvenation, The History of an Idea* (Robert Hale, 1967), which is much better than Patrick McGrady's *The Youth Doctors* (Arthur Baker, 1969). David Hamilton's *The Monkey Gland Affair* (Chatto & Windus, 1986) focuses on, and is sympathetic to, Voronoff.

# GLOSSARY

**Bacterium** (pl. bacteria): A very large group of single-celled micro-organisms (q.v.), most of which are harmless to man (non pathogenic), but a number of which cause serious disease. Bacteria are classified according to their shape: spherical (*cocci*), rods (*bacilli*) and comma-shaped (*vibrio*).

**Contagious disease**: A disease which is transmitted directly or indirectly from one person to another.

**Endemic**: An adjective applied to a disease which occurs more or less constantly in a locality.

**Epidemic**: An outbreak of a disease which claims many victims, often over a large geographical area.

**Fungus**: A very simple form of plant life. Responsible for such diseases as thrush and athlete's foot.

**Incubation period**: The time between contracting an infectious disease to the appearance of the first symptoms. The incubation time is usually reckoned in days, though the incubation period for some diseases, e.g., AIDS and leprosy, may extend to years, even decades.

**Infectious disease**: One that is spread from person to person without direct contact, infection occurring as a result of droplets of exhaled moisture containing pathogenic micro-organisms (q.v.).

**Inoculation**: The intentional introduction of a micro-organism into the body of the host in order to produce a mild form of the disease and thereby give protection from more severe forms of the disease.

**Micro-organism**: An organism, either animal or plant, only visualized under the microscope. Includes bacteria, (q.v.) and protozoa (q.v.).

**Pandemic**: A disease covering a very large geographic area.

**Protozoa**: A group of unicellular micro-organisms which includes *Plasmodium*, the sub-group causing malaria and transmitted by the bite of the anopheles mosquito.

**Rickettsia**: A micro-organism (q.v.) smaller than bacteria but larger than most viruses. Carried by ticks, fleas and lice, they are responsible for such diseases as typhus, trench fever and Rocky Mountain spotted fever.

**Vaccination**: Inoculation with an attenuated or related form of a micro-organism in order to give protection through immunity from the more severe form of disease. The term was most often used in protection against smallpox.

**Virus**: A micro-organism (q.v.) smaller than a bacterium, often only visible with an electron microscope, which generally live *within* the cells of the host. Viruses are responsible for a number of human diseases, including influenza, measles and smallpox.

# Index


Abracadabra, 28
Acquired Immune Deficiency Syndrome, *see* AIDS
Act of Union, The, 91
Addison's disease, 161, 162
Adrian VI, 21
*Aëdes aegypti*, 5
AIDS, 9, 11, 230–40
  African provenance, 234–6
  controls, 236–8
  HIV, 238–40
  and homosexuality, 232
Akhenaten, 138, 139
Alexander the Great, 33, 241
Amerindians, 1, 9, 66, 67, 69, 130, 199ff.
Anatomy Act, The, 40
*Ancient Mariner, The*, 97
Animalculae, 78
Auenbrugger, Leopold, von, 77
*Avariés, Les*, 224, 225
Avicenna, 133
Aztecs, 10, 49

Bacon, Roger, 242
Baker, Sir George, 168
Banting, Frederick, 169, 170
Baudelaire, Charles, 9, 214
Beardsley, Aubrey, 95, 97
Becket, Thomas à, 49
Bedson, Professor Henry, 64
Beethoven, Ludwig van, 109
Benedetto, 202
Berni, Francesco, 20
Best, Charles, 169, 170
Bethercourt, Jacques de, 204
Bilharzia, *see* Schistosomiasis
Bills of Mortality, 60
Bismarck, 152
Black Death, *see* Bubonic Plague
Blackwater fever, 176
Blains, 13
Blistering, 136
Boccacio, 17, 19, 20
*Bohème, La*, 80
Boswell, James, 73, 226–8
Brawne, Fanny, 70
Bristol, 23
*British Medical Journal*, 180, 182, 185
Brontës, 75, 76, 100
Brown, Charles, 99
Brown-Séquard, Charles, 242
Bubo, 13
Bubonic Plague, 4, 6, 9, 11, 13–32
  and astrology, 25
  (arrival at) Caffe, 16
  causes, 24–7
  (and the) Church, 21
  clinical description, 13–15
  and Dancing Manias, 29
  derivation of name, 15
  (and) doctors, 21
  in England, 22
    last outbreak in, 31–2
  (and the) Flagellants, 29
  in Ireland, 24
  in London, 23
    and Fire of London, 31
  mortality, 15
  origin, 15
  pneumonic, 13, 15

provenance, 15
remedies, 27–9
search for scapegoats, 25–7
social consequences, 23
spread, 16–24
Bures St Mary, 174
Burney, Fanny, 124–6
Byron, Lord, 81, 110–12

Caffa, Siege of, 16
Caius, Dr John, 9
Caligula, 142
Camus, Albert, 32
Cancer
of the jaw, 155
of the throat, 150–3
Caroline of Anspach, 60
Carriers
in genetic diseases, 140
in infectious diseases, 8
Carroll, James, 194ff.
Casimir, 26
Catherine the Great, 61, 217
Cattell, 101
Caventou, Joseph, 190
Cellini, Benvenuto, 216
Celsus, 4
Charles II, 136, 137
Charles V, 144, 145
Charles VIII, 201
Chateaubriand, René de, 74
Chauliac, Guy de, 21
Chekhov, Anton, 97; Chapter 5: endnote 2
Cheselden, William, 119
Chickenpox, 5, 6, 10
Cholera, 9, 32–48
Broad Street outbreak, 46
causes, 42–4
clinical description, 32
in Hamburg, 34, 47
medical reaction, 36–9
mortality, 33
in Paisley, 41
provenance, 33
and social class, 39
spread, 33, 38
in Sunderland, 33–9
Chopin, Frederic, 74
Christian VII, 217
Churchill, Lord Randolph, 220, 221
Churchill, Winston, 162, 163; Chapter 8, endnote 18
Clap, *see* Gonorrhoea
Clark, Dr James, 70
Claudius, 143
Clement VI, 20
Cleveland, Grover, 155, 156
Colchicine, 118
Coleridge, Samuel Taylor, 97, 100
Columbus, Christopher, 1, 11
Condamine, Charles Marie de la, 190
Condoms, 210
*Confessions of an English Opium-Eater*, 98
Constantinople, 16
Consumption, *see* Tuberculosis
Cortés, 10, 65
Counter-irritants, 136, 137
Coward, Noel, 243
Cowpox, 5
Crabbe, George, 99
Crabs, 227
Creativity, and illness, 95–114
Cro-Magnon medicine man, 1
Cumano, 202
Cupping, 130–2

DDT, 191
*Dame aux Camelias, Le*, 80
Dance of Death, 27
Dancing manias, 29–30
Danzic, 20
Daudet, Alphonse, 219
Daudet, Léon, 101
*David Copperfield*, 80
Deafness, 108–10
*Decameron*, 17
Defoe, Daniel, 30, 110; Chapter 2: endnote 9
De Quincey, Thomas, 97, 98, 99, 100
Devonshire colic, 167–8
Diabetes (mellitus), 168–70
Dickens, Charles, 81, 100

Dimsdale, Dr Thomas, 61
Diphtheria, 8, 154
*Doctor Faustus*, 101
Don Carlos, 146–8
Donizetti, Gaetano, 217
Dumas, Alexandre, 82
Dunfermline Abbey, 91
*Dunciad, The*, 113
Duplessis, Marie, 80

Eden, Sir Anthony, 163
Edward I, 26, 90
Edward III, 21, 22
Edward VII, 228
Ehrlich, Paul, 222
Eisenhower, Dwight, 160
Elizabeth I, 55
Ellis, Havelock, 101, 102
Epilepsy, 3, 106–8
Eskimos, 69

Ferdinand II, 201
Filariasis, 175–6
  clinical description, 175
Finlay, Carlos, 194
Flagellants, 29
Flaubert, 214
Fleas, 13
Florence, 17, 19, 71
Fore indians, 170–2
Fracastoro, Girolamo, 204
Francis I, 213
Franklin, Benjamin, 66, 119
Federick III, the Noble, 150–3
French, Sir John, 153
Frère Jacques, 120–1

Guaiac, 208, 216
Gajdusek, D. Carleton, 171
Galen, 55, 82, 178
Galton, Francis, 101, 102
Gas gangrene, 4
Gaugin, Paul, 215
Gautier, Margarite, 80
Gautier, Théophile, 215
General Paralysis of the Insane (GPI), 198
George III, 148–50
George IV, 116, 119, 149
Goncourt brothers, 81
Gonorrhoea, 6, 226–8
Gout, 115–19
  remedies, 118
  sufferers, 116–18
Goya, 108
Grassi, 187ff.
Great White Plague, *see* Tuberculosis
Gregory of Tours, 55
Grenville, Charles, 34, 35, 37
Grunpeck, Joseph, 202
Gurdjieff, George, 82

Habsburgs, The, 143–8
Hadlow, W.J., 171
Haig, Sir Douglas, 153
Haiti, 12, 236
Halford, Sir Henry, 34; Chapter 2: endnote 12
Hansen, Armauer, 83
Haemophilia, 139–40
Harris, Frank, 220
Hecker, Dr, 15
Henry VII, 117
Henry VIII, 216
*Hereditary Genius*, 101
Hippocrates, 6, 8, 53, 87, 116, 117, 130, 177
Hitler, Adolf, 165
HIV, *see* AIDS
Huayna Capac, 65
Humoural theory of disease, 127
Hunter, Dr John, 160, 212, 213, 218
Huntington's Chorea, 173–4
Hutchinson's teeth, 198
Huxham, John, 167
Huxley, Aldous, 72

Incas, 65
Infectious hepatitis, 8
*Insanity of Genius, The*, 103
Ivan the Terrible, 216

Jacob-Creutzfeld Disease, 172
Jacquier, 178
Jane the Mad, 144ff.

Jenner, Edward, 62–3; Chapter 3: endnote 6
Jews, and Bubonic Plague, 25–7
Johnson, Lyndon, 162
Johnson, Dr Samuel, 73, 97, 102
Juana La Loca, *see* Jane the Mad
Julio-Claudian emperors, 142–3
Jussieu, Joseph de, 190
Justinian, Plague of, 15

Keats, John, 70, 80, 82, 95, 99; Chapter 5: endnote 4
Kendal Black Drop, 97
Kennedy, John F., 161, 162
King's Evil, 72
Koch, Robert, 47, 79, 187, 188
Kretschmer, 102
Kriton, 6
*Kubla Khan*, 98
Kuru, 170–2

Laënnec, René, 77–8
*Lancet*, 34, 37, 39, 172
Lancisi, Giovanni, 178, 180
Latta, Thomas, 44
Laudanum, 81, 97ff.
Laura, 22
Laveran, Alphonse, 178ff.
Lawrence, D.H., 70–1, 82, 95
Lazarus, 86
Lazear, Jesse, 193ff.
Leeching, 132–6
Leopold I, 122, 123
Leprosy, 8, 9, 83–94
  in Bible, 85–6
  clinical description, 83–4
  in history, 87–91
  and Robert Bruce, 91–3
  social consequences, 87–91
  stigma, 93
Lincoln, Abraham, 67
Locke, John, 105
Lombrosdo, Cesare, 103
Louis XI, 130
Louis XIV, 120
  anal fistula of, 75
Louis XV, 61
Ludendorff, Erich, 153
Luther, Martin, 9

MacArthur, J.R., 170
Macaulay, Lord, 57
Machiavelli, 19
Mackenzie, Morrell, 150–3
Mad Cow Disease, 170
Madness
  and genius, 102
  and personality, 102–6
  and royalty, 141–50
Magdalene, Mary, 86
*Magic Mountain, The*, 101
Malaria, 5, 8, 10, 176–92
  clinical description, 176–7
  control, 189–92
  history, 177
  and mosquito, 180–8
  pathology, 178–80
Malformations, congenital, 110
*Man of Genius, The*, 103
Manet, Edouard, 215
Mann, Thomas, 101
Mansfield, Katherine, 76, 82
Manson, Sir Patrick, 176, 180ff.
Marcus Aurelius, 55
Maria Theresa, 61
Marseilles, 20, 21
Marten, Benjamin, 78
Mary, Queen of Scots, 57, 150
Mather, Cotton, 66
Mather, Increase, 65
Maupassant, 213, 214
Measles, 5, 8, 9, 10
Melcombe, 22
Mercury treatment, 206–7
Messina, 17
Metchnikoff, Ilya, 242
Milton, John, 116
Møller-Christensen, Dr, 86, 87, 93
Mongols, 16
Montagu, Lady Mary Wortley, 60, 113, 123; Chapter 3: endnote 4
Montezuma, 10, 65
Moran, Lord, 162; Chapter 8: endnote 17
*Morbus Dominorum*, 116
*Morbus Gallicus*, 203, 214

Mosquitoes in spread of disease, Chapter 10
Mussis, Gabriel de, 16
Mussolini, Benito, 164
*Mycobacterium leprae*, 83
*Mycobacterium tuberculosis*, 5, 69
  resistance to drugs, 83

Naples, siege of, 198, 201–3
Napoleon III, 101, 123
Nebuchadnezzar, 141
Nelmes, Sara, 62
Neosalvarsan, 222
Nero, 143
New Guinea, 170–2
Newton, Isaac, 105–6
Nicholas V, 21
*Nicholas Nickleby*, 81
Niehans, Paul, 243
Neitzsche, Friedrich, 217
Nisbet, 103

Oberammergau, 24
*Ode to a Nightingale*, 99
Orwell, George, 132
Opium, 97ff.
Oxford, 23

Paganini, Nicolo, 82
Paisley, 41
Paracelsus, 209; Chapter 11: endnote 4
Paré, Ambroise, 27, 130
Parkinson's disease, 165
*Pasteurella pestis*, 4, 11, 12, 13
Pelletier, Joseph, 190
Peloponnesian War, 53
Penicillin, 229
Pepys, Samuel, 30, 106, 121–2; Chapter 2: endnote 8
Pericles, 53
Peter the Great, 216
Petrarch, 17, 22
Pettenkofer, Max von, 47
Philip II, 145
Philiskos, 6
Phipps, James, 62
Phthisis, *see* Tuberculosis
Pisa, 17
Pitt, William, 119
Pius II, 21
Pius XII, 243
Plague of Athens, 53–4
Plasmodia, 176–88
*Plasmodium falciparum*, 5, 176ff.
Pliny, 132
Poe, Edgar Alan, 81
Poliomyelitis, 8, 9, 158
Polo, Marco, 16
Pope, Alexander, 112–14
Porphyria, 150
Pox, *see* Syphilis
Princess Joan, 21, 23
Procopius, 15
Progeria, 241
Proust, Marcel, 133
*Psychology of Men of Genius*, 102
Purging, 127–30
Pythion, 6

Quarantine, 28, 34ff.
Queen Alexandra, 228
Queen Anne, 58, 73
Queen Mary (wife of William III), 57
Quinine, 189, 190

Rameses V, 50
*Rattus rattus*, 13
Reed, Walter, 194ff.
*Remembrances of Things Past*, 133
Rhazes, 27, 31
Richard III, 9
Rickets, 112
Rickettsial organisms, 48
Robert the Bruce, King, 91–3
Rocky Mountain Spotted Fever, 48
Roosevelt, Franklin, 158–60
Ross, Sir Ronald, 180ff.
Rossetti, Dante Gabriel, 81, 100

St Anthony's Fire, 166
St Denis, 203
St Nicaise, 62
*Salmonella typhi*, 5, 8
Salvarsan, 222

Sand, George, 74
Scarlet fever, 8, 9
Schistosomiasis, 4
Schubert, Franz, 217
Scott, Sir Walter, 75, 100
Scrofula, *see* Tuberculosis
Severn, Joseph, 100
Shelley, Percy, 70, 82, 100
Shingles, 6
Siddal, Elizabeth, 81, 100; Chapter 4: endnote 8
Sixtus IV, 21
Sleeping sickness, 10
Smallpox, 5, 6, 8, 9, 10, 56–68
  clinical description, 50
  early history, 55
  and Elizabeth I, 55–7
  eradication, 67
  famous victims, 57–9
  inoculation, 60
  and Jenner, Edward, 62–3
  in nineteenth century, 63–4
  and Plague of Athens, 53–4
  spread, global, 64–7
  and the Stuarts, 57
  in twentieth century, 68
  vaccination, 62, 63
Smenkhkare, 138, 139
Snow, John, 44–8, 140
*Spes phthisica*, 95
Spitalfield Church, 68
Sproat, William, 38
Stern, Erich, 95
Stevenson, R.L., 97
Stones
  in the bladder, 119–24
  famous victims, 121–4
Stuart royal family, 57
*Study of British Genius, The*, 101
Sweating sickness (English), 9
Swift, Jonathan, 108
Sydenham, Thomas, 118
Syphilis, 1, 8, 11, 101, 192–225
  in Bible, 199
  causes, 205–8
  clinical description, 197–8
  famous victims, 214ff.
  in Naples, 201–3
  protection, 210, 211
  provenance, 198–201
  remedies, 205–8
  social consequences, 208–11
  spread, 203
  and women, 221–6

Tabes dorsalis, 198
Tallyrand, 50
Tetanus, 4, 6
Thompson, Francis, 99
Thucydides, 8, 53
Tiberius, 142
Titan, 19
Tokens, 13
*Traviata, La*, 80
Trepanation (of the skull), 1
*Treponema pallidum*, 197, 200
*Trypanosoma gambiensi*, 10
Tsetse fly, 10
Tuberculosis, 1, 3, 6, 8, 9, 69–83; *see also* Creativity and Illness, Chapter 5
  affecting Keats and D.H. Lawrence, 70–2
  (and the) arts, 80–2
  (in the) Bible, 72
  clinical description, 69
  diagnosis, 76–8
  famous victims, 74–6
  germ theory, 78–80
  history, 72–3
  modes of spread, 73–6
  pathology, 77
  treatment, 83
  twentieth-century update, 83
Tutankhamun, 138, 139
Typhoid, 5, 8
Typhoid Mary, 8
Typhus, 3, 9, 48–9
  clinical description, 48

Van Gogh, Vincent, 101
*Variola major*, 50
Victoria, Queen, 139–40
*Vibrio cholerae*, 32
Villalobos, 202

Villemin, Jean-Antoine, 79
Virchow, Rudolph, 151, 152
Voltaire, 209
Voronoff, Serge, 242

Walpole, Robert, 123
Washington, George, 66, 101, 154
Waterhouse, Benjamin, 66
Whelks, 13
Whooping cough, 6, 9
Wilde, Oscar, 217
Willis, Francis, 148
Wilson, Woodrow, 156–8
*Wuthering Heights*, 80
Wolf, Hugo, 217
Wolsey, Cardinal, 216
Worms, 3, 4, 165
  varieties of, 4

Xenopsylla cheopis, 48

Yangtze Valley, 10
Yaws, 200
Yellow fever, 192–6
  clinical description, 192
  spread, 193

Zigas, Vincent, 171
Zola, Emile, 221
Zwingli, 9